ISILWANE

THE ANIMAL

ISILWANE

THE ANIMAL

TALES AND FABLES OF AFRICA

CREDO MUTWA

DEDICATION

I dedicate this book to my late friend Magqubu 'Ntombela' Madolo and to my friend Dr Ian Player. I would also like to dedicate it to all those who died, who suffered in sorrow, in the war to conserve my country's dwindling wildlife.

PUBLISHER'S ACKNOWLEDGEMENTS

The recording of Credo Mutwa's work has been facilitated by the efforts of Lesley Ann Tintinger and Johann Beyers.

Struik Publishers (Pty) Ltd
(a member of the Struik Publishing Group)
Cornelis Struik House
80 McKenzie
Cape Town 8001

Reg. No.: 54/00965/07

First published in 1996

Editor: Hilda Herman
Project editor: Jenny Barrett
Designer: Gaelyn Quixley
Cover designer: Gaelyn Quixley
Illustrator: Bowen Boshier

Reproduction: cmyk Prepress
Printing and binding: CTP Book Printers, Parow

ISBN 1 86825 970 6

CONTENTS

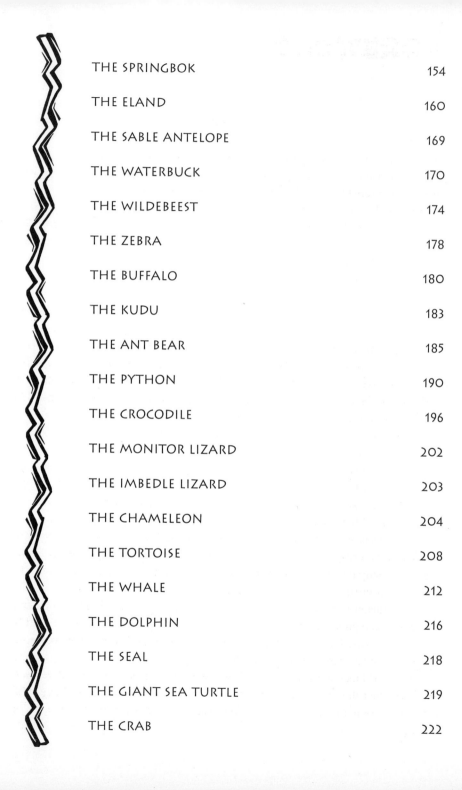

FOREWORD

Credo Mutwa: seer, sage, sangoma, *inyanga*, healer, psychic and storyteller. No single word can describe this most remarkable human being. One thing is certain, though – Credo Mutwa will go down in history as a man who was able to bridge a gap between white and black South Africans and start a healing process.

I was introduced to Credo Mutwa by a mutual friend and one of South Africa's greatest conservationists, TC Robertson. I clearly remember being taken by TC, as he was affectionately known, to where Credo was working. From the moment he began to speak, I knew Credo had a great depth of wisdom. I later read his book *Indaba my children*, and marvelled at his exposition of history; it is an insight into the oral traditions of South Africa that no one else could have written.

For me it was always a comfort to know that Credo Mutwa was available to answer questions about the many different cultures of southern Africa and beyond to the countries north of us. In 1976, after a conference in Johannesburg where Credo delivered an address, I asked him what the people in Soweto were dreaming about, as it was a time when the Nationalist government was being particularly severe. Credo replied that the women were dreaming of fire and smoke, and that serious trouble was coming. Sure enough, a few months later the Soweto riots erupted, and South Africa was never the same again. Something had snapped in the psyche of the black people and apartheid was doomed.

Credo Mutwa's storytelling ability and his detailed knowledge of both wild and domestic animals are clearly illustrated in this book. What I find particularly striking is his deep respect for the natural world and the place of the animal. Credo stresses that in the past, African people did not regard themselves as being above the animals, trees, fishes and birds. These were all seen as part of ourselves, and nature was contained both within and without us. He castigates the arrogance of modern western society which has taken dominion over the Earth. He asks the question, 'How can we escape from this ugly trap into which our short-sightedness, greed and gross stupidity have landed us?' then answers his own question thus: 'We must take a great spiritual step backwards.'

In his brilliant introduction to this book, Credo takes us on a long journey into the past of the great continent of Africa. He brings to life ancient beliefs foolishly scorned by many European travellers and missionaries as superstitious nonsense.

Credo Mutwa tells us that when the white people first came to Africa, they found a world teeming with animals from the Cape to central Africa and beyond. We know that the white man, with a terrible urge to kill or tame anything wild, embarked upon a slaughter with modern weapons that has never been equalled in human history. Today, with the rising tide of ecological awareness, western society is becoming increasingly conscious of the fact that we have been on the wrong path. Credo says that many people in the western world believe that conservation in Africa is a new thing, imported by the colonial powers, but we who have worked in the Mfolozi and other game reserves in Zululand know that conservation and protected areas existed long before white people came.

Wild animals, Credo tells us, were thought to be blessings from the gods and vital to the continued existence of human beings. Credo writes, 'Black people used to believe that animals were the blood of the Earth,' and goes on to say that there was a belief that human existence upon the Earth was dependent upon the large animal migrations criss-crossing the continent.

People in the modern western world have separated almost everything: white and black, man and woman, and they believe that we are separate from the Earth. James Lovelock in his book *The Gaia Hypothesis* shows that we are a part of the Earth, and that it lives and breathes. Lovelock was initially hounded by scientists for his beliefs. Now, more people accept his view. My friend, colleague and mentor Magqubu 'Ntombela' Madolo, who, many years ago, revealed to me some of the African mysteries, is a similar case in point. Magqubu could not read or write, but he had a wisdom and knowledge that was far superior to that of so-called educated people, and a natural and intuitive understanding of the world in which we live. He always insisted that the Earth was alive, and that we were brothers and sisters to the animals, trees, plants, grass, birds. Credo Mutwa, too, explains here that the old African people always knew that the Earth was alive.

There are many interesting facts in this book, but it is equally a book of great beauty, of poetry and prose. The praise songs to the elephant, the rhino, the hippopotamus, will touch even the hardest of hearts.

Those of us who have heard the roar of a lion at first light, the sound of it echoing against the stone krantzes, will appreciate the praise song to this king of predators. '*Ngonyama*, thunder of the valleys' is how Credo Mutwa portrays this animal, at the same time describing perfectly the sound of its voice. It is a sound that vibrates the sternum.

Isilwane – The Animal is a great book written by a great man for a world that has become sick and bent on self-destruction. To read it is to become alive again and to know that we must fight with every weapon at our disposal to ensure that nature is no longer abused, otherwise there will be no hope for man or animal – only the cockroach will survive.

IAN PLAYER D.M.S.

INTRODUCTION

Through *Isilwane – The Animal*, I hope to open the eyes of the world to traditional African attitudes, folklore and rituals which have governed the relationships between the people of Africa and the animal world.

Under Western civilization, we live in a strange world of separatism; a world in which things that really belong together and which ought to be seen as part of a greater whole are cruelly separated. The result of this separatist attitude is that humanity is denied a great deal of valuable knowledge. We are led into a forest of confusion when we try to learn about ourselves, our mother, the Earth, and the universe of which our planet is an infinitesimal part.

Although there are many alternative attitudes, it is very clear that during the last five hundred years or so the human race has made minimal, if any, progress in understanding itself, the world and the universe beyond. The much-touted discoveries made by men such as Copernicus and Galileo, when viewed objectively, were really not discoveries at all, but rather *rediscoveries* of discoveries made hundreds, if not thousands, of years before.

People upon the plains and in the valleys of Africa knew, long before Galileo and Copernicus were born, that the Earth orbits the sun and not the other way round. Africans and people of other nations across the world knew thousands of years ago that the Earth was round; they knew that the world is but one of many worlds where living beings exist.

The Bushmen of the Kalahari Desert knew that no-one could live on the moon, and that it lacked air and water. There is the legend of a stupid hunter who so feared living with other Bushmen that he decided to fly on magic wings to the moon. There he died of thirst and hunger because there was neither water nor animals upon that bleak satellite.

Today we see the human race running around in circles, like a mad dog chasing its own tail. We have seen things hailed as great discoveries which will change the future of humanity, end in cul-de-sacs of futility. Today, the same type of confusion prevails in all fields of human thought.

There is confusion in the way we view ourselves, there is confusion in the way we view the Earth, there is even confusion, believe it or not, at the core of every one of the world's great religions. I can state this with confidence, as I have studied most of these religions and even joined some of them.

But why the confusion? It is due to the way we view things: the way we view the atom, the stars, life on Earth, and the way we view the Deity Himself or Herself. But the most dangerous and destructive view by far – one which has changed human beings into rampaging, destructive and mindless beasts – is that we compare ourselves with other living things.

Western man is taught that he is the master of all living things. The Bible itself enshrines this extreme attitude, as do other great books. Repeatedly one hears of Western people talking about nature as if it were man's mortal enemy: one hears dangerous phrases such as 'untamed nature' or 'interrogating nature with power'. One hears of the strange belief that man is superior to all other living things on Earth, and that he was especially created to be overlord and custodian of all things, animate or inanimate.

Until these attitudes are combated and erased from the human mind, Westernized human beings will be a danger to all earthly life, including themselves.

We are conditioned to regard nature as crude and primitive, to regard all stretches of forest, bush or savannah as things that ought to be cleared before the so-called master of all, the human being, can rule supreme over the denuded valleys and the ravaged plains.

A very dangerous attitude that ought to be erased from our minds and those of our children is that human beings can build a glittering technological future without animals, and without trees; a future in which food will be synthesized (only heaven knows what from), in which there will be no disease and no death. This Utopian attitude encourages human beings to ravage the Earth in the hope that our descendants, who will inherit our denuded world, will somehow, using the might of the electron and waving the magic wand of technology, create a new paradise.

One thing that I, as a traditional African, angrily frown upon is that, in Western civilization, God is removed from the orbit of human life to some faraway, never-never heaven. Expelling God from everyday life leaves the field clear for super-capitalists, colonialists and other plunderers to rape the Earth, to destroy nature, to ravage priceless natural resources with cold impunity.

African people have the amusing saying that once a tribe has sent its chief into exile, slaughtered its elders and traditional healers, and kicked out its warriors and praise-singers, it turns into a nation of long-fanged, man-eating cannibals. Throughout the world this is what human beings have become: big-bellied, insatiable, unbelievably greedy cannibals.

We have become a nation like the legendary monkeys who, according to one African story, were placed by the great Earth Mother on a sacred fig tree to guard it. They developed such appetites that they not only ate all the figs but also devoured the bark and the wood of the tree. When the great Earth Mother returned, she found the tree reduced to a rotting stump and the skeletons of all the monkeys who had died of starvation after eating their own tree.

How can we escape from the ugly trap in which our own shortsightedness, greed and gross stupidity have landed us? How can we get out of this prison?

We must take a great spiritual step backwards. We must adopt the view of creation that was held not only by ancient Africans, but also by native Americans and many other people of the ancient world: that creation is one great and beautiful whole, one revolving sphere of the purest, greenest crystal, a sphere to be viewed from all sides as one thing, instead of a number of shattered fragments upon the dark desert of human folly.

We must stop – immediately – regarding ourselves as superior and special creatures created in the image of some imaginary god. This dangerous, chauvinistic view has led us to the very edge of destruction. We must bring the Almighty back into our lives – not just on Sunday or Saturday, but every hour and day.

And, as strange as this may sound to those who believe in it, we must stop believing that man's ultimate destiny is in some heaven beyond the dark curtain of death.

In olden days people viewed heaven and Earth, the spiritual and the physical, as one beautiful thing. People viewed God as being not only with us on Earth and in heaven, but also within us. We were taught by ancient Africans that we are part of God (as a little pebble is part of a great mountain), and because of this, we should beware of doing anything against the teaching and the nature of God.

In old Africa we did not regard ourselves as superior to the animals, the trees, and the fishes and the birds. We regarded ourselves as part of all these living things. We believed that far from being specially created, we were, in fact, the weakest of all the creatures that God created. This feeling of weakness instilled in our souls a deep dependence upon the living nature around us.

We believed that human beings could not exist without animals, birds and fishes, or the greenery that whispers all around us. We used to believe that in every one of us there lay a spiritual animal, bird and fish with which we should keep contact at all times, to anchor our family upon the shifting surface of this often troubled planet.

We believed that within us were the oceans, the rivers, the sky and the mountains. We believed that we had nature within and beyond ourselves. For this reason, many African gods were depicted as part animal and part human. For instance, the great Earth Mother, whose Zulu name is *Nomkhubulwane*, or simply 'Ma', is often depicted with only one human leg, while her other leg is that of an animal – an antelope, elephant or rhinoceros. At other times she is depicted as having one fully human leg and another, usually the left leg, with roots where one would expect to find toes.

The great Earth Mother, together with other lesser goddesses, was believed by African people to be capable of changing her shape to that of any animal, bird or fish whenever she chose, and this is why Zulus call her *Nomkhubulwane*, a name which means 'she who chooses the state of an animal' – in short, 'the shape-changer'.

Nomkhubulwane is a goddess believed to be a trinity within herself. She is thought to consist of a young woman whose name is *Nomndende*, which means 'lady of the big buttocks' or 'lady of the big hips'; a middle-aged woman, called *Nomkhubulwane*; and, as her bad aspect, *Nomboyi*, a hideous, ugly, wrinkled old hag, with fangs like a shark's.

The great Earth Mother is capable of changing her shape into beautiful and gentle birds, animals and reptiles. She is capable of assuming the shape of an animal such as a springbok, an eland, an impala, a lizard, or a python. She is believed to be able to change her shape into a rhinoceros, an elephant, a giraffe, a lion or a lioness at will.

But in her bad and cruel aspect, she is believed to be capable of changing her shape into only two animals: the hyena or the crocodile. Some say that she likes to change into a vulture. This is the most popular belief about this most ancient of African goddesses.

Initiation schools still exist in scattered parts of Africa, where one learns about the deepest spiritual mysteries of our people and our country. We are taught that the reason that our forefathers told us that our gods and goddesses were capable of changing shape, or were part animal and part human being, is that they wanted to instill in the minds of their descendants the oneness of the human being, the animal and the Deity.

By making us believe that the highest gods were part animal and part human being, we were taught to look upon animals with great reverence, love and respect. If you are taught that God often has the head of a lion and the body of a human being, you will treat all lions with respect.

In my travels to many parts of the world and in the course of my studies of ancient history and religions, I have noticed with interest that all the nations which treated nature with great respect, recognized people's dependence on her bounty as human beings, created civilizations in which nature was worshipped as a Deity, and did not separate nature from human life had, among their gods and goddesses, beings who were part animal and part human being.

The ancient Egyptians who depended upon the Nile had many such gods. The ancient Sumerians, too, had in their pantheons gods who were part animal and part human being. The god *Ningishieda* was depicted as being part bull and part human being.

I have also noticed that all the native races of America – South, Central and North – had gods exactly like this. In the United States, for example, I found the Hopi people believing in, among many other spiritual beings, a female being which they call *Hanu-Manu*. *Hanu-Manu*, the goddess of maize and greenery, is depicted as a beautiful American-Indian woman with bright green skin and long, black hair.

African people depict *Nomkhubulwane* in exactly the same way – as a green- or silver-skinned goddess with long, black hair. The Egyptian god of fertility, *Ozaries* or *Asaar*, is also depicted as having green skin.

It is interesting to note that, among the Zulu people, when a person is born with a particularly dark skin, he or she is not called black-skinned, but green-skinned. The Zulu word for black is *mnyama*. This term is never used to address a dark-skinned person to whom we wish to show respect. We rather use the term *luhlaza*, which means 'green' or 'green-skinned'.

In ancient times, all the men and women who trained as traditional healers or sangomas and who had particularly dark skins were specially selected to learn about plants and animals, and ways of combating disease in both of these life forms. At one time, my grandfather toyed with the idea of training me as a healer of domestic animals because of my dark skin.

Isilwane – The Animal will reveal African attitudes to animals: domestic, wild, on land, in the sea and in rivers.

When you talk of wildlife conservation nowadays, many people assume you are talking about something new, a miracle born of our supposedly enlightened era, a sign that human beings are beginning to care about the world in which they live, and about animals and other forms of life. But wildlife conservation is as old as Africa.

When white people came to this land, they found the plains and the valleys of the so-called Dark Continent teeming with wildlife. From the Cape to Central Africa and beyond, the land was alive with millions of animals. Great herds used to migrate the length and breadth of Africa. Millions of springbok, wildebeest, zebra and buffalo swarmed across the land, like bees around a beehive.

What many people do not realize is that these huge, wild herds existed because the native people of Africa regarded them as a blessing from the gods – as something unbelievably sacred and vital for the continued existence of human beings. Black people believed that animals were the blood of the Earth and that as long as there were migrations criss-crossing the country, human existence on Earth was guaranteed.

No-one ever interfered with these great migrations because they really believed that wildlife was the soul, the very life-blood, of Mother Earth.

When white people came to Africa, they had been conditioned to separate themselves spiritually and physically from wildlife. In the vast herds of animals they saw four-footed enemies to be crushed and objects of fun to be destroyed for pleasure. They slaughtered wild animals by the million.

It never occurred to white pioneers that these animals were protected by the native tribes through whose land they migrated. It never occurred to them, with their muskets, rifles and carbines, that black people worshipped these great herds and regarded them as an integral part of their existence on Earth.

Many hundreds of years ago, a wise old man called Pinda Moleli prophesied that one of the first indications that the end of the world had come would be the disappearance of herds from the African plains. The herds have almost disappeared and Pinda Moleli's prophesy appears to be coming true.

In old Africa, every tribe had an animal that it regarded as its totem, an animal after which the tribe had been named by its founders. It was the sacred duty of this tribe to ensure that the animal after which it was named was never harmed within the confines of its territory.

In addition, Africans knew that certain wild animals co-exist with others, and that in order to protect the animal after which the tribe was named, it was essential to protect those animals with which the sacred one co-existed.

In KwaZulu-Natal, for example, there is a tribe, the Dube people, for whom the zebra is the totem. These people not only protect vast herds of zebra in their tribal land, allowing them to roam wherever they choose, but they also protect herds of wildebeest because they realize that zebras co-exist with wildebeest.

The zebra has very good eyesight during the day but very poor eyesight at night. The opposite is true for the wildebeest. And so these two very dissimilar animals are always found grazing together in the bush for mutual protection. The old Africans knew that to protect the zebra effectively one had to protect the wildebeest, the warthog, the bushpig, the eland, the kudu and other animals sometimes found grazing with zebra in the bush.

But the old Africans knew that it was not enough simply to protect those animals which grazed with their tribal totem. It was essential to protect those animals which preyed upon the sacred animals.

Thus, those who protect the zebra and all other grass-eating animals that graze with it must also protect the preying lion. People knew that although the lion was the zebra's enemy, it was a natural and necessary enemy that would weed out the weaker zebra and ensure the survival of the fittest.

There were other tribes, such as the Batswana Bakaru and the Bafarutsi, which regarded the baboon as their totem. They knew that protecting baboons alone was not enough. The leopard which preyed upon baboons had to be protected, along with those plants upon which the baboons fed. The people knew that if they did not protect these plants, they would starve in the bush and start feeding on the crops in the people's corn- and maizefields. If this occurred, baboons would become man's enemy.

The Batswana Batloung tribe, whose name means 'people of the elephant', were sworn to protect the elephant. They also protected the rhinoceros and the hippopotamus, which they regarded as the elephant's cousins. It was believed that an elephant would not injure a person who carried the Bafloung name.

But what if an elephant became a rogue and started devastating villages? What if an elephant became a destroyer and started terrorizing the people? If this occurred, the tribe's king would call a gathering of his wisest people, among whom would be the traditional healers. They would throw the bones of divination and seek the answers from spirits as to exactly why the elephant had become an enemy.

If the diviners found that the elephant was sick or had been harassed by human beings in any way, strenuous efforts – some of them quite dangerous and bizarre – were made to entice the rogue elephant away from Bafloung territory without it being killed. However, should it prove absolutely necessary to kill the elephant, a group of hunters who were not of the Bafloung nation had to be brought in from far away.

The hunters would kill the elephant and then flee as fast as they could, back to their native land, for if they were caught having killed an elephant in Bafloung territory, they too stood a chance of being killed. A reward in the form of cattle would be sent by the Bafloung to the hunters for their troubles.

If one of the hunters were killed during the elephant hunt, as often happened, he would be given a hero's burial by the Bafloung. He would be regarded as one of the Bafloung nation and be honoured in spirit by the people he had helped.

One of the most important pillars upon which the traditional religion of African people rests is a belief in reincarnation and the transmigration of souls. There is the belief that when you die, you are reincarnated immediately after death as that type of animal which your people regard as their totem.

The Zulu people had twelve totems, among which were the elephant, the lion, the leopard and the fierce snake that is known as the mamba. Zulu people believed that when one of their kings died, he would be reincarnated as a mamba. If, after the death of a king, a mamba was seen entering the king's kraal, this was taken as a sign that the king had returned to his people, inside the body of the mamba. While the mamba was in the hut, that hut and several others next to it would be evacuated of all human life. The mamba was allowed to stay in peace inside the hut for as long as it chose.

Zulu people never willingly killed a lion, as it was the symbol of their king and his surrogate. In old Zululand, any stranger who killed a lion lived to regret it!

There were tribes who had certain birds as their totem and who protected them with their lives, if necessary. Some tribes who had particular trees as their totem also guarded these with their lives.

Among the Batswana and the Basotho people there was a very ancient tribe called the Mgwana, 'the crocodile people', who regarded the crocodile as their totem and their holiest animal symbol. If a Mgwani was killed by an elephant, he was deeply mourned, but if a Mgwani was killed by a crocodile, it was believed either that he had been greatly honoured by one of his ancestral spirits or that he had angered them.

In the land once called Rhodesia and now known as Zimbabwe, there is a tribe of people who also regard the crocodile as their totem. These people are the Tangwane people, a name which also means 'people of the crocodile'.

The Tangwane people were deeply humiliated by a group of white colonialists, among whom was a particular gentleman from England who held black people in utter contempt. The white officers and other officials caused great suffering to a very holy chief, called Rekhi Tangwane, whom they had treated cruelly and with disrespect. One day, in my presence, a group of Tangwane elders met under a tree and solemnly placed a curse on the worst of the white officials. They prayed to the great crocodile of heaven to bring immediate death to the white man who had insulted and injured their chief. They made an image of this man from clay and then they shattered it ceremonially with a crocodile carved out of Rhodesian teak.

A few weeks later, a vehicle in which the official was travelling stalled while crossing a river. The official was seized and savagely mauled by a crocodile which appeared from nowhere. Someone managed to shoot the crocodile and save him, but he later died from the severe injuries. Needless to say, the Tangwane people believed that one of their ancestral spirits had been sent to punish the man, and his lingering, painful death was regarded as quite befitting the crime committed against their holy chief.

The lives of ordinary human beings are full of coincidences and so is history. Today, there are many South African game reserves set aside to protect wild animals. What is amazing to a student of tribal history is that many of these game reserves were established by white operatives in areas which had already been claimed as lands of animals by some of our greatest kings, hundreds of years ago. For example, everyone knows about South Africa's Kruger National Park, but very few realize that it was a sacred land of animals where great Shangani kings forbade all hunting without royal permission.

In KwaZulu-Natal, the Umfolozi Game Reserve and the Ndumo Game Reserve were first proclaimed by Shaka as far back as 1823, when that great and far-sighted, though fiercely warlike, Zulu monarch set aside areas where animals were to exist without interference by human beings. A game reserve was not just a place where animals dwelt in peace, it was set aside with gods and animals in mind. A game reserve was regarded as the sacred place of the gods where no hunting or shedding of blood was allowed. In the Umfolozi area, only the king was allowed to hunt animals, and then only on very sacred occasions.

Africans did not hunt animals for fun. They were hunted for food and for religious reasons. In many instances a religious hunt was conducted by the king once, and once only, during his lifetime.

In the land now called Botswana there exists a very spiritual place which, these days, is called the Tuli Block. The great King Khama, who ruled the country during the nineteenth century, forbade all hunting for a very strange reason. It is said that King Khama and his men were hunting in the Tuli Block near the Shashi River, one of the holiest rivers in southern Africa, when they suddenly saw, descending from the heavens, a great, growing sphere of light. The light hovered above the ground for a long time and was seen by more than a hundred armed warriors. It is said that, clearly visible inside this glowing sphere of light, there were two gigantic, man-like entities which stood facing each other and performing mysterious tasks with their hands.

After this incident, King Khama declared the entire Tuli Block a sacred place where all hunting and shedding of blood was forbidden for all time.

If you want to learn about the true greatness of the black people of Africa, you must examine the hundreds of wise sayings of every tribe and nation. Here, you will discover the depth of African traditional wisdom and knowledge. If you study these proverbs you will find, for example, that Africans knew about the importance of a healthy, clean environment long before other people.

The African people knew, just as the native American people knew, that if you destroy the environment, you will ultimately destroy the human race. Among many African proverbs to do with the environment and with animals is this one: 'That which scratches the wild animal, also scratches the human being.' This proverb means that if you do evil to wild animals, evil will ultimately rebound on your fellow human beings.

A remarkable Tswana proverb states that 'He who buries the tree will next bury the wild animal, and after that, bury his own ox, and ultimately, bury his own children.' This saying indicates that people were aware, even in ancient times, of the interdependence of all living creatures upon this Earth, and that if you harm one, you harm others and, in the end, yourself.

Although African people kept livestock in the form of cattle, sheep, goats and chickens, they were sometimes forced by necessity to go into the wilds in search of animals whose skins could be used for blankets, bags, and items of attire. These animals were very often dassies (also called rock rabbits or hyraxes) or black-backed jackals, and from time to time, large antelopes.

The hunt was always governed by very strict rules and taboos. Elders kept a close watch on all the hunters to make sure that no-one brought down more animals than was necessary for meat and for skins. You were not allowed to hunt more animals than you actually needed, and you were not allowed to leave the carcass rotting in the bush. This was regarded as very unlucky.

In other words, you were not allowed to bring back more than you could carry or more than your family could use within a given time.

Hunting was always preceded and followed by elaborate rituals: a knot was tied in the tail-hairs of the animal which had been brought down, as a gesture to the soul of the dead animal requesting it to forgive the hunters for robbing it of its living home and wishing it a speedy rebirth.

Africans carefully studied the animals' way of life and all hunting was forbidden when it was mating season and when animals were pregnant with young. It was regarded as the blackest of bad luck for a hunter to bring down a pregnant antelope. If this happened, it was believed that one of the hunter's wives would die during childbirth.

Although Africans had domesticated animals such as dogs and cats, they often enlisted the assistance of wild animals under certain circumstances in their daily lives. For example, all large African villages produced piles of bones from the meat eaten by the villagers, especially military kraals which housed as many as ten thousand warriors. These warriors were great meat-eaters and piles of bones accumulated outside the stockade of each kraal.

The warriors encouraged large groups of hyena to live in the bush, as these scavengers disposed of the bones. The warriors and their families also encouraged warthogs and bushpigs to live peacefully outside the kraal – and sometimes inside the kraal. The role of these greedy animals was to dispose of left-over food scraps in the form of corncakes and stale maize porridge.

African kings rejoiced every time migrating animals thundered through their kingdoms, for they knew that these animals would leave a great swath of dung along the route. When the rains came, the bush would be green and the grass would grow tall as a result of the fertilization of the land by the herds.

It is a fact well known to all students of Zulu history that the vulture enjoyed special favour in the eyes of Zulu kings, as did hyena and jackal. These birds, which were known as *izinyoni-ze-nkosi*, or 'the birds of the king', helped to dispose of the corpses of executed criminals which were dumped in deep gullies not far from the kings' great kraals.

Criminals were not given the honour of a decent burial under Zulu culture, but were thrown into a gully after execution for vultures to feast upon. Even today, the Zulus have a saying, 'You shall die and be eaten by vultures,' which refers to a person who will be punished for committing a heinous crime.

Africans occasionally captured living wild animals to extract what they regarded as medicinal substances. For example, they knew that the eland produced much richer milk than a domestic cow and that it had powerful medicinal properties for helping children. When a Zulu child was weak and sickly at birth, the child was often fed eland's milk. The eland cows were specially captured and milked for this purpose before being released and sent scampering back into the bush.

Zulus sometimes captured living hyena, plucked hairs off their tails and then released them back into the wild. They believed that the tail-hairs of a hyena, and even its whiskers, could induce sleep in sleepless children if the hairs were burnt on charcoal.

It is a known fact that African warriors wore headdresses made from, among other things, the feathers of birds such as ostriches, herons and eagles. However, many people do not know that a warrior never wore the feathers of a bird that he had killed, as this was regarded as very unlucky. The bird had to be alive when the feathers were taken from its wing or tail, and then be released. Great care was taken to remove only those feathers which would in no way impair the bird's flight or wellbeing.

When I was a young boy, my grandfather taught me how to capture a bird and remove two of its feathers. A hole was dug that was big enough for me to stand upright in. A lid of saplings and green branches was laid over the hole and a young dassie or hare was tied to the top. When a bird, such as a large eagle, soared down to snatch the animal, the boy hidden under the lid would reach out and pluck two feathers from the tail or the wings as it struggled to lift its prey. It was a risky task which, if one was careless, would result in badly lacerated arms. If you did it carefully, though, you were rewarded with two feathers from a live eagle which would then soar heavenwards, carrying its prey with it, and you would earn the praise of your elders and peers for your great cunning and courage.

The everyday life of the African of old was governed by scores of taboos, many of which related to the protection of nature, the environment and wildlife, and the protection of domestic animals against acts of cruelty by human beings.

Certain trees were not allowed to be cut down for any reason whatsoever, and there were others which could be cut down only on very special occasions or for very serious reasons.

Among the Batswana people, for example, there is a type of acacia tree known as the *moosu* tree which is only cut down when a local chief dies. It is used to make firewood for the ritual fire that is lit outside the king's home, to light the king's soul to the next world. No-one, even today, is allowed to cut down a *moosu* tree. If you do, the Batswana will publicly accuse you of wishing for the death of their king and you will be severely punished for this crime.

The *umphafa* tree grows in KwaZulu-Natal and other parts of South Africa. No-one was allowed to cut a branch from this tree without first obtaining the permission of the chief or king. In olden days, this tree was used to make cattle-pens because the wood is never eaten by termites and it can last for years. Even if the king had given his permission, you were only allowed to cut off old branches. Cutting off new branches was strictly forbidden, and no more than two branches could be removed from each large tree.

Traditional healers used the bark of different trees in their battle against disease, but when a traditional healer went into the bush to source medicinal bark or roots, he or she was not allowed to take so much bark that it could cause the tree's destruction. The traditional healer believed that if the tree from which he or she obtained the bark was destroyed, all the patients treated with the bark from that tree would die.

So it was in the interests of the traditional healer to keep the tree from which he or she had taken medicinal bark alive and well. No ring-barking was allowed, and only bark from very old branches could be taken.

If modern poachers and defilers of the environment think that game reserve wardens and environment protection officers inflict harsh punishments upon them, they should actually breathe a sigh of relief. In old Africa, if you were caught polluting the environment in any way, no fine or apology was acceptable. Death, and only death – often the most cruel imaginable – was the punishment.

The story is told of a young man who lived in the days of the great King Jobe of the Mthethwa people. He had the strange and offensive habit of urinating into any river or stream he came across. One day, King Jobe was told of this, and decided to make an example of the offender.

The young man was seen urinating into a spring and was promptly arrested by warriors and brought before King Jobe. With a cruel smile upon his face, King Jobe ordered that the young man drink huge volumes of marula beer, which is a very diuretic liquid. Then the young man was fed a huge meal of corncakes and fat goat's meat.

Then the king ordered that a piece of raw hide be tied around the young man's penis so that he was unable to urinate, and a large mealie cob forced into his anus to prevent him from defecating. The helpless young man was then buried up to his waist in a hole in the ground to ensure that he was incapable of relieving himself. He suffered horribly for several days before the king dispatched him with a savage battle-axe blow to the head.

In old KwaZulu-Natal and in other parts of the country, the ancient laws of protecting Mother Earth were enforced to the letter.

If a person was caught throwing refuse or a dead animal into a river or stream, or caught cutting down a tree which the law forbade, then that person was tied hand and foot, his or her belly was slashed open, and the intestines pulled out and tied around the branches of a thorn tree. The victim was left to die a horrible death. Sometimes the victim's eyes and lips were stitched closed with sinew and then he or she was forced to walk through bush where there were man-eating animals.

If you were responsible for killing a sacred animal, you were first beaten unconscious by a troop of women and then, if you were male, you were publicly castrated or, if you were female, your breasts were slashed off. It was said that the great Earth Mother is a very sensitive and quick-tempered goddess, and that only the hideous death of those who offend her can placate her and prevent her from taking revenge on the rest of the tribe.

The short-sighted, arrogant and mindless modern savages who pollute our rivers with industrial effluent and defile the skies with acid rain, and the skulking poachers who murder rhinoceros throughout the continent of Africa today, really ought to consider themselves lucky that they were not born a century or more ago. Had they done what they are doing today in the days of King Jobe, they would have had many hours of regret before the dark angel of death came to relieve them from their agony.

It is not an exaggeration to say that African people had more laws governing people's behaviour towards the Earth, plants and animals than they had governing other acts of human behaviour. When crops were planted, we conducted rituals not only with the aim of ensuring a good harvest, but also to thank the Earth Mother and to apologize for injuring her sacred flesh in order to plant food.

When we hoed to get rid of weeds, rituals were performed as a form of apology to the weeds for having to remove them to save our crops. We understood that weeds were not evil, but were plants which had the misfortune of growing where we had planted our food crops.

At harvest time, we left some of our corn standing so that passing birds could share in the bounty of our fields and, by sharing, bless us and ensure us of plenty of food. Sometimes large fields of corn and millet were planted. These were sacred to the goddess and were offered to the vast armies of birds to eat. No human being could enter the sacred cornfield.

These sacred fields were ploughed far from the ordinary millet, maize and corn, and they were left unfenced. Over the centuries, people had discovered that the star gods sometimes communicated with human beings through these sacred fields. Time and again, strange circular depressions were seen in the centre of these fields. These depressions were called *izishoze zamatongo*, the great circles of the gods.

These circles are an amazing sight to see. The stalks of corn or millet are never cut by the gods when they form these depressions. It appears as though a great, circular, disk-shaped force has descended on the field. It presses the corn firmly into the ground, without breaking the stalks or damaging the plants. Then the force appears to spin, resulting in the strange spiral appearance of the fallen stalks. Words cannot describe such a phenomenon, which I have seen more than thirty times in the course of my life as a traditional healer. Whenever a circle appeared in the fields, the people rushed to erect a fence of poles around the circle. They would dance and perform other sacred rituals honouring the star gods and the Earth Mother.

All the kings and chiefs awaited the arrival of these circles. The appearance would be cause for celebrations which lasted several days. These celebrations were accompanied by prayers to the gods to watch over the people and to talk to them through the sacred circles.

When Africans ploughed the sacred and the ordinary grainfields, they never raked out the stumps of the previous year's corn. They were ploughed under to feed the soil and keep it fertile.

Many tribes practised a strange ritual, especially during winter, when they gathered all the left-overs from their meals in grass baskets every two or three days and took them to the cornfields where they were ceremonially buried. This was done while the fields were fallow and was called 'feeding the grandmother'. This ritual, which our grandparents told us was thousands of years old, was practised as recently as my childhood years, until it was forbidden by over-zealous and ignorant missionaries.

In olden times, African tribes were forced by law to recycle the ash from cooking fires. If the village's ash dump showed signs of growing too big, some of the ash was taken away in baskets, mixed with sand and water to form a cement-like paste, and used to repair hut floors. It was also used to build paths in front of huts and the low mud walls that bordered these places.

Ash was also made into a paint and used to rid cattle of ticks. If a cow was heavily infested with ticks, you dug a hole, filled it with ash and water, mixed it into paint similar to whitewash and then, using a broom, painted the cow with it. Ticks would drop off the beast and it would be relieved of its agony.

Some tribes, such as the Batswana, had another ingenious way of ridding cattle of ticks using wood ash. They would dig a hole just outside the entrance to their cattle-pens and fill it with ash. When the cattle were driven in and out of the pen, they passed through this heap of ash, and this caused the ticks to drop off.

Ash was also used as a disinfectant. If anyone died of an infectious disease, they were buried in an ash dump. Very deep graves were dug and some ash was poured into it before the person was buried. When the grave had been filled, a heap of ash was poured over it to prevent the disease from killing others. Africans believed that negative spirits were afraid of wood ash, and it was used freely in combating these entities.

Some people believed that ticks were the offspring of evil spirits as they could not stand being covered with ash.

One of the laws protecting the environment was that high-ranking people were strictly forbidden from eating particular types of food. It was believed that certain foods, which were freely eaten by ordinary people, would cause droughts and other ecological disasters if consumed by high-ranking people.

For example, there is a very nutritious bean which the Zulus call *indumba* (cowpea), which is particularly delicious when boiled in water with a little cow fat and salt. Traditional healers and clairvoyants are forbidden from eating *indumba*. It is said that if a sangoma or an *inyanga* eats these beans, all the good spirits will take flight and ill-luck in the form of cattle disease or man-killing epidemics will call upon the community.

There is also a kind of sweet cane, called *imfe*, which many Zulus love to chew when it is in season. Delicious as it is to eat, and beneficial though it is because of its fibre content and tooth-cleaning properties, *imfe* is forbidden to chiefs, princes and princesses. It is said that if a person of royal blood breaks the taboo and chews *imfe*, a great illness will affect cattle and human beings, and crops will perish in a great drought.

One day, King Langalibalele, who lived in the Natal Midlands during the nineteenth century, yielded to temptation and chewed some *imfe*. A great blight ruined his people's cornfields and a savage disease that had never been seen before in that area swept away hundreds of cattle. To this day, traditional historians always point out Langalibile's mistake. He is called the king who chewed *imfe* and caused the death of his country.

Before I end this introduction to *Isilwane – The Animal*, let me tell you about two more taboos, the breaking of which is said to bring great disaster to the offender's land.

Many years ago, when I was still a child, one of my father's half-brothers kicked down the door of his rondavel and caught his wife and a neighbour in bed together. My father's half-brother took his knobkerrie and beat the man to within an inch of his adulterous life. And then he took a sjambok and beat his wife. The matter was brought before the tribal court in the chief's village and my father's half-brother was fined five head of cattle because he had broken the taboo that forbade wife-beating. It was believed that if a man thrashed his spouse during the growing season, the great mother goddess and the female ancestral spirits would withhold rain from the country as punishment for this offence.

While corn, maize, millet and pumpkins were growing in the fields, no-one was allowed to beat any female for any reason, even if she had committed a crime.

Herd-boys carried long whips with which they controlled cattle while they drove them between the pastures and the cattle-pens. During the growing season, you were not allowed to use your whip on cows, nanny-goats and ewes. You could crack the whip to frighten a cow into returning to the herd if she showed signs of wandering, but you were not allowed to whip her.

African laws and taboos were sometimes very strange indeed.

One of the holiest substances known to Africans is salt. Salt is regarded as the sweat of the great Earth Mother, crystallized by the sun god for the benefit of human beings and animals. For many centuries, Africans treated salt with respect, and in many urban and rural areas of South Africa this is still the case. The ancient laws of Africa die hard.

I wish you happy reading, enlightenment and peace.

CREDO VUSAMAZULU MUTWA

PART I
DOMESTIC ANIMALS

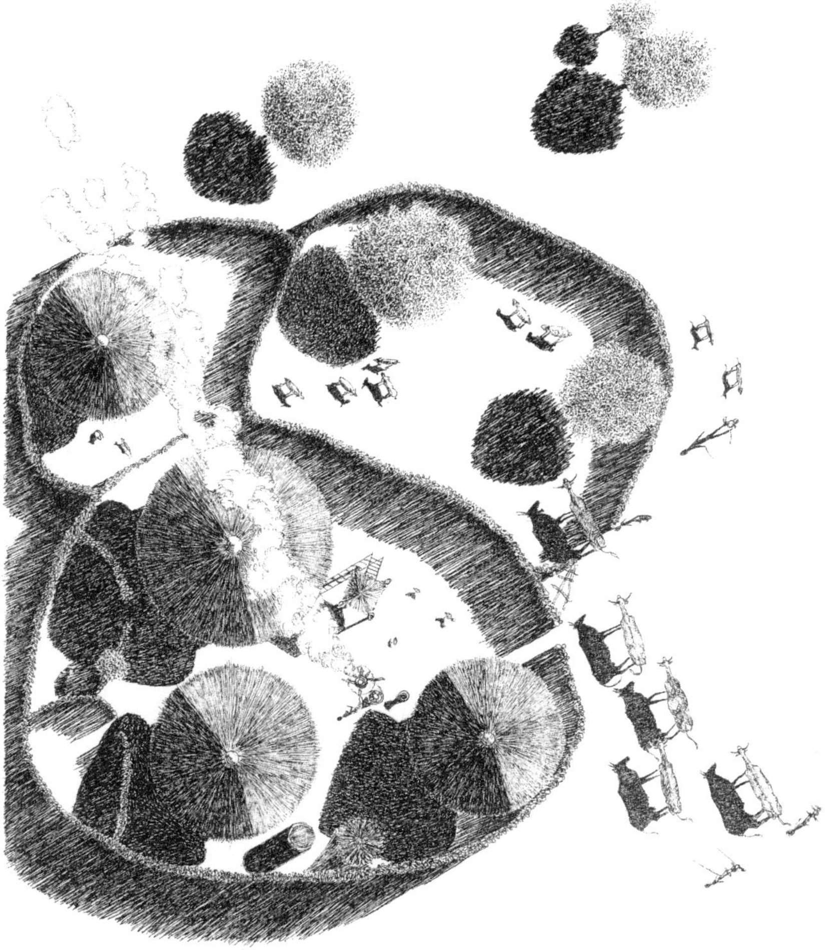

PRAISE SONG TO THE CAT

You are a gentle-looking calabash that hides lightning inside it
You are the beautiful one who hides a sharp cruelty
You are the proud one whom no-one can ever tame!
Feared by the *mantindane* and the *tokoloshe*
You are the one whom the mice treat with reverence and before whom the rats flee
You are the cat!
You, whose eyes shine like fires, like cold fires in the darkness
You, whose ears hear everything
And whose nose can smell everything
You are the cat, the tamer of human beings and not tamed by them!
You are the animal whom we all fear, the darling of sorcerers, the beloved of witches and the treasure of sangomas.
You are the cat whose very footstep is a whisper
You are the cat whose claws hide red lightning
You are the cat, the guardian of the village, protecting us alike from enemies we can see and enemies we cannot see!
No evil spirit dare set foot where you are heard mewing, oh cat
No *tokoloshe* dare intrude where you wash your face!
Sent by the greatest gods to shield the world from unseen demons and from visible rats and mice, the carriers of the most fearsome of diseases and the bringers of weeping to the villages
Oh cat, tamer of human beings!
Oh cat, master of all life!
I honour you when I come home
I give you your food which you often disdainfully refuse, telling me that my

fortune must change for the better!
Oh cat, when I sleep, before I lay myself down upon the mat at night, I must send you outside to guard me while I am asleep,
That no night-walking *mantindane* may intrude where I hide,
That my dreams may not be disturbed by the knobkerrie of the *tokoloshe*,
That the *umkhovu*, the zombie, may never dare to undo the thongs that bind the woven door of my hut.
I honour you, cat
May the gods and the ancestors always see to it that I have milk and fat meat to delight you!
For they say that he who denies food to a cat will suffer blindness for the rest of his days.

MORE THAN JUST A PET

Domestic cats were kept by Africans for practical as well as magical reasons. Domestic cats were kept to eliminate mice and rats in their huts and kraals. But there was another practical reason: wherever there is a cat, the snake is conspicuous by its absence. It was not only rats or mice that found their way into huts and damaged foodstuffs – some types of poisonous snake hid in huts and were known to bite people while they were sitting or sleeping.

When I was young, living in rural Zululand (now KwaZulu-Natal), I saw many people being treated for poisonous snake bites after they had been bitten inside their huts. Inside a typical Zulu beehive grass hut, most of the floor was kept free of utensils and all the pots and the calabashes were placed on a raised platform at the far end, opposite the door. This raised platform, called *ithala*, was situated in the part of the hut known as *umsamo*.

Zulu grass huts had no windows, which meant that the light was dim inside. When you entered a hut it often took quite some time for your eyes to adjust to the semi-darkness. Many people would enter a hut, walk over to the pots and calabashes and start rummaging among them for food. They wouldn't see a snake hidden among the utensils. The next thing, that person felt the snake's fangs sinking into his or her hand, sometimes with fatal results.

For this reason, Zulus kept cats in their huts. They even had special enclosures filled with fresh river sand for cats to stay in. Zulus especially spoilt their cats. Milk and meat were always on the menu. And when a cat came striding into a hut, it was not uncommon to hear its owner singing a specially composed song, praising that pampered animal.

The eating habits of a domestic cat were carefully observed by its owners. If a cat appeared to have a poor appetite it was immediately taken to the local sangoma for treatment. There were herbal medicines aplenty to keep domestic cats fighting fit.

PROTECTOR AGAINST THE *TOKOLOSHE* AND THE *MANTINDANE*

When night fell, cats were often chased from the huts, especially large tom-cats. If a person owned a tom-cat and a female cat, only the female cat was allowed to remain inside. The reason for this brings us to the magical use that Africans had for cats. There are certain mysterious creatures of which Africans are mortally afraid; creatures that prowl the bush when night falls under the African skies.

Throughout Africa, there is a belief that domestic cats have the power to protect people not only against rats, mice and poisonous snakes, but also against the dreaded *tokoloshe* and the even more feared and abhorred *mantindane.*

African people believe that when a cat sees a group of *mantindane* approaching a village, it will always start howling, thereby alerting its owners to the danger and frightening away the alien creatures. I can testify to the fact that, especially on farms and in rural black villages, cats, as well as dogs, often set up a fearful racket for no logical reason, especially in summer. When you listen to the noise, not only with your physical ears, but also with your spiritual inner ear, you can sense that these animals see something out of the ordinary.

Africans believe that treating a cat properly guarantees that it will protect you against the *tokoloshe* and the *mantindane.*

THE *TOKOLOSHE* AND THE *MANTINDANE*

From the Cape right up to Zaïre, there is a fearful creature known as the *tokoloshe.* It is short, thickset, round-headed and furry, with a round snout and a pair of glowing, bright red eyes. It has pointed ears and a thick, bony ridge extending from above its forehead to the nape of its neck. This creature, short though it is, is extremely aggressive and viciously cruel. It specializes in sexually assaulting women and challenging benighted travellers to stick fights which it triumphantly wins.

In the course of my career as a traditional healer I have come across many women who have been sexually molested and even raped by this terrible creature, which moves in the shadowy field where the real and the unreal, the visible and the invisible meet.

As a *sanusi*, I have treated many men who have been beaten and frightened out of their wits by the *tokoloshe*. However, there are some people, especially white sceptics, who believe that the *tokoloshe* is nothing more than a figment of African superstition and fertile imagination.

With over fifty years of experience, I must appeal to these sceptics to think again. The *tokoloshe* is real – it does exist. I have seen the way it injures men and women who are unfortunate enough to fall into its clutches. When Africans fear the *tokoloshe* they are not fearing a figment of their imaginations. Instead of being laughed off by sceptics, the *tokoloshe* deserves investigation.

There is another creature which is not unlike the *tokoloshe* in its love of inflicting bodily harm, and which is also greatly feared. The Zulu name for this creature is *mantindane*. Like the *tokoloshe*, the *mantindane* stands about three-and-a-half feet tall. Unlike the *tokoloshe*, which is a powerfully built, almost chimpanzee-like creature, it appears extremely frail. It has a large, bald, egg-shaped head which can be as large as a fully grown watermelon, and it has very weak-looking jaws. Its mouth is little more than a slit and the nose is rudimentary, with nostrils like comma-shaped holes. The creature's eyes are very strange and resemble beans. They are slanted and covered with what looks like thick, jet-black plastic or horn. It has a very thin neck, narrow shoulders and long, thin arms, and its hands, although resembling those of a human being, are very thin and long. Its long, thin and bony fingers have more joints than those of a human being.

The creature's two spindly legs end in long, delicate feet. The *mantindane* is civilized and highly intelligent, and unlike the *tokoloshe*, which appears stark-naked, it always wears some type of garment that reaches from its neck and covers its limbs completely. The colour of this creature's skin is a strange greyish white with slight pink overtones.

Like the *tokoloshe*, the *mantindane* treats human beings who fall into its hands cruelly and with utter contempt. It kidnaps males and females and scoops out flesh from their legs, thighs and even buttocks and upper arms. Unlike the *tokoloshe* which is solitary, *mantindane* operate in groups. There can be as many as twenty of these vicious creatures in one group.

Sometimes a gang of *mantindane* will kidnap a person and ill-treat him or her. They will then release the person, only to kidnap them again a few months or even a few years later.

I have met many black men and women throughout Africa who have been kidnapped by these creatures several times, and who bear scars on their bodies that testify to their terrible ordeals at the hands of these strange and fearful beings.

I have personally fallen victim to *mantindane* – not once, but three times – and I still carry scars on my body that testify to the truth of what I say.

CATS MUST BE WELL LOOKED AFTER

African people believe that cats, being magical animals, are capable of putting curses of a most terrible nature upon people who ill-treat them, under-feed them or allow them to fall ill.

Zulu kings and queens kept as many as forty cats in their royal huts and, needless to say, these cats were terribly spoilt and pampered.

All African kings had a special servant who was known as 'the keeper of the cats'. This was a trusted man or woman, a person whose courage was beyond dispute, whose duty it was to guard the king's cats with his or her life. Sometimes enemies of the king would kidnap one of the monarch's cats and then send a message to the ruler, threatening to cast an awful spell over him and his family unless he paid a ransom in the form of cattle or goats, or both. Needless to say, the king very often paid the ransom demanded in return for his precious cat.

The keeper of the cats also protected the felines against sorcerers who regarded them as a delicacy. When a black wizard or witch felt his or her powers ebbing with old age, they would enter a village secretly, steal one of the villagers' cats, take it to a cave far away in the mountains and ceremonially eat it.

There are sangomas in many parts of South Africa who tell fortunes by simply gazing into the eyes of a cat in very much the same way gypsies in Europe gaze into a crystal ball. These sangomas are often very accurate in their divination.

HOW THE CAT CAME TO LIVE WITH HUMAN BEINGS

This story takes place in the oldest of old days, during the time known as *Ncwebamatshe*. This was the time when the rocks were as soft as clay – so soft that you could pinch them into shapes with your fingers.

Kinto was a brave, cunning and wise man, and a trickster. He was a leader of his people – a position he had acquired by means both fair and foul.

People lived in caves in those days and they lived in fear. The world was filled with fearsome monsters, many of which were bitterly hostile towards human beings. There were great serpents that roamed the land, some of them so huge that they could easily be mistaken for mountains. There were great birds, bigger than an ostrich – some even bigger than an elephant – which ran across the plains or flew through the heavens. Against such creatures, human beings could do nothing except hide.

One day, Kinto was sitting next to a warming fire deep in the bowels of his cave, shaping weapon-heads out of stone. All of a sudden he heard loud screams coming from the bush below his cave. Within a few moments, a crowd of men, women and children came running towards his cave, fleeing from something which had driven them with terror almost to the brink of madness.

'What is it, my brothers and sisters?' asked Kinto.

'A giant!' replied the people, running for the depths of the cave. 'There is a giant out there! He suddenly appeared out of nowhere, and is seizing and devouring people – one after the other – like little mice! Save us, great Kinto! Save us with your great wisdom! Help us!'

'What do you want me to do?' asked Kinto. 'What can I do against a giant?'

'You are the great Kinto,' cried the people. 'Your cunning and courage are without equal in this land. Help us, great Kinto, or we shall die. For a long time you have been our leader. For a long time we have looked up to you and we know that if anyone can help us against rampaging monsters, that person is you!'

Kinto struggled to his feet. He was lame in one leg and he could not move very fast. He hobbled painfully towards the entrance of the cave and arrived there just in time to see the monstrous giant emerging from the dense bush at the bottom of the mountain. He watched with a terrified and sinking heart as the lumbering monster made its way up the mountain like a huge, grotesque ape. The giant was ugly, with a face like that of a baboon. His beard was grey, his hair a thick bush on top of his head. And even from that distance, Kinto could smell the unwashed body of the giant.

Frightened out of his wits, Kinto turned to flee. But as he did so, he stumbled on a loose stone and fell. The giant must have seen him, because he hurried up the mountain and, before Kinto could struggle to his feet, the giant entered the cave, stooping low.

'Aaaagghh . . . little human being,' said the giant, laughing, as he hauled Kinto to his feet. 'Why are you unable to run like the others?'

'Because I am a cripple, giant,' replied Kinto. 'My leg was broken long ago . . .'

'Who broke your leg?' asked the giant.

'Oh, great giant,' replied Kinto, 'it is the custom of our people that if you are elected as leader over them, they break one of your legs with a very big stone, so that you cannot escape.'

'Aaaagghh . . . so they broke your leg? This is why you could not escape from me. Now little human being, I know that your people are hiding deep inside this cave. Call them out. Tell them to come here!'

'But I cannot . . .' started Kinto.

'Call them out!' cried the giant.

Kinto called to the people and they slowly made their way out from the depths of the cave. There were many frightened faces and sweat-covered bodies.

'What do you intend doing, giant?' asked Kinto.

'You and I, old crippled one,' said the giant, 'are going to play a game. Over the next few days you are going to choose the people whom you think I should eat. You are going to pick them out for me. And when I have eaten all of them, it will be your turn!'

'But I cannot allow you to eat my people,' cried Kinto. 'I am their leader, I cannot allow any harm to come to them!'

'Oh yes you can,' rumbled the giant. 'If you do not select two people each day, I shall come into the cave and devour all of them!'

And so it became Kinto's painful duty to go into the depths of the cave each morning and select two people for the giant to devour. Some of the people went willingly to their fate, but others were reluctant and Kinto had to stun them with his club and drag them across the cave for the giant.

'You are doing your work well, my friend,' said the giant on the fifth day.

'But why, oh giant, don't you eat me?' cried Kinto. 'I am tired of bringing you my friends to eat. Please eat me!'

'You are a poor, wrinkled old man and there is not much meat on you,' said the giant. 'But I shall soon remedy that! Every day after dinner, I shall go into the bush and fetch nutritious fruits and wild spinach to feed you so that you can get fat quickly. And to make sure that neither you nor your people escape, I shall tie you near the entrance to the cave like a tame animal. Then I will close the mouth of the cave with a great stone to keep your people from escaping!'

The giant did exactly what he said he would do. Each day after dinner he went deep into the forest and brought back a bag of ripe and delicious wild fruit to feed Kinto.

'Eat up, little man! Eat up!' said the giant whenever Kinto's appetite appeared to be lacking. 'I want you to be nice and fat by the time I eat you!'

Each time the giant left, Kinto prayed for a miracle, for anything that would save him and his people from the horrible giant. As the days passed there were fewer and fewer people left in the darkness of the cave. Only twenty men, women and children were still alive.

'Help me, great spirits of the sky and the Earth!' Kinto prayed. 'Help me to save my people and myself from this merciless monster!' While Kinto was still muttering to himself and praying, he looked up and saw a strange animal sitting on a distant rock. It was a small but beautiful animal, black and white, with large, yellow, intelligent eyes, small, pointed ears and a fat, furry body.

'Greetings, human being,' Kinto heard the animal say. 'Do you need help?'

'You have the power of speech! You can speak!' cried Kinto.

'Of course I can speak, stupid,' said the animal. 'I am one of the cleverest animals on Earth!'

'What kind of animal are you?' asked Kinto.

'I am called Mausana, the cat,' it replied. 'I am known far and wide for my great cunning and fearlessness. I ask you again: do you need help against the giant?'

'I do, I do!' cried Kinto. 'This is the answer to all my prayers! But what can you, such a little, weak-looking animal, do against the giant that holds us captive?'

'I can do a lot,' answered the cat. 'Listen, I have a very good plan.'

'Do you want to tell me about it?'

'Yes,' replied the cat, 'but on one condition . . .'

'Name any condition!' cried Kinto.

'I will help you on the condition that, after I have saved you and your friends, I and others of my kind may live with you to the end of all time.'

'Agreed! Agreed! Agreed!' cried Kinto. 'Tell me about your plan!'

The cat rose from the rock on which it had been sitting, stretched itself luxuriously, and then ambled over to where Kinto crouched, tethered like an animal with a long leather rope, the other end of which was fastened to an old, dead tree which stood just outside the entrance to the cave.

'I can sense the giant's return,' said the cat. 'Now listen, here is my plan. This very day we shall deal with the giant and he will no longer trouble you.'

The cat whispered its plan into Kinto's ear. Kinto doubted the plan would succeed, but anything was worth trying to save the last remaining people.

When the giant returned from the forest, he brought with him the usual bag of wild fruits which he forced Kinto to eat. When Kinto had eaten his fill, the giant gave him a bowl of fresh water to drink.

'I want you to have a lot of blood in you when it is your turn to be eaten,' said the giant to Kinto, 'I do not enjoy bloodless morsels.'

When Kinto had had his fill, the giant released him from the leather rope that held him captive and ordered him to get into the cave and select the fattest people he could find.

Kinto staggered to his feet and the giant sat down at the entrance to the cave. Instead of going to the depths of the cave to fetch the people as the giant had demanded, Kinto reached down behind a rock and brought out the cat.

Then he hurled the cat with all his strength at the giant's head and dashed forward, just as the cat had instructed him to do. As the cat landed on top of the giant's head, it dug its claws deep into the giant's scalp. The giant sprang to his feet, howling with anger, fear and pain. Kinto ran forward and seized the cat firmly by its tail, forcing it to dig its claws even deeper.

'Don't do that!' roared the giant. 'Let go of its tail! Let go of its tail!'

Such was the giant's agony that he became completely blind and, in trying to escape and trying to shake the cat off, he ran into a great rock and fell to the ground, stunned. When consciousness returned a few moments later, he turned and ran down the mountain towards the dense bush, with the cat clinging fiercely to his scalp and scratching him for all it was worth! The giant screamed a loud, sky-shattering scream of pain – a scream that grew fainter and fainter as he fled for his life, trying to shake the cat from his head.

Later, when the sun had set, Kinto and the surviving people saw the cat return with a proud and mischievous expression on its furry face.

'Well, friends,' said the cat. 'I got rid of that giant!'

'Where is he?' asked Kinto.

'Don't worry about him, he will never return – except, perhaps, as a ghost in your dreams! In blind panic he ran and ran, with me clinging to his scalp, until he came to a great precipice. He was about to fall to his doom, when I jumped off his head onto the branch of a tree. He tumbled over the edge and now lies among the snarling rocks, with his bones completely broken!'

'Thank you, oh cat! Thank you! Thank you! Thank you!' said Kinto.

And the people said, 'You have saved us!'

'But do you remember your side of the bargain?' asked the cat.

'Of course we do!' said Kinto and the people in unison.

'Well, I have brought my friends and relatives with me.'

A long procession of cats arrived at the cave: tom-cats, female cats and kittens of all colours and sizes. The people were astonished. Within a short while it was apparent that they were not the masters, not the keepers of the cats. The cats were the keepers of the human beings.

PRAISE SONG TO THE DOG

You are the great devourer, oh dog, whose praise song I sing now
You are the first sangoma possessed of the powers of seeing into
the future!
When you sense a death coming into the village, you will stand under the
moon and howl
For you feel the agony of the departed one before the others do!
You are the watching eye that protects our slumbers
You are the bark that frightens away thieves and other intruders
You are my friend, closer than my brother is to me
You are my shelter when the mountain wind blows cold
You are the one who crosses the river first, showing me that no
crocodile lies in wait
You are the one who defends our villages
You are the one who cleans our *lapas*
You are the dog, the wise one on four legs, the diviner, the healer,
the sangoma!
You are the dog, the one to whom tomorrow as well as today and
yesterday are one
You are the dog, whose loyalty is beyond question and whose love is deeper
than the seas upon which the white men sail their ships
You are the dog, whose affection is higher than the skies and more enduring
than the mountains of uKhahlamba!
You will die before I come to any harm, oh dog
To you, love is all and all is love
To you, life is a song and not an empty mirage, cursed by old men in their
sunset years!

Dog, as long as man walks upon this Earth
You shall find your way, your place in his heart
Dog, as long as man walks these plains, he shall need you.
No animal can replace you in his heart, nor in his life
No animal can hold before his eyes the same light that you do!
You are the opener of hearts, the bringer of love even from the hardest of souls.
Dog, you are the music in my heart and the praise song on my tongue
Dog, you are the smile upon my lips and the caress of the tips of my fingers!
For every ounce of love I show you, you return a full pound of the same
Every droplet of tenderness and loyalty that I give you, you return a whole river full of it!
Inja, dog, the devourer of darkness
Long may your voice be heard on the plains of Africa
Long may you bring smiles to the orphaned child
Long may you still tears from the widow's eyes
Long may you bring companionship and comfort to the wrinkled hearts of ancient men!
Bayete inja!

MAN'S BEST FRIEND

Throughout Africa, the dog is called by a name that means 'the purifying devourer'. The Zulu word for dog is *inja*, and in Sesotho or Setswana it is called *ntja*. Both words have to do with eating or devouring.

A dog is called this by the Zulu, Basotho and the Tswana peoples, because it is said that in ancient times the dog finished off the meat left over by cave-dwelling hunters and their families. If the dog had not been there, the lives of the hunters would be in danger as vicious scavengers, such as hyena, would invade the cave in search of the leftovers.

According to legend, it was not human beings who first tamed dogs or cats. Solitary animals approached human beings and lived near to and, eventually, among them. Human beings were efficient food-finders, and cats and dogs, being intelligent by nature – although rather lazy at times – found it in their interests to remain close to human beings.

In olden days as well as fairly modern times, Africans took great care of their dogs, because the dog was not only the human being's friend, it was also his protector and saviour. A loyal dog would often give its life to save that of its owner.

I remember clearly what used to happen when we were young. I attended a school that was situated on the far side of a wide river. The river was inhabited by crocodiles, especially after heavy rains, and I witnessed some very disturbing and heart-rending scenes.

When a group of pupils approached the river with the intention of wading across, their dogs insisted on crossing first and of their own free will. If the dogs reached the opposite bank unharmed, the schoolchildren knew there were no crocodiles in that part of the river and they could cross safely. But if one of the dogs was suddenly seized and dragged away by a crocodile, the children had no option but to wait for a group of adults to help them across the river, and watch out for any crocodiles that lurked in the water.

Sometimes we crossed the river with our dogs paddling behind or beside us. Occasionally, one of the dogs would suddenly vanish underwater with a loud yelp of agony and fear. Given the choice between taking a human being or a dog, a crocodile preferred the dog. I do not know why.

In olden days, when a Zulu king sent a trusted servant on a dangerous mission to a strange land, he said a very old Zulu proverb: 'The river which is unknown must first be forded by your best dog.'

Although KwaZulu-Natal enjoys predominantly beautiful, warm weather, it can become so cold that snow forms upon the great Drakensberg range and the Ulundi mountains. Whenever we herded livestock on such bitterly cold days, we always made sure our dogs came with us to keep us warm. If a herd-boy in the veld had no means of lighting a fire to keep himself warm, all he needed to do was gently call his dogs and order them to lie as close as possible to him. The dogs' bodies would generate enough heat to keep the herd-boy warm.

When we lay under the stars guarding our parents' cattle against stock thieves and the night was bitterly cold, we had good reason to thank our four-legged friends whose furry bodies kept us warm.

DOGS OF WAR

Africans did not use dogs only for hunting or guarding their kraals and villages. Specially trained dogs were used in war because of their ability to track down and deal with enemies. War dogs often wore collars fitted with razor-sharp blades, and whenever the dog approached an enemy, it could use its armed collar to lacerate the enemy's legs.

Dogs were used to send messages from village to village and between tribes. A square piece of white softwood on which a message had been burnt with a hot needle would be tied around the dog's neck before it was sent running. These messages were often cryptic. A paste consisting of soot mixed with animal fat could be used to paint a message onto the flanks of the messenger dog before the dog was set free to run through enemy lines and look for help. The message could also take the form of two or three bead necklaces.

It may interest you to know that in the long and bloody war that finally led to the independence of Namibia, Ovambo villagers used dogs to warn hidden Swapo fighters about the presence of South African troops. If the South Africans were coming from the south, the Ovambo villagers made a mark on the dog's tail. If they were approaching from the north, they would mark the dog's nose; from the east – on the right side of the dog, and from the west – on its left side. The Ovambo have made use of this form of bush courier service for centuries.

Many years ago I worked in a country called Rwanda-Burundi (today it is two separate countries, Rwanda and Burundi). Here I found two tribes which had been at war with each other for many years. One of the tribes was called the Watutsi and the other the Bahutu. The Watutsi are tall warriors, some almost seven feet tall, while the Bahutu are Africans of average height.

In a war in which spears were used (prior to the horrific proliferation of automatic guns throughout Africa), the Watutsi people won battle after battle against the shorter Bahutu because of their height and their expertise in combat. But the Bahutu people had a secret weapon in the form of a dog called a *basenji* – a very fierce and fearless creature which, for some reason, is unable to bark. The Bahutu used these dogs to defend their villages against Watutsi attackers. The *basenji* dogs would attack the Watutsi warriors by biting the backs of their legs and bringing them down so that Bahutu spearmen could dispatch them.

In many parts of southern Africa, dogs used for warfare were often disguised in strange ways with bark cloth and oxide paint to give them a fearsome appearance. Some were disguised as mythical animals with two or three heads, while others were painted with fearsome patterns and had their ferocity increased by rubbing an onion-like bulb on their gums. This bulb mildly irritates the gums, causing the dog to bare its fangs. Dogs were also fed a diet of mashed scorpions (with their stings removed) and minced meat to increase their fearlessness and ferocity. This practice is still followed in many areas of southern Africa.

Africans took good care of their canine friends, whether they were domestic dogs or dogs of war. It was regarded as a disaster for a dog to fall ill, and traditional healers have more than one hundred different herbal preparations that are used specifically to heal sick dogs.

HELPING THE SICK

When a dog bites a person who is not an enemy, the people of the village sometimes take a few hairs from the dog and place them, together with a powdered herbal preparation, on the wound. This causes the injury to heal rapidly and prevents the victim from being attacked by dogs in the future.

Dog excrement has great medicinal value. It is used to treat many illnesses in central and eastern Africa and parts of southern Africa. When I was working in Uganda, I fell victim to one of the most painful diseases: typhoid. I was sick, utterly delirious, and if I had not been helped I would have died. A medicine woman named Opanga saved my life.

I did not know how sick I was or what was forced into my mouth on a daily basis as I lay very close to death. When I started recovering, I learned that she was using dried dog excrement to snatch my life from the arms of eternal death.

TELEPATHIC COMMUNICATORS

One encounters many amazing things while travelling through Africa. In old Africa, traditional healers instructed all dog owners how to establish daily telepathic communication between themselves and these loyal animals. Very often, the results were spectacular. I remember how one of my mother's brothers, who had made a fine art of telepathy between himself and his pack of four ridgebacks, was saved from a horrible death in the coils of a large python. He managed to send a mind-call (as we call telepathy) to his dogs far away, to come to his assistance. The ridgebacks ran a distance of just over two miles, in time to attack the python with ferocity and to save my uncle.

FAITHFUL TO THE END

There is another story about one of my uncle's dogs which saved him from a python. The leader of the pack was a huge brute called Bushman. He played a strange part in my life and planted in my soul a deep love of all dogs.

Bushman lived for a long time and became quite old. Eventually, he was unable to go out with his children and grandchildren into the bush. He just lay under the granary, close to the hut in which I lived, with his head resting flat upon his paws, his old eyes still gleaming with hidden fires which would soon be dimmed – fires of love, great courage and amazing intelligence.

As a child I had few friends, but when I was twelve years old, I met a very naughty boy named Sigodi. We soon got into many scrapes, one of which earned us a caning from the teacher at the local mission school.

One day, Sigodi and I were lost in dense bush not far from the mountains. We spent a whole day trying to find our way out, only to discover that we were walking around in circles and getting extremely exhausted, hungry and thirsty.

Night fell, a night of pure terror, and we huddled together, two lonely souls from which all mischief had been washed by fear, listening to the yapping of jackal and the threatening laughter of distant hyena. Two very frightened little boys spent the night under a rock, shivering with terror more than cold.

As the sun rose, we heard shouting and calling from far away, from a search party which had set out to look for us. But we were unable to respond to the calls because our mouths were dry and our tongues were beginning to swell with thirst. And then suddenly, just before midday, we both saw a strange sight: staggering towards us out of the bush was the old dog, Bushman.

His tail hung low between his legs, his eyes were dull, and his head was hanging as though he were on his last legs. Bushman came close to us and paused, obviously expecting us to follow him, which we did. And then, miracle of miracles, we came to a stream where we slaked our thirst, slowly and carefully at first, as the older boys had taught us. We drank our fill, and although we wanted to rest, the old dog would not allow it. He growled and glared at us over his shoulder, commanding us to follow him, whether we liked it or not.

We rose from the refreshing waters of the stream and followed the old dog, which to our amazement had not drunk with us. Bushman led us out of the bush, up and over a rocky hill. He led us straight to the Hlazakazi mission station. When we entered the yard, he disappeared.

Before we could look for Bushman, Sigodi and I were greeted by excited schoolchildren and adults, because the story that we were lost had spread throughout the reservation. When we reached my uncle's kraal, after being well fed by the mission-school teachers, we told him how Bushman had led us to safety. My uncle's eyes widened with surprise and one of his wives said to us, 'Surely what you are telling us cannot be the truth?'

She went on to tell us that Bushman had died early on the morning the search party set out to look for us. He had died without moving an inch from where he lay under the granary.

My uncle, who was an excellent tracker, went to investigate where we had been lost. He found only our tracks and not those of the dog we said had led us out of the dense bush. Then an old man said to my uncle, 'Something must have led them out of that place because many children have been lost there in the past and have never returned. Something must have led the two boys to the mission station.'

To this day, I do not know what that 'something' was. All I do know is that Bushman led us out of the bush, several hours after he had died.

THE PRICE PAID FOR ILL-TREATING A DOG

Africans believe that there are diseases caused by witchcraft, diseases caused by the gods and diseases caused by human weakness. But they also believe that certain diseases attack you if you or a senior member of your family have been cruel to animals.

There is a disease in Africa, regarded by some as related to glaucoma, which causes a young person's eyelids to swell. These swellings soon fill with pus and burst, and the disease is the greatest cause of blindness among Africans.

Many people believe that it is the result of someone denying food or proper nutrition to dogs in his or her home or their parents' home. A great stigma is attached to this disease, and anyone who develops it is soon looked at askance by neighbours, who are sure to think that he or she is being punished for being cruel to animals.

Zulus call a wart by a name which means 'the pointer'. If a person develops a wart on his or her nose, it indicates that this person is a dog hater who has been punished by the dogs' spirits. It is also regarded as a sign from the gods that this sinful person should mend his or her ways before more punishment is visited upon them.

Because of the stigma attached to these growths, many Africans go to great lengths to remove warts from their faces. In old Zululand, if you were troubled by warts, and all herbal means to combat them had failed, you had to go to a prince or princess who, by touching you with his or her royal finger, could make the warts disappear.

BONE OF ASSISTANCE

In the olden days, when traditional healers were still free to practice surgery, the bones of dogs were often used in bone-transplant operations. If a warrior had a splinter of bone chipped off his shin by an enemy battle axe, one of his dogs was killed in a ceremony and a matching splinter was removed from one of the dog's legs. The splinter of bone was boiled and placed on the warrior's injury, and many, many times, the transplanted splinter of dog's bone melded with the human bone and the warrior's limb would be saved.

This gave rise to the belief among Zulu people in particular that God had specially created dogs to save human beings.

There is a Zulu proverb that states, 'The bone of a dog smiles together with the bone of a human being,' and this refers to the great spiritual bond that has always existed between human beings and dogs – and which is something that still exists to this day.

HONOURING THE DOG

To African tribespeople, the dog was a very important animal. It was believed that without dogs, a community of people could not survive. Children were taught that a dog was to be honoured at all times, and be treated with friendship and respect. You were not allowed to kick or swear at a dog. If food ran low in the village, people had to take into account that dogs too had to have their rations. Very often human beings had to share their own food with their canine friends, even if it resulted in great human suffering.

With only one notable exception, the tribes throughout southern Africa were forbidden by law to eat dog meat, even during times of famine. In the whole of southern Africa there is only one tribal group which ritually consumes dog flesh and even they, this tribe which I will not name, ate dogs as a sacrament, as part of the ritual of absorbing the strength, speed and voracity of the canine. Dogs were only eaten when war was imminent and then only by the warriors, who ate the flesh to increase their aggression in battle.

THE DIFFERENT BREEDS OF DOG

Africans kept several breeds of dog. In addition to the ridgeback, which was called the *umgodoyi*, there was a very powerfully built breed of dog that was so rare it was kept only by kings and chiefs. This dog, known in Zulu as *ubhova* or *igovu*, had a voracious appetite, especially for meat, which made it rather expensive for ordinary people to keep. It was not fast, but it was powerful enough to bring down any intruder. It did, however, need constant grooming and regular feeding.

King Shaka is said to have kept two such dogs during his reign and the story is told of how a group of wanderers from the south, from the land of the Xhosa, paid him a courtesy visit. When these travellers left, it was discovered that one of Shaka's dogs, the female, had been stolen.

Shaka was heartbroken at the loss of his animal, and the story lived on in the annals of Zulu folklore. It was used in several proverbs aimed at teaching people not to trust strangers. For example, the proverb, 'It is a stupid king who shows a stranger where he keeps his *ubova* dog', means that you must not tell strangers where you keep your wealth.

Storytellers described the *ubova* dog as large, usually rusty brown in colour, with white paws and a white-tipped tail. It had a very large mouth and floppy ears, and when it barked, even the baboons on the distant hills were afraid.

The *ichalaba* was even faster and stronger than the ridgeback, and had a more powerful bite. This was a hunting dog with a very thin stomach and the Zulus nicknamed Shaka after this dog. One of the names for this dog translates as 'that which is hungry' or 'that which looks hungry, although it has eaten'.

The *ichalaba* dog was used to pursue and bring down fast-moving animals like impala, springbok, klipspringer and duiker. Zulu kings sometimes used the klipspringer horns as part of their necklaces, as containers for powders with magical powers to protect the king against assassins and poisoners. In order to bring down these fast-moving, high-jumping antelopes, an agile dog such as the *ichalaba* was essential. The *ichalaba* was also used for tracking criminals. Zulu warriors pursuing a runaway chief's wife often used *ichalabas* and ridgebacks to track and capture her. A chief's wife who ran away from the harem had to be recaptured at all costs to prevent enemies of the tribe from using her to harm the chief.

If a man stole something of great value to the king, he was hunted by very powerful dogs. The story is told of a sacred necklace, of which I am the keeper, that a thief once stole during the reign of the great King Dingiswayo. A troop of warriors, accompanied by six dogs, soon tracked down the thief. It is said that the thief could not escape the fast-running royal dogs. He was cornered, and made the mistake of seeking refuge at the top of a small palm tree. The dogs formed an unbreakable barrier around the tree, glaring up with expectant eyes at the man hiding among the leaves.

The man threw the necklace at the dogs but they did not move. They just stood there and glared up at him. Then one of the *indunas*, Mapepela, who was leading the force of man-hunters, cut down the tree with his battle axe. The thief fell to the ground, but before he could get up and run away, the dogs tore him apart.

People were often plagued by sorcerers who terrorized the community by riding a baboon backwards round and round the village fence every night. To deal with such unwelcome intruders, highly trained and powerful dogs were used to attack first the sorcerer and then the baboon. The baboon would take off after a furious battle with the dogs, but the sorcerer was dealt with mercilessly.

Here is one story that cannot prevent me from smiling: A Zulu king would often give a present of two *ubova* dogs to a man whom he really did not like, or if someone aspired to the kingship, and his intentions were known to the king, the king would send that person a warning gift in the form of *ubova* dogs. The ruling king's aim was to ruin the challenger. To feed an *ubova* dog was very expensive, and if it became sick, it required the services of the best animal sangoma in the land. These people were rare and their fees very expensive.

If you were given a dog as a gift you had to ensure that it came to no harm. If the dog became sick or died, you would be unlucky for the next ten years. The more precious the dog and the more rare the breed, the greater the care that had to be taken and the more expensive it was to ensure its wellbeing.

If an *ubova* dog suffered from diarrhoea, it cost the owner two cows for a special sangoma, skilled in the treatment of animal diseases, to treat the dog and save its life. To this day you will hear Zulus say, 'I have been given a dog suffering diarrhoea.' ('I have been given a gift, which is ruining me financially.')

Much to my amusement, I once heard a man in Soweto using that expression. He had been given a Mercedes Benz by a kindly employer who left South Africa during the late 1960s. It was so expensive for this poor man to keep the car running that he angrily sold it to a scrap-yard dealer – after smashing it in irritation with a hammer and, furiously drunk, shouting in the street that his employer had given him a dog suffering from diarrhoea!

HOW THE DOG CAME TO LIVE WITH HUMAN BEINGS

I am Sopaduza, the hero of heroes, the bravest of the brave. I am the one whom the world shall never forget. I am the one whom singers will always remember. I am the strangler of lions; the tamer of wild buffalo. I am the strongest of the strong. I am Sopaduza and this is my story.

But this is also the story of a strange animal that I have never seen before – one that was to tame my own heart and change the lives of all human beings throughout the world.

One day I was lying in my grass shelter, my weapons at my side – my mace of heavy wood that had shattered many skulls, some human and some animal, my quiver of many bone-tipped arrows, and the great bow with which I let those arrows fly. I was sent by my grandfather on a sacred task that was fraught with great danger. There was a beast at large in the land, and it had killed many of our people. It was so small, so beautiful and appeared to be so gentle, one wondered how it could commit such great atrocities. This creature was known as *mbuthi-ya-Nbange*, the goat of the great skies.

It was about the size of an ordinary goat. It had a similar shape, cloven hooves, a head like a goat's and long, glossy, snow-white hair like no goat that existed on Earth had. This animal had one horn on its head that grew long and straight between its ears. It was the horn that gave this creature its awesome power. The strange thing about an *mbuthi-ya-Nbange* was that it could shoot its horn off its head with great force and fearsome violence. It shot off the outer covering but left the raw pink bone inside. With the twinkling of an eye, it would grow a new ebony-black horn.

The *mbuthi-ya-Nbange*, this fantastic creature which had come from the stars, was capable of sending a stream of horns, each one as sharp as a needle and as tall as a man, in rapid succession to impale any enemy.

My grandfather decided that I was the best person to track down the beast and eliminate it. At that time, the beast had already accounted for over five hundred of the bravest men in my tribe.

I vowed never to return home unless I was wearing the skin of this unbelievable animal from the stars. As I lay in my grass shelter in the deep bush, I heard a strange whining sound. I listened, and there it was again, not far from where I lay. I was weary from following the *mbuthi-ya-Nbange*, but I stood up, picked up my weapons, my bow and my club, and slung my quiver with its arrows over my shoulder. I listened carefully and again I heard the whining sound. It sounded like an animal, maybe a wolf or a jackal, in great distress, and I set out to investigate.

I followed the sound to the edge of a donga that yawned before me, a great gully, and I listened again. I heard the strange whining sound again and looked down. At first I saw nothing in the dense bush, then there, lying under a tree and injured, was the strangest animal I have ever seen.

The animal had obviously fallen and injured one of its legs. Although the animal looked like a wolf, it was like no wolf I had ever seen. It was like no jackal that I had ever seen. It was large and very powerful-looking. It was a golden colour and had pointed ears, almost like those of a wolf, but it had white patches on its body, especially its belly, its face and three of its four legs.

'What kind of animal is that?' I asked myself.

I was then suddenly conscious of the fact that I was hungry. I had not eaten for a number of days. Was that animal edible? Our people ate jackal and wolf without question. Could I eat that animal?

Gripping my club, I carefully made my way down the side of the gully, towards the animal. It saw me coming, but it could not move, it could not escape. Its leg was swollen – badly sprained or perhaps broken.

As I raised my club to shatter the animal's skull, I noticed that it was a female and obviously pregnant. There was something in the animal's eyes which sent a mute appeal to my spirit. It was incapable of speech, unlike most other animals that live on Earth, but its eyes spoke to me more strongly than any words could have done.

'Spare my life, do not send me into the darkness!'

I felt my arm weakening and slowly lowered the club. I stood looking down at the animal, wondering what I could do. Then I approached the animal, its eyes never leaving my own. I knelt down next to the animal and gently reached out my hand and touched its head. There was something about this animal that drew my soul to it. There was an intelligence in this creature's eyes which filled me with amazement. What kind of beast was this?'

I found myself stroking the creature's head, and noticed that it wagged its tail. Here was friendship, here was love.

I decided to find some food in the forest because I was truly hungry. And as the spirits would have it, a herd of antelope came storming out of the bush and raced along the edge of the gully above me. Quickly drawing one of my arrows, I fitted it to the bow, drew back the string and let the arrow fly. The sound of the string was like music to my ears. The arrow sped straight and true for the largest antelope and caught it in the chest. The antelope reared on its hind legs, uttered a loud bleating sound and tumbled into the gully and on to a rock not far from where I stood. I walked over to the antelope and skinned it with my stone knife. Within a few moments I had started a fire and had tasty bits of antelope meat roasting over the flames.

I ate like a lion, I ate like an elephant, I ate until I could eat no more. And then I heard the same whining sound that had brought me to the gully. I looked over my shoulder and I saw that the strange, injured animal was watching me. Its eyes carried an appeal that I could not ignore.

'Are you a meat-eating animal? Do you eat meat, strange beast?'

I cut a large piece of meat from the antelope carcass and carried it over to the animal. It looked at me and wagged its tail as I approached. I placed the piece of meat close to the animal. It ate greedily, it ate ravenously and then it looked up to me for more. I gave it more meat, and still more. When I was sure that the animal had eaten its fill, I decided to smoke the rest of the antelope meat to preserve it.

While I was smoking the meat, another thought came to mind. Something told me that the strange, injured animal needed water. I took my calabash and went to the stream at the very bottom of the gully to scoop out water, first for myself and then for my new-found friend. The animal watched me with great anticipation as I placed the calabash close to its mouth, but it could not drink. It thrust its tongue into the calabash.

'Ah,' I said, 'you drink like a wolf, my friend. You drink like a jackal. You are almost of the same tribe.'

Once more I went out into the gully. I was searching for something that would hold water. Eventually I found a large nut, almost as big as my head, which I cracked open to form a wonderful drinking vessel. I poured water into it and carried it over to the animal. It lapped up the water thirstily.

I camped in the gully for several days, tending to the sick animal which had become my friend. I made a poultice out of leaves, warmed it on the fire and applied it to the animal's leg. At first the animal fought fiercely and tried to bite me, but I knew what I was doing and the animal's swollen leg had to be healed.

Day after day I tended the animal, giving it meat and water and putting more poultices on its injury. It was getting better and the swelling was definitely subsiding. When I was sure that the animal was truly healed, I got up, picked up my things and decided to move on – after all, I had a sacred task to accomplish!

I had been walking through the bush for some time when I noticed, to my great surprise, that something was following me. It was the strange animal. We became companions and were inseparable. It helped me when I hunted antelope by hobbling around and worrying the antelope from the rear, making it easy for me to bring one down. We had many days of fun together.

But my four-footed friend grew in size as the life within her body grew. I knew that soon the time would come for the creature and me to part. After all, it would not, or so I thought, follow me once it had given birth to its young.

One day the creature disappeared. I realized that the time for our parting had come. But I was wrong. After a few days, I heard a strange barking sound, a demanding sound – one that I sensed was intended for me alone. I set off to investigate and found the animal lying under a tree. All around it were other animals, its young. I counted six round, fat things which suckled greedily from the mother's many teats. As I stood looking at the animal, her eyes appealed to me: 'Don't abandon me!'

And so I, Sopaduza, the hero of heroes, became the servant of an animal. It had captured me; it was taming me. I was responding to the animal's demands for water, food and companionship. I stayed.

One day, after a brief hailstorm had passed over the land, there was a sinister smell in the air that was all too familiar to me: the *mbuthi-ya-Nbange*, the dreaded goat of the skies, was nearby. I knew that this strange and fearsome beast loved to stalk human beings and I knew that the animal was seeking my life.

I waited, weapons at the ready, with deep apprehension in my heart and a raw terror tearing at my bowels, demanding that I scream aloud with fear. Part of me wanted to flee, to desert the strange wolf-like creature, but part of me wanted to stay and face the *mbuthi-ya-Nbange.*

It was just before sunset that I saw a snowy-white shape emerge from the dense bush. It was a beautiful, goat-like animal with a long delicate neck, glossy, snow-white, flowing hair all over its body and a long, thin horn between its ears. It was coming straight for me and, even from a distance, I saw dark death in its huge, dark brown eyes.

'I see you, human being. I have followed you this great distance and more. I see you, biggest of your kind. It will give me great pleasure to send you to the place of darkness. It is I, the *mbuthi-ya-Nbange.* You must turn and face me, ugly one!'

Before I knew what was happening, a strange hissing sound passed my head. The creature aimed its first horn and I knew there were more to follow. I threw myself to the ground as the second horn came whizzing through the air. It struck a tree close to my head and went right through the trunk. Such was the force behind the horn.

I knew that the horns were poisonous, and that one scratch meant death for any human being or animal at whom the *mbuthi-ya-Nbange's* wrath was directed. I had to avoid this. But how?

The *mbuthi-ya-Nbange* rushed towards me with great speed. It moved like a bolt of white lightning through the bush. I felt my courage deserting me. No human being could summon enough courage to face such a monstrous animal. I knew that my moment of death had come. I knew that I could not survive.

It sent horn after horn in my direction. I threw myself flat behind a rock. I knew that my strength was leaving me. I could not bring myself to fire arrows from my bow; my arms were numb. And then, something leapt over the rock behind which I was crouching and the *mbuthi-ya-Nbange* stood over me. It was astride me and there was death in its eyes.

'Ah, human being,' it said, 'tell me, are you afraid? Are you afraid of the *mbuthi-ya-Nbange*? Are you afraid of the goat of the stars? I love creatures that are frightened of me! It fills me with great happiness!'

I felt the terror within me increase beyond all imagination, but this made the white monster dance with ecstasy.

'Ah, the terror of death, human being, the thing that sustains me. I drink the flames of fear that emanate from the minds of frightened human beings and you are giving me more than my fair share! Your death is only a few heartbeats away! A very painful death! You shall curl up, you shall scream and the flesh shall boil from your body when I drive my horn into you!'

But before I could do anything, something stormed out of the bush behind the *mbuthi-ya-Nbange* and I heard a terrible sound as my friend fastened her jaws on one of the *mbuthi-ya-Nbange's* hind legs. The dust flew as the two animals fought furiously, locked into a bloody life-and-death struggle. My courage returned – I had to help my friend!

I stood up, tore an arrow from my quiver, raised the bow and let the arrow fly. It struck the *mbuthi-ya-Nbange* in the neck. Another arrow left my bow and pierced one of the eyes of the terrible monster. I prayed that the *mbuthi-ya-Nbange's* horn would not touch either of us.

The *mbuthi-ya-Nbange* thrashed about, its rage and fear ringing out like silent music. The third arrow sank deep into the *mbuthi-ya-Nbange's* evil heart. As it writhed about, I threw down my bow and seized a heavy stone that lay on the ground, and I shattered the monster's skull and horn. I skinned the *mbuthi-ya-Nbange* and left its snow-white skin to dry on a tree.

I built a new shelter of dry grass and twigs with the intention of camping there until I had recovered from the experience. At my side was the animal, the dog that I now call *Muthuthi*, the one who teaches me many things.

Muthuthi was to become my battle companion in many fights. I draped the skin of the *mbuthi-ya-Nbange* over my shoulder and all the heroes who saw me were afraid of me. They knew that I had slain the animal that no-one thought could be killed.

And as *Muthuthi's* progeny grew to maturity and fathered or gave birth to more of their kind, people appealed to me to give them one of *Muthuthi's* pups or grand-pups.

I, Sopaduza, hero of heroes, had discovered the magical animal known as *inja*, the dog. It is said that when my time came to enter the land of the spirits, the great gods decided to honour me by raising my spirit to the stars where I found the spirit of *Muthuthi*, who had grown old and gone before me into the land of the dead. We can still be seen, my dog and I, up there in the sky, still hunting, seeking, fighting and winning.

This is the story of how dogs came live with human beings. Had I, Sopaduza, not taken care of *Muthuthi*, the dog, we would never have known the beauty and love of keeping such an animal.

PRAISE SONG TO THE ROOSTER

Usually individual roosters are given particular praise songs by their owners. I have a large rooster at home which I praise as follows:

I say, cock-a-doodle-doo
You, who wake me up in the morning before others have awoken
You, who scratch first and eat before others have eaten
You, wakener of old women and old men
Saying cock-a-doodle-doo
Wake up and empty out all your chamber pots
Because the sun is about to appear in the east!
You, cock with the long spurs
Fighter of many battles
You, whose comb is as red as the headdress of King Shaka at the
battle of Koghi
I say to you: May you be so fertile that your eggs will fill every valley
Your children will delight every hen and every hawk that flies in the sky
I will not feast upon you
Cock of cocks
Rooster of roosters
Only the vultures shall share your flesh among them
Because you are my friend
You are my wakener
You are my alarm
And you are my guide
Bayete!

BELOVED AND RESPECTED FOWL

African people have a deep love and respect for poultry, and in the past they kept them not so much for food as for medicinal and magical purposes. There were tribes in South Africa where a hen or a cock was worth far more than a cow, a bull or an ox. In fact, some tribes in the Shangane and Tsonga nations of South Africa payed their bride-price not with cattle – as was the case with the Zulus, the Southern Sothos and the Batswanas – but with poultry. Where a Zulu would honour the bride's family with nine head of cattle, a member of these tribes would pay nine hens or eight hens and one cock.

MEDICINAL USES

African people believed that poultry had great magical powers and properties, and they were used for treating certain illnesses, putting curses on hated enemies, and appealing to the gods and the ancestral spirits.

In southern Africa, black people refer to poultry by a very strange name. The name for poultry is *inkuku* in Zulu and *kuku* in Setswana. Both words mean the same thing: 'the picker-up' or 'that which picks someone up'. The words come from the verb *kuka* which means 'to lift'.

The reason for this name is that this creature lifts you from a state of weakness to a state of recovery and strength.

'How?' you may ask.

With its soup! When an African suffered from an exhausting illness, among the many treatments a traditional healer would prescribe a healthy broth of poultry soup, once or twice every ten days.

Sometimes this soup was eaten with a little salt, and sometimes it became the main ingredient in a herbal mixture which was taken orally. Poultry soup was prepared and half a handful of powdered *sibaya* root was added to it before it was given to a person with a bad chest cold. (The *sibaya* root is a painkiller and loosens phlegm. It has powerful fever-reducing properties, and acts in exactly the same way as menthol by opening clogged bronchial tubes.)

Traditional healers of all tribes kept large numbers of poultry, and when influenza or the common cold swept the land, many old hens which were fattened with age and no longer produced eggs in large quantities were slaughtered.

In the early townships around Johannesburg, enterprising traditional healers pounded a quantity of eucalyptus bark, put it in an iron pot with some fowl fat and boiled it. Some of the eucalyptus perfume would be absorbed by the fat, which was carefully strained into bottles. These were tightly sealed and stored in a cool place.

When someone had a cold, the eucalyptus-perfumed fowl fat was rubbed on the chest, the upper lip, and the back of the neck. It was also rubbed on muscles to lessen the severe pains of rheumatism and reduce the effects of a cold. Elderly people rubbed the fat on their feet on cold nights, to keep them warm and ensure a good night's sleep.

Among the many strange diseases found in Africa there is one which we call 'the fat chicken illness'. This is an embarrassing skin disease where the skin becomes so dry it develops scales like a reptile. However, Africans have an effective treatment for it: they use poultry fat into which the strongly-scented leaves or bark of certain trees have been pounded and boiled. This perfumed oil is rubbed on the body, limbs and face of the sufferer, often with very good results. It is also used to treat a young person whose hair has fallen out in round patches.

The afflicted person must also eat fat, whether it is from goats, sheep or poultry. But the best fat for this purpose comes from guineafowl or Egyptian geese.

UNRAVELLING THE FUTURE

Since time immemorial, we have wanted to know what the future holds in store or us. Some threw what are known as the 'bones of divination' and studied the way in which they fell, while others watched the movement of clouds or the flight of migratory birds across the expanse of the blue heavens. Yet another way of predicting the future was through fowl.

The traditional healer first drew a circle on the mud floor of a hut with a mixture of white clay and water. Then he drew a number of magical symbols at regular intervals along the circumference. Each symbol had to be about 15 centimetres long. When he had finished drawing, a young girl of about fourteen or fifteen years of age had to place a small amount of chicken feed (ground sorghum or maize) onto each design.

When this had been done, a number of hens and chicks and one or two cocks were brought into the hut, placed in the circle, and carefully watched by the traditional healer and the people with him. As the fowl rushed to eat the grain placed on the sacred symbols, the fortune of the people – good or bad – was revealed, according to the first symbol from which the fowl ate.

If the fowl ate grain from negative symbols, the people knew that there would be trouble in the near future. If they ate the grain placed on positive symbols, the people knew that the future would be filled with good things.

COMBATING BAD LUCK

When a person suffers repeated misfortune, loses money, is assaulted for no reason, or is unlucky in love and in other ways, there is a very special treatment, involving a hen, which can be performed by sangomas.

A hen is sacrificed, its fat is removed, and the person is smeared from head to foot with the suet. Then the person is given a steam bath using water in which fragrant, luck-bringing herbs and powdered roots have been boiled. This treatment is repeated until the person's luck starts changing and bad fortune is replaced with good fortune.

The meat of the sacrificed fowl is not eaten. It is thrown away, usually in a deep hole or, in urban areas, on a township rubbish dump.

In a similar form of treatment, after the person has completed the ritual bath, a fowl (usually a black one) is dipped into the herbal water, then taken – alive and unhurt – some distance away, where one foot is tied to a tree or a telephone pole near crossroads. This fowl is supposed to carry away the patient's sins and bad fortune, and woe betide someone who takes this fowl and eats it. In many townships like Soweto, hungry people come across such fowl, cut them loose and take them to their shacks for supper – and they all die. It is very dangerous to take home a fowl which has been used to remove a curse!

One day, in the shantytown known as Kliptown, a poor old woman was shopping with her two teenage daughters when the elder of the two girls saw a red hen tethered by one leg to a telephone pole close to the road. She immediately drew her mother's and sister's attention to this hen, but the mother angrily forbade the children to release the hen. She told them it was a cursed hen. But the elder daughter was wilful and stubborn, and when they had finished shopping, she crept out of the shack and went with a friend to find the hen.

The girls took the hen to the friend's shack, killed it, plucked it, cooked it, and invited three more friends to the chicken feast. When the five girls had finished eating, they drank a bottle of beer and lay down on the floor to sleep.

The next moment there was a terrible sound of splintering wood and collapsing corrugated iron. When the people ran out of their homes to investigate the commotion, they found that a huge truck had swerved off the road in an attempt to avoid another vehicle, and had careered into the shack where the five girls were sleeping. Four were killed and the fifth was seriously injured. When she recovered from her terrible injuries, she told the story of the chicken that her friend had found tied to a lamppost.

When a person undergoing treatment for madness begins to show signs of recovery, the sangoma who has been healing that person sacrifices a fowl in honour of the patient's ancestral spirits. But before the fowl is sacrificed, the patient is made to kneel on the floor and the fowl is placed gently on his or her head. If the fowl jumps off the patient's head, the sangoma knows that, although the patient is showing signs of improving, he or she is far from healed and the sacrifice is cancelled. If, however, the fowl rests calmly on the patient's head for about five minutes, the sangoma knows that the patient has recovered. The sacrifice proceeds and the treatment for madness is discontinued.

Often, when a fowl is sacrificed, it is killed quickly and its intestines removed immediately. Their slow movement is studied by the traditional healers to learn the patient's fortune, be it good or bad.

When an African's home is being protected against physical enemies and negative spirits, the *inyanga* or traditional healer prepares a number of hardwood pegs, usually about 16 centimetres long, and smears them with protective medicine which consists of several kinds of root mixed with the fat of certain animals.

When this has been done, the pegs are placed in a grass basket and the throat of a rooster is cut over them. Each peg is then formally blessed and instructed by the traditional healer to guard the home against all visible and invisible foes. The pegs are driven into the four corners of the yard in which the house stands and at each corner of the house itself. One special peg, the largest and longest, is driven into the space between the two posts of the gate which leads to the yard.

These protection rituals keep sangomas busy in nearly all the townships and rural communities, because many people want their houses protected, not just once but once every year. These pegs are supposed to protect the house and those who dwell in it against thugs, thieves, the *tokoloshe* and lightning.

APHRODISIAC QUALITIES

As a rule, Africans did not eat hens' eggs, except as an urgent aphrodisiac. If a young African male felt himself getting a bit weak in bed, he would, on the advice of a traditional healer, swallow half a handful of powdered *bangalala* root, which is a potent aphrodisiac, with a good draught of full-cream milk. Then he would take a fresh hen's egg, make a hole in it, add a pinch of finely ground rock salt, shake the egg and suck out the shell's contents. He had to steel himself against vomiting. If he did this for eight to ten days, things really got better for him in bed and his rod of manhood began to function as intended.

Let me hasten to add that this treatment was only undertaken by *married* men and women. Young, unmarried people were strictly forbidden from eating eggs, whether they were raw, boiled or fried. Black people believed that if young people were allowed to eat eggs freely, they would mature and become sexually active before the proper time, before their minds were stable and educated enough to meet the challenges, adventures and problems of adulthood. Promiscuity was strictly frowned upon in tribal communities.

The reason for young people being forbidden from eating eggs was often carefully hidden from them. If unmarried men or women asked an elder why they were not allowed to eat hens' eggs, when married men and women freely indulged in this form of nutrition, they were told that if they ate eggs, they would turn into thieves. This was a thin disguise for an important truth. If the young person had access to such a powerful aphrodisiac, he or she would not turn into a thief of other people's property, but a thief of sex.

Africans believe that rooster flesh has aphrodisiac qualities, especially when it is eaten with certain traditional vegetables and fruits.

When I was young, I saw Zulu wives greeting their husbands who had returned from many months of working in Johannesburg's gold mines with a huge supper consisting of rooster meat, boiled to perfection, sweet potatoes, pumpkin, green spinach, and other delicacies – to say nothing of hard-boiled hens' eggs and fried winged termites.

The pampered husband needed no second bidding when this supper was placed before him. Blessed with a huge Zulu appetite, he soon tucked in and pigged out on the bounty. That done, he would take a huge swig from a pot of bubbling sorghum beer. When the lights in the hut had been put out and the love mats spread, to the accompaniment of the owls outside, things would happen in the hut that would be screamingly delicious – I can assure you of that!

TALKING TO THE ANCESTORS

Africans who cannot afford either sheep or goats to carry out sacrifices to their ancestors, or to celebrate their children's birthdays or any of the other traditional ceremonies have to make do with poultry. And because traditional poultry breeds are fast vanishing from the homes of black people, especially in urban areas, they find themselves forced to use battery hens.

Many ultra-conservative old people and tradition-bound sangomas protest when this type of hen is used. Battery hens are regarded as soulless, lifeless creatures because they lay eggs which have not been blessed by the seed of a cock and are sterile. But the force of change is stronger than traditional conservatism and battery hens are being used more and more frequently in ceremonies held in urban townships. However, serious healing ceremonies, where a person's life and wellbeing are at stake, still demand the use of traditional poultry. For this reason, many sangomas keep large numbers of poultry in their back yards (the authorities permitting, of course).

PRAISE SONG TO THE GOAT

I hear you cry, oh *imbuzi*, on the altars of our ancestors
I hear you cry, oh goat, in the shrines of our forefathers
You are the one who asks the questions
That is the meaning of your name
The animal which asks questions
Questions which often have no answer
You are the delight of the old men
Old men without teeth who grow strong on your milk
You are also the delight of the gods
The angry gods who adore your flesh
You are the creature that came from the heavens
Sent by the gods to human beings on Earth
That whenever we seek knowledge from those above
We must make you ask the gods the question
You are a cousin of the impala that roam the plains of our fatherland
They cannot ask any questions, but you can
For you, oh goat – you are the wisest of the wise!
Your hooves have etched the soil of Africa deeply
Your bleating has been heard from one end of the land to the other
You are the joy of our children, the joy of our little sons and daughters who
love to caress your beard, and to brush your ears, and to count
the rings in your horns
Your hide keeps our grandmothers warm and our grandfathers from shivering
Your eyes are as gentle as those of a lover
But your butting is as forceful as that of a Bapedi warrior!
You are the lover of the trees

You are the one who remains alive when other animals have long since
perished from the face of the land
For you are the *imbuzi*, the asker of the questions
You are the goat!
You are the animal!
Our sisters often say that your smell is overpowering, but they fail to
understand that it is the perfume of wisdom
Our brothers often say that your beard is ridiculous, but they do not know
it is the beard of wisdom
Our cousins often say that your genitals dangle like drunkards' calabashes
inside a beer-brewing hut
But they do not know that they are the gonads of fertility itself
The gods revere you, oh *imbuzi*
And the demons fear you below
For you are the goat, the one who asks many questions
Bayete!

THE QUESTIONING ANIMAL

The goat is an animal with a long, very complex and amazing history. Zulus call the goat imbuzi, while the Xhosas call it *ibhokhwe*, which is a corruption of the Dutch word for a goat or an antelope, *bok*. The Sotho- and Setswana-speaking tribes of southern Africa call a goat *pudi*, while some tribes among the Venda, Tonga and Shangaan people call the goat *mpundzi*. All of the names used for a goat mean 'that which asks a question' or 'the questioning animal'. (In Zulu, the word for question is *umbuzo*, and the person who asks a question is *umbuzi*.)

But why is a goat called 'the questioning animal'?

Because it is the one animal, we are told by our great teachers, that black people of many tribes have kept for hundreds of years – not so much as a source of meat, but as a means of communicating with the gods and ancestral spirits, and asking questions of these invisible or barely visible beings.

MAGICAL POWERS

There is the belief that one can tell whether or not a goat has magical powers by the colour of its hide.

We are taught that black goats possess the most powerful magic of all, and that that type of goat should be used in communicating with the spirits of the dead in the direst emergencies. The Zulus call a black goat 'the goat of calling up, or talking up' the ancestral spirits.

A goat with a reddish-brown hide is believed to have the power to prevent conflict and bloodshed. It is interesting to note that during the long years of endemic violence that swept through countless black townships during the mid-1970s, many reddish-brown goats were slaughtered by desperate and frightened people, who were praying for peace and asking their often uncaring ancestors for protection.

An all-white goat is used to bless a marriage ceremony. It is also used in a ceremony to exorcise a ghost from a haunted house.

A black-and-white goat is used as an animal of thanksgiving to the ancestral spirits for prayers which have been granted. It is believed that a goat with black-and-white markings is sacred to the great Earth Mother, because it represents both night and day, positive and negative forces.

A red-and-white goat is also used for thanksgiving ceremonies, arranged to thank the gods and the ancestral spirits for bringing an end to conflict or disagreement between people.

When an apprentice sangoma undergoes initiation, he or she must constantly ask the ancestral spirits to show to him or her in a dream the exact colour or colours of the goat of admission, the shape of its horns and even its sex. Once the initiate has had such a dream, all efforts must be made by the teacher and the student's family to obtain a goat of which the colour, shape of horns and sex exactly match those of the dream.

GOATS MUST BE TREATED WITH RESPECT

African people believe that all goats are born to be sacrificial animals. Their purpose in life is to serve human beings and to protect them with their lives. For this reason, a goat must be treated with the utmost respect and reverence. It must never be whipped like an ox, be sworn at like a slave, or suffer ill-treatment at the hands of human beings.

And even when it is being slaughtered, it must be slaughtered only by those who are trained and skilled enough to cause the sacrificial animal the minimum of pain and agony.

It is said that if a goat is slaughtered by careless people and takes a long time to die, it will bring bad fortune to those who have slaughtered it. Furthermore, its spirit will block the prayers the people are trying to send to their ancestral spirits.

Since time immemorial, certain men and women have been specially trained in slaughtering goats and cattle. Very often they are trained not only to slaughter animals with the minimum of pain, but also to study the livers and entrails of the slaughtered animals and to read the fortune of the people making the sacrifice. It was important to have a reader of entrails in order to learn whether or not the ancestral spirits were pleased by a sacrifice and were prepared to grant the wishes of those who had made it.

For example, if a goat had been sacrificed on behalf of a sick person and the goat was found to have a deformity in one of its internal organs or legs, this was taken as an omen that the sick person's recovery would be slow. If a foetus was found inside the goat, this was a sure sign that the patient would die.

It was believed that a goat was capable of absorbing a person's illness and, through death by sacrificial knife, would remove the illness from the sick person, allowing him or her to recover.

For this reason, some African tribes performed a ritual which has been misrepresented by anthropologists. The goat to be slaughtered was placed on the back and shoulders of the patient. This was done for ten to fifteen minutes while the goat absorbed into its soul the patient's illness. The patient then had to whisper to the goat what he or she wished it to achieve for him or her by laying down its life under the knife. This is why you sometimes find a sick black person bringing his or her mouth close to the snout of a goat. The patient must whisper to the goat exactly what he or she wishes it to ask the ancestral spirits. Bestiality and satanism have absolutely nothing to do with these rituals, contrary to what certain white anthropologists have concluded. This gross misrepresentation merely displays abysmal ignorance.

EVERY PART OF A GOAT CAN BE USED

Every product of a goat is useful. Goat's milk is used to treat sick babies, especially those who suffer from asthma or whooping cough, and to build up their resistance to disease.

One of the remedies for whooping cough consists of goat's milk in which a few leaves of wild dagga have been boiled. This also helps to open the chest of a baby suffering from asthma. My grandmother on my father's side gave me this treatment when I was a baby. She mixed wild dagga and herbs with goat's milk and brought it to the boil in a small, clay pot. When the mixture was cold, she spooned it into my mouth and rubbed chicken fat, perfumed with *sibaya* leaves, onto my chest and back.

Goat droppings are used in a magical mixture given to babies suffering from measles. They are boiled in water with a herb called *umhlonyane* and given to babies with a small bone or horn spoon. The purpose of this medicine is to bring out the child's skin rash and so shorten the period of illness.

HOW THE GOAT CAME TO LIVE WITH HUMAN BEINGS

It is said that when the world was first created, there were all the animals on Earth, but no goats and no sheep. One day, human beings murdered the sun god who had come to stay among them and teach them. As a result of this horrible deed, God punished the world with a great flood that drowned many villages.

The flood was so great and the water masses rose so high that even the mountains drowned. And when the flood ended and the surviving human beings began rebuilding their villages and repopulating the Earth, a wise old man, named Mparungu, spoke to the great God:

'Oh Father of the Heavens, I know that we have sinned before you. I know that the terrible punishment you visited upon the human race for murdering your son was more than deserved.

'But, Great Father, it is important that human beings keep in touch with God at all times. It is important that we know what you like and dislike. How do we get in touch with you? How can we know what you expect us to do?'

It is said that God, who was still angry about his son's death, answered:

'Go to that mountain and there you shall receive my answer.'

Mparungu took his great stick and walked painfully up the mountain. It was a long climb for the old man, but he eventually reached the summit. At first he saw nothing, but being a pious man, he waited patiently. The sun set, night fell and Mparungu remained on the mountain.

Early the following morning, Mparungu heard a strange sound that he had never heard before. It was the bleating of a goat which was quickly answered by another goat. Mparungu went to investigate and there he saw two animals, the likes of which he had never seen before.

It was obvious that one was a male and the other a female. Mparungu addressed another question to God:

'Great One, is this your answer to my prayer?'

And the angry voice of God said, 'Yes, it is!'

Mparungu said, 'Great One, please forgive me. What is the meaning of these animals? What are they?'

God did not answer. Then the male goat suddenly spoke: 'You must ask us, human being.'

'You can speak?' said the surprised Mparungu.

'Yes, I understand your language. The Great One has sent us, the goats, they who ask questions, to be a link between God and human beings on Earth. You will find our milk nourishing for your little children. You must treat us well and, when occasion demands, you must sacrifice one of us. We shall remain with you for all time, such is the wish of the All Highest, the Whisper Among the Clouds, the Voice in the Hearts of All Living Things.'

THE SHEEP

THE VOICELESS ONE

The Batswana people, the greatest and the most skilled sheep farmers in southern Africa, call the sheep *nku*, a word with the literal meaning, 'the dumb or voiceless animal'. The Zulus call a sheep *imvu* and the Xhosa people of Transkei call sheep *igusha* which is a corruption of the Hottentot name for this animal: *gus*. They all mean 'the voiceless animal'.

Sheep are called by this name because unlike a goat, which bellows blue murder while it is being slaughtered, the sheep dies quietly. Xhosa and Zulu sangomas never use sheep in any of their ceremonies because if they do, the ancestral spirits will fall silent, like sheep, and never talk to them or through them again.

Xhosa and Zulu sangomas are forbidden from eating mutton. If forced to eat mutton through hunger, the sangoma is compelled to undergo a five-day purification ceremony afterwards.

TREATING RHEUMATISM WITH SHEEPSKIN

Among Batswana *dingaka*, or traditional healers, the sheep is the animal chosen for ceremonial and healing purposes. The Batswana people possess the best cure for rheumatism that I have ever come across in my travels throughout Africa.

They slaughter and skin a sheep, strip the patient naked and wrap the warm hide around him or her. This must be worn for about half a day. When the sheep's hide is wrapped around the patient, the wool side faces outwards so that the patient's body is in contact with the warm, fatty inner side of the skin. After a few hours the patient's symptoms subside noticeably, the muscles becoming less stiff and painful.

After many years of observing this form of treatment, I have come to the conclusion that there must be something in sheep-fat that reduces rheumatoid pain. Another successful method of treating rheumatism that is practised by the Batswanas is to rub the patient from head to foot with raw sheep-fat, using a piece of sheepskin or wool.

Another interesting form of treatment involves binding a number of flat, thin, polished copper sheets to the patient's body and lightly sprinkling them with salt water before wrapping the fresh sheepskin around the patient. Usually two copper sheets are used. One is tied to the small of the patient's back and the other to the patient's chest. This treatment is used on hot days when the weather is clear and sunny, and when the patient can sit outside in the sun for several hours.

COMBATING MADNESS WITH SHEEP'S BRAINS

The Batswana and Zulu people believe that a worm lives inside the brain of a sheep. It is called *ituku*, which means 'the worm of insanity'. It is believed that a sorcerer can remove such a worm from a dead sheep's brain and use it to bewitch a person, causing him or her to become mad.

The *ituku* worm is carefully dried and burnt with pungent healing herbs which are then placed, while smoking on charcoal, under a mad person's nostrils so that the smoke may be inhaled. This form of treatment causes the mad person to sneeze and, as soon as this happens, people believe that he or she has sneezed out the worm of madness.

When a person is being treated for madness, he or she is forbidden from wearing any copper ornament and is fed a regular diet of half-cooked fresh sheep's brains and a lot of skilfully boiled freshwater fish, until he or she shows signs of recovery.

African people believe that when a person goes mad, it is because the worm of insanity has eaten many holes in that person's brain. Feeding the victim a diet of sheep's brains and fish is believed to close the holes created by the worm. When Africans tell a person that they should eat a thousand sheep's brains, they are actually insulting him, implying that he is hopelessly mad.

When treating a mad person using sheep's brains, traditional healers are very careful to use only the brains of female sheep. It is believed that if you feed a person the brain or flesh of an aggressive animal, such as a ram, that animal's aggressiveness is passed on to the sick person.

THE FAT-TAILED SHEEP OF THE TSWANAS

The Tswanas believe that fat-tailed sheep are their most prized possessions, and these animals are used only in the most sacred of ceremonies and rituals.

There is no greater gift one can give to a Tswana than a fat-tailed sheep. When a young man is negotiating marriage with the parents of a Tswana girl, the first thing they will demand of him is a fat-tailed sheep called *mokwele*, which means 'the opening' or 'the talking sheep'. This sheep must be big and fat and it is eaten the moment it arrives by the girl's family and those whom they have elected to represent them in the negotiations with the husband-to-be.

The fat of a fat-tailed sheep is not only used in the treatment of diseases, such as rheumatism, but also in magical mixtures that cause enemies to be unable to speak out against you. If a Tswana faces a serious court case, he often goes to a traditional healer who gives him, among other things, a putty-like mixture of various luck-bringing and protective roots that have been ground to a powder and mixed with sheep fat and that of a lion or a crocodile. The sheep fat in the mixture is intended to bring about total confusion in the people who testify against the accused. It is also intended to strike some of them dumb, like sheep, and render them completely incapable of offering coherent evidence.

Sheep fat is also used in mixtures prepared to ensure success in certain business undertakings and transactions. One type of mixture is given to a team of football players to rub on the soles of their feet before they put on their boots and walk to the playing field. The mixture is believed to paralyze the opponents, making them slow and clumsy like sheep, and thus enable the side to score goals. I have seen football officials forcing an entire football team into the showers to wash their feet of whatever medicine they may have smeared on them to intimidate the other team.

PRAISE SONG TO THE COW

B*uya, buya, buya, mama-we*
Buya, buya, buya, mama-we
Come away from the bush, mother of our home
Come away from the bush, lady of the four legs
You are the sun that rises in our morning
You are the river that moves on four legs, the river that brings us
the milk that lives
You are the one whose udders are full
You are the one whose belly is huge
You are the mother of the calves
You are the mother of our babies.
Buya, buya, mama-we
Come back, away from the bush
Where the lion and the leopard are king
Come back, away from the bush
Where the thief who steals cattle is the chief
Oh beautiful cow!
Oh wild one, untamed!
Oh one of the long tail!
You, who are the sweetheart of every bull in the land
Our mother, Nomazala, cow that my father gave me
Buya, mama-we
The sun is setting beyond the purple mountains
The smoke rises peacefully from the villages
The smoke of the cooking fires
The smoke warming the old ones' bones

Buya, mama-we

Let us return home

Let us return home, cow that my father gave me!

WHO INTRODUCED CATTLE TO AFRICA?

Cattle are the most important domestic animals kept by Africans throughout Africa. There are many different stories about how they came to possess these very valuable animals. One story holds that many centuries ago, a beautiful princess named Rarati brought cattle from a mysterious land to the black people of the Uganda area.

Another story, which was told by Masai storytellers, states that the Masai people were given cattle by a very wise old being whose face shone like the sun, whose attire was bright gold and silver and bronze, and upon whose back grew four monstrous wings like those of an eagle. The storytellers say that this being, who came from one of the stars in the skies, was named Urugwantai. It is said that Urugwantai brought the first herd of cattle to the Masai aboard a great, golden raft that flew through the heavens. He told the Masai that they had been specially chosen to be the keepers and protectors of cattle for all Africa to the end of all time.

The story goes on to relate how Urugwantai fell in love with a beautiful Masai girl who was murdered by Ningalu, Urugwantai's jealous wife. When Urugwantai discovered this, he put a curse upon Ningalu and turned her into a horrible vulture, the ugliest of all vultures, that flies through African skies to this very day. It is said that the heartbroken Urugwantai boarded his golden raft and flew back to the land of the stars, never to be seen again.

LOOKING AFTER CATTLE

More wars have been fought in Africa over cattle than over any other animal. In days gone by, the ability to acquire cattle, by fair means or foul, was the yardstick by which a man's worth was measured. A young African could acquire cattle by working as a herdsman for a person who owned a lot of cattle and be paid a young cow at the end of every year for his services.

Looking after cattle was a very demanding and often dangerous task. The herdsman had to be prepared to deal with emergencies such as wild animals, especially lions. A pride of lions could pounce on a herd of cattle and inflict tremendous damage on these docile animals before help arrived.

The herdsman also had to be prepared to face gangs of cattle-thieves – a very common thing in ancient as well as present-day Africa. To lose cattle to a gang of cattle-thieves was regarded as the deepest disgrace, and some cruel chiefs executed without pity any herdsman whose cattle had been stolen. A herdsman had to be trained in all forms of combat, ranging from unarmed combat to the use of deadly weapons. He had to be prepared to fight a group of thieves on his own, and to this end, he not only honed his fighting skills, using a variety of weapons, but also kept a large pack of dogs. These dogs were trained to defend the herd against men and wild beasts, and on their own, could round up the cattle and drive them home at great speed if anything happened to the herdsman.

The herdsman had to form a good working relationship with the leading bull or bulls in the herd. For this purpose, he developed a system of calls and whistles which were well known to the bulls, and which he could use in an emergency to instruct them to lead the herd to the safety of the village. Very often, the leading bull was so well trained that the cattle-thieves had great difficulty in driving the cattle away. The bull would frustrate the cattle-thieves by scattering the herd if it sensed that the herdsman had been killed. For this reason, many cattle-thieves developed a strategy of capturing the herdsman alive and forcing him to use his system of whistles, calls and songs to assist them in driving the cattle.

Many stories and fables are told of how rampaging bandits captured a herdsman and forced him to help them drive the cattle away. But, in almost all of these stories, the clever herdsman manages to turn the tables on the cattle-thieves, recover the cattle and lead them home.

CATTLE AS INDICATORS OF WEALTH

In the language of the Zulu people, cattle are called *izinkomo*. The singular of this word is *inkomo*, which is the generic term for domestic cattle, be they cows, oxen or bulls. In Sesotho and Setswana, the word for cattle means 'the great wealth'.

In olden days, people who did not own cattle were regarded as the poorest of the poor, and a man who only had a few head of cattle was contemptuously looked down upon by those people who had large herds. It was not uncommon for very wealthy men and women to divide their herds into several groups and to keep different groups of cattle in different parts of the country. For example, Tswana kings kept herds in the land now known as Botswana as well as in the Free State in South Africa.

Many tribes who kept large herds banked cattle against cattle disease. They would take a large herd of cattle and place it in the keeping of a tribe that lived many days' journey away. If the cattle which that person kept at home were devastated by cattle disease or stolen by cattle-thieves, he or she could recall the herd of cattle left in the care of the distant tribe.

This practice was also followed when a tribe migrated from one area to another. Many people no longer realize how dangerous it was to travel by foot though ancient Africa. There were wild animals by the thousand in every stretch of bush and savannah, including carnivorous animals, such as lion, leopard and cheetah, and hundreds of Cape hunting dogs and hyena. These animals could substantially reduce a migrating tribe's herds of cattle, sheep or goats. There were also other deadly enemies, such as the tsetse fly, cattle disease and hostile tribes, as well as dangers that cannot even be imagined today.

And so, before a tribe moved from its territory, it entrusted most of its cattle herds to one of the remaining tribes. The migrating tribe only took enough cattle to see it through its long journey, as a source of milk and food. On reaching its destination, the migrating tribe would wait a number of months, or even for years, before sending emissaries and warriors to bring the cattle that had been left behind.

As this was an African version of a business transaction, the tribe which had maintained the migrating tribe's cattle would receive in payment a percentage of the calves of the cattle which had been in their care. The remaining cattle would be returned by the warriors and emissaries to the tribe to whom they belonged.

Human nature being what it is, though, the tribe entrusted with the migrating tribe's herds sometimes flatly refused to return the cattle. A state of war would then exist between the two tribes and would continue until peace was made.

In olden days, Africans used cattle in many different ways. Cattle were the medium of trade between tribes and between nations. Some tribes manufactured grindstones which were bartered with other tribes for cattle, and there were also tribes which owned and operated great iron mines, such as the ancient mines in Thabazimbi in the Northern Province. The latter bartered iron ore for cattle – ten lumps of iron ore, each one about the size of a baby's head, could be exchanged for one ox, fifteen for a bull and twenty or twenty-five for a cow.

As unbelievable as it may seem, in ancient Zululand, pumpkin was such a rare vegetable that each one was regarded as being worth one cow! But what was so special about a pumpkin? It was a very rare item in those days, and was secretly grown by wise men and women in hidden places, far away from villages. Pumpkin-growers believed that pumpkins had purifying powers and that those who ate them would enjoy bodily health, wellbeing and beauty. This is why pumpkins were so expensive.

A story is told about a queen named Madiye who exchanged a pumpkin for a cow and gave it to the elder of her two sons, whom she favoured. This display of blatant parental favouritism is said to have so infuriated the younger prince that he actually broke away from his father's tribe and formed his own tribe – which he named the Zulu tribe.

CATTLE AND SPORT

Africans used to gamble with cattle. They had games, similar to chess, which were originally played using live cattle but are nowadays played with stones of different colours. One such game is called *morabaraba.* It is played by two people, one using white pebbles and the other using black pebbles, which are called cattle.

Cattle races were held in which trained oxen, ridden by young warriors, raced each other on a great, circular racetrack. These cattle races were preceded, accompanied and followed by very colourful religious rituals. They were usually performed in October, during the time of the ceremony of the first fruits.

A very dangerous sport is illustrated in one of the caves in South Africa where Bushmen once lived. In this sport, four or more fearless young men and women took turns somersaulting over an angry bull. The bull would be released in the centre of an enclosure and these young people, risking serious injury or even death, would run towards the angry beast, seize it by the horns and somersault over its back. Although sometimes people died under the hooves of the bull, it did not deter others from taking part in the sport, again and again, when the first fruits arrived.

THE ROLE OF CATTLE IN THE ECONOMY

By far the most well-known African transaction involving cattle, which is still practised today, is the *lobola* custom, where a young man pays nine head of cattle, usually cows, to the family of his wife-to-be.

Many people who are ignorant of African religion and culture believe that these cattle are the bride-price paid in the same way the warriors in the writings of Homer paid a bride-price in gold, bronze and other precious things for their wives. However, African *lobola* should under no circumstances be confused with the Homeric bride-price. It does not involve buying a woman, because African religion holds that no-one has the right to buy a woman or, for that matter, any other human being.

The Zulus have a saying, 'You cannot buy a woman, she is not a cow; you cannot purchase a wife, she is not a home.'

So what is *lobola*?

Nine cattle are involved in this transaction, and this should give you a clue. Each head of cattle represents a month in which the young man's wife-to-be lay in her mother's womb. *Lobola*, therefore, is an ancient ritual which honours women – in this case, the mother of the wife-to-be.

Tswana and Sotho-speaking tribes call *lobola* 'the things that have to do with the female' or 'the things of the female'. By presenting cattle to his prospective in-laws, the young African man proves that he is capable of supporting their daughter in the manner to which she is accustomed. It is also a pledge that he will be a responsible husband and a loving, dutiful and responsible father to any offspring that God and the ancestral spirits might present to him and his wife.

Another interesting custom involving cattle was the one followed when a strange person arrived in our territory from far away. If this person was destitute and had no cattle of his or her own, the king would grant a piece of land on which a home could be built, and the neighbours would lend a number of cows for milk and a bull to serve those cows.

The newcomer was supposed to keep the cows and the bull, and even slaughter them if the occasion demanded. But that person was honour-bound some day to return some of the calves born while the cattle were in his or her possession to the people who had offered assistance. This form of cattle banking was known as 'bringing life' or 'bringing wellbeing'. To bring life to whom, you may ask? To bring life to the newcomer. You welcomed the person into your community and offered cattle so that he or she would not starve. Your goodwill would be rewarded with offspring from the cattle you had loaned to that person.

This was what Africa was like in the past: a beautiful, sharing, human Africa, governed by a philosophy which we call *ubuntu* – the path of the human being.

In olden days, fines for offences were paid in cattle, sheep or goats. Light fines were paid in fowl or grain. Whereas most of the animals paid in fines became the property of the king or the *induna*, there were situations where the fine was paid to the victim. For example, if one man hit another man with a stick and broke his arm, the offender, after being duly tried by the chief, was fined a cow which was given to the victim. Sometimes the sentence did not end with the fine paid to the victim, and the offender's own arm was broken with a stick!

If a man assaulted another man and damaged one of his eyes, the offender was fined two cows. One cow was given to the king and other to the victim. And then the offender's eye was subjected to a powerful blow from the fist of the strongest warrior in the land, so that he too could know what it is like to look at the world through one eye.

If a man insulted a woman by calling her a bitch, he was severely punished. He was fined three head of cattle: two were given to the king and one was given to the victim in compensation. Then the man was forbidden by the king to have intercourse with any woman for a period not exceeding two years. By insulting this woman, he had indirectly insulted all the women in the land, including his own wife.

The cow presented to the insulted woman would be slaughtered in the chief's village and all the women in the area would be invited to eat. Every part of the cow would be cooked except the tail, which would be hacked off after the beast had been slaughtered. The tail was used in a very unusual way. The man who had insulted the woman would be tied to a tree with his face to the trunk, his loin-skin would be ripped off and the women would take turns to beat his buttocks black and blue with the tail of the slaughtered cow.

If a man insulted a virgin by insinuating that she was no longer a virgin, the king would order all the virgins in the land to converge on the offender's home, wailing at the tops of their voices and shouting that they had been insulted. They could select the best cow in the man's kraal and stone it to death while they put terrible curses on the man. Then they would slaughter the cow and simply leave it in the bush for the hyenas and vultures to enjoy. The man would be banished from the community for about a year, on the understanding that he would be killed without mercy if he so much as showed his face in the land before the period of exile expired.

THE COW IS THE LIFE OF THE HUMAN BEING

It was not uncommon for Africans to sacrifice their lives to rescue cattle that had fallen into dongas or were trapped in quicksand. There was a saying, 'The cow is the life of the human being.' In olden days, if an ox, a cow or a bull had been injured in any way, all efforts were made to save the life of the animal. In my travels through Africa I have seen many instances of cows or oxen which had escaped from the claws of lions having their terrible injuries tenderly nursed by their owners with poultices and compresses, until they recovered.

Some years ago, I was exploring the Magabeng region with the famous archaeologist, Adrian Boshier, and his wife, Joan, when we came across a group of Bakone people who were stitching a gash in the haunch of an ox which had been injured by the blade of an ox-drawn plough.

The Bakones used a heavy, sailmaker's needle and a double length of twine which was normally used for weaving grass mats. The way they performed this operation indicated that they were familiar with such injuries and knew how to deal with them. The ox was sedated with a strong mixture of *dahwa* tubers mixed with dagga leaves during stitching. Then warm resin was poured over the injury to keep out infection and flies. We left the kraal a few hours after the stitching to explore further afield. When we returned two weeks later, the stitches had been removed and the injury was healing well.

In olden days, clever cattle-owners collected urine from their calves and cows and kept it in large, clay pots in a specially-built hut next to the cattle-pen. The urine was often collected in a rather amusing way. A waterproof leather bag was tied around the body of a calf in such a way that when it urinated, the urine poured into the leather bag. When the bag was half-full it was removed from the calf and the contents poured into a clay pot.

The urine was used to disinfect cattle injuries. For example, if a bull was injured by another bull during a fight, the urine was heated and used to disinfect the injury before a herbal poultice was applied. Sometimes the urine was used cold, but its antiseptic properties were beyond question.

When I was young, everyone who kept cattle swore by the disinfectant qualities of calves' urine. Occasionally they used it to treat human illnesses, and euphemistically called it *nkongozelo*, 'that which has been gathered with respect'.

Zulu kings kept special cattle which were known as *inyoni kayiphumuli*, which means 'the restless bird'. These cattle, of the traditional Nguni breed, were pure white with black ears. They were revered as the soul of the nation and called 'the cattle of the sun'. They were kept in special enclosures inside the king's kraal and no other cattle were allowed to graze where these sacred beasts grazed. When one of the cattle died, its skin was made into two shields for those warriors whose loyalty to the king was beyond question and formed part of the thousand-strong force known as the *amafanenkosi* – 'they who must die with the king' – the most trusted bodyguards of the Zulu monarch.

These cattle were rarely slaughtered, and then only on very special occasions. During a solemn rainmaking ceremony, high on the summit of a flat-topped, sacred mountain – such as the Madlozi mountains in Zululand – two sacred beasts would be slaughtered at the king's command. Their meat would be eaten only by carefully selected people who would collect those bones that had not been broken or smashed in a great pile at the centre of the summit. There they were ceremonially burnt, with a large pile of wood, by the king and his people, who requested the rains to fall on their rain-starved territory.

REQUESTING THE SPIRIT OF A DECEASED MAN TO RESIDE IN A BULL

There is a very old custom which is still practised by many people in the land of the Tsonga and Shangaan peoples. About a year after the death of a great person or a family head, members of the dead person's family attend an auction to buy a cow (if the dead person was female) or a bull (if the dead person was male). They select the biggest and best-looking animal they can find. When the animal is brought to the village, it is taken to the grave of the dead person and, at nightfall, the local sangomas call up that person's spirit and beg it to enter the bull or cow and possess it. They will do this for three or four days in succession, until they are sure the beast is possessed by the spirit of the dead person. They will study omens for several days after that to make sure that the dead person is reincarnated in the beast. Then, in a ceremony which is conducted very early in the morning, the beast is formally named after the dead person and it is kept, honoured and respected, cleaned and nursed, exactly as the dead person was in the last months of his or her life.

If a member of the dead person's family goes to the trading store and buys, say, a roll of material to make clothes, it is first presented to the beast, which is told how much it cost and where it was bought. Then the roll of material is taken to the *ndumba*, a hut specially set aside as the temple of the ancestral spirits which is a feature of all the Tsonga and Shangaan homesteads. The roll of material is kept there for a number of days before it is used to make clothes. Even if a radio or items of furniture are bought, they are all presented formally to the beast which carries the name of the deceased person.

If the beast dies, it is immediately replaced with a similar beast which is once again believed to be the reincarnation of the dead person.

These beasts are always present at all feasts performed by the family; at all weddings and burials. The beast must share the family's every joy and every sorrow. If the family wants anything from the ancestral spirits, they address their prayers to the beast – or rather to the spirit of the dead person which is believed to be inside the cow or bull. If rain is requested, the animal is sprinkled with water by four sangomas standing at four points around the animal. If the family asks for money, a small handful of coins is brought close to the beast's nose so that it can see what is required. If a baby is wanted, a clay statuette representing a baby is placed on a table or on a low mud wall in the centre of the kraal and the beast brought to see it and told what is required.

LAWS AND TABOOS REGARDING CATTLE

In all African cultures, keeping cattle was governed by many laws and taboos. Cattle had to be let out of the pen and be back in at certain times – neither too early nor too late – every morning and evening. The herdsman had to make sure that the dew had evaporated from the veld before the cattle could be let out. He also had to see that the cattle ate the right food every day and that they all had enough water to drink. He was not supposed to disturb the cattle while they were chewing the cud. If he did, the cattle would become depressed and would not yield sufficient milk or tender meat when slaughtered.

Africans of all tribes, and of all the nations through which I have travelled, were very careful to keep their cattle happy and content. Herdsmen played musical instruments that produced notes which, based on many centuries of experience, were known to have a restful and relaxing effect on all the cattle in their care.

When the cows were milked, a young person had to stand outside the cattle-pen and play a special musical instrument which would make the cows relax and let their milk flow freely. Sometimes it was necessary to bring a calf close to its mother if she was nervous. The herdsmen had to take care not to over-milk the cows, as milk for the calves had to be left in the mothers' udders. The milk left for the calf was carefully calculated according to the known yield of each cow. If, for example, the cow had enough milk to yield two wooden milking pails, only one pail was milked.

According to African law, no menstruating woman was allowed to walk into a cattle-pen. A newly-married woman, in particular, was not allowed to walk across her father-in-law's cattle-pen. No-one was allowed to use bad language at milking time, whether directed at other human beings or at the cattle – and especially not at the cows being milked. There is evidence that seems to confirm the belief that cattle, sheep and goats, like cats and dogs, have very deep feelings.

We were told as young boys that cattle have a sense of humour, like human beings. We were also told that they have a deep sense of grief. Cattle are aware of death and, when they are faced with it, they grieve and fear. A phenomenon which is well-known to anyone who has ever kept cattle is cited as proof that they experience grief when another cow or bull has been slaughtered or killed in an accident. We often saw, and I still see, cattle entering the area where a cow has been slaughtered and bellowing over the drying hide of the beast and its stomach-contents.

For this reason, a strictly observed law was that no beast could be slaughtered or skinned in the presence of another. It had to be removed from the rest of the herd and taken away for slaughtering. Its hide had to be taken to a place where other cattle would not see it and mourn over it.

Those whose duty it was to slaughter cattle were advised to bury the contents of the beast's stomach immediately in order to prevent other cattle from finding it. It was believed that if cattle were allowed to grieve over the hide, blood or stomach contents of a slaughtered animal, it would bring bad luck to the cattle owner and his family.

We were taught that cattle understand human speech and jokes. They also understand and revel in being flattered by human beings. For this reason, every leading cow, bull or ox in a chief's or wealthy man's herd had a special name, and a special praise song or praise chant was always recited whenever this animal was nearby.

Our people also believed that like dogs, some cattle – especially cows – had the powerful ability to see into the future. If a cow foresaw disaster it would signal this by lowing continually and for no reason. And it always did this in the direction from which the disaster would appear.

When I was a young boy, the people of our valley and a group living nearby were always locked in sporadic faction fighting, especially at Christmastime. Whenever a war-party intended attacking our valley, some of our cows would start lowing in the direction of the enemy's approach. Our dogs would join in the uproar, ceaselessly howling as loudly as they could. Then we knew for sure that the animals were warning us about an attack. We knew from personal experience the truth of the ancient African saying, 'Very often your dog and your cow are far better seers than you are'.

In ancient times, there were men and women who were highly trained as 'cattle midwives'. They were greatly loved and highly respected by all the people in the land. It was their task to keep a close watch on calving cows and, if necessary, assist them. These men and women were believed to be children of the moon, and they were experts in treating illnesses in cattle, sheep, goats and fowl, cats and dogs. They knew exactly what to do if they found a cow having difficulty giving birth. They knew exactly what to do if a poultry disease afflicted a village. They knew exactly which herbs or mixtures to give to young calves suffering from diarrhoea.

THE BEAUTIFUL COW THAT ENDED A WAR

In the area now known as Mpumalanga there is a river named after a cow. Unfortunately the river's name is incorrectly spelt these days, and only when we revert back to its original name does the meaning become apparent. This river, which starts in Mpumalanga and flows through Mozambique towards the Indian Ocean, is called the Komati River. The correct name to be used is *Inkomati.* The Zulus and Swazis belong to the great Nguni stock of black nations. In the language of the Zulu and Xhosa peoples, a cow is called *inkomazi,* but the Swazi people avoid sounding the 'zi' and pronounce it 'ti'. When a Zulu refers to a cow, *inkomazi,* a Swazi will call it *inkomati.* Thus the Komati (or Inkomati) River is really the Cow River.

But why would people name a river after such an ordinary creature as a cow? Well, the cow that it refers to was a very special cow. And this is the story . . .

We do not know the river's original name, but the story goes that at one time the Mangwane and Mambayi peoples were locked in a terrible war of extermination that lasted for more than four decades. The tribes were equally strong. Both could put many warriors on the battlefield and both tribes were equally brave and ferocious in battle. Neither nation could gain advantage over the other and claim victory.

One day, under the leadership of their kings, the two tribes met for what was to be the last and greatest battle of their long war. The battle went on for four days – such was the rage and hatred that boiled within the souls of all the warriors. It is said that at the end of the hideous bloodletting, during which twenty-five thousand warriors lost their lives, the two kings were badly wounded. Both realized that they were dying.

One king said to the other, 'My brother, my fellow human being, don't you think this slaughter has gone on for far too long? What have we gained from the bloodshed? What have we brought upon our people, except misery, pain, fear and hatred?'

The second king replied, 'I could ask the same question, my brother. Here we lie like two fools in the bush, our lives ebbing redly away, and for what purpose?'

The first king said, 'It would be wonderful if, as we die, we could leave peace behind us so that our children and our children's children will never see such carnage as we see around us this day. War is madness personified; war is blasphemy against the ancestral spirits and the gods. We must stop this nonsense, and we must stop it while we still breathe.'

The second king said, 'But how are we going to do that?'

The first king answered, 'We must allow the gods themselves to tell us whether we should continue this war or make peace. You are dying, I am dying too. It is up to us as kings, together with the gods, to leave to our children either a heritage of peace, friendship and love, or a bloody legacy of war, carnage and destruction. What is it to be?'

The second king replied, 'Let the warriors who survive break off the war. Let us declare a truce between us, my friend, and let the warriors go out and search for an omen – any omen that will tell us whether the gods want us to continue or stop this war.'

It is said that the warriors declared a truce, put away their headdresses and their battle shields, and broke all of their spears except one. The warriors stood facing each other on the battlefield.

'Go and look for a sign from the gods,' cried one of the dying kings weakly.

The warriors scattered across the land. They scoured the land in search of an omen, a sign, anything that could be taken as a message from the gods. Then one search party was suddenly galvanized into action when a young warrior cried out, '*Inkomati! Legani inkomati!*' ('The cow! Look at the cow!') All the warriors rushed in response to the cry and they came across an amazing sight.

The river moved slowly, forming reed-bordered pools here and there. Standing knee-deep in the silvery water of one of these pools was a pure white cow. It was one of the most beautiful beasts the men had ever seen. There was scarcely a blemish on her body. Her horns were long and jet-black like polished ebony. Her ears were black and small. Her nose was black. She was beautiful! It was a very strange sight. There was no village for miles, yet here was a solitary, snow-white cow, standing in water and drinking it.

And to make the scene even more miraculous, the storm-clouds which had been roaring across the land for several hours parted. To the east was a rainbow so beautiful, so fantastic, so delicate, it arched from one cloud to the other like a mighty bridge built by an artistic god.

'*Inkomati!*' shouted the warriors.

The wise men of both nations immediately went into council. They threw the bones of divination and were told that this cow had been sent by the gods as a sign that the two tribes should make peace. The cow had to be sacrificed and its white hide used to wrap the two kings who were close to death.

A great peace ceremony was held in which the two dying kings ate small pieces of the white cow's sacred liver. When the two kings died, their bodies were wrapped in the white hide of the sacred cow and they were buried together upon one of the foothills of a mountain range. Thereafter, there was peace between the Mangwane and the Mambayi peoples.

PART II

WILD ANIMALS

PRAISE SONG TO THE HYENA

You are the *impisi* that pieces together the assegais of our forefathers
You are the living broom of our great-grandmothers, with which they swept their villages
You are the one who walks splay-footed
Who passes through the night unseen
Whose eyes gleam like stars in the darkness, frightening both the *mantindanes* and the sorcerers.
You, *impisi*, are the friend of the warriors and those that walk through the night
Strange creature that purifies the whole land
Worshipped alike by the great gods, the amatonga, and by men and women
You laugh in the night as you leave
You deceive with your voice saying, 'I am going over there!' when, in fact, you are about to enter our villages
Hyena, many are those who despise the appearance of your face
Many are those who call you a coward
But you are a friend of warriors
You are a purifier of battlefields
You are a purifier of feasting grounds where both the tooth and the spear have eaten their fill
Bayete, animal of ancient times!
Hail hyena!

THE PURIFIER WITH THE UNSAVOURY REPUTATION

There is an animal which has a very objectionable reputation among many African tribes. It is known for its cowardice, and as a crude and ungrateful scavenger, a beast which cleans up where nobler beasts have feasted. This is the hyena, an animal whose ugliness and cowardliness have for many generations made it a byword in Africa for all that is unsavoury.

However, this animal once had a noble purpose. Together with the vulture, it was used by African people to clean up the environment near villages and kraals.

Some African people know the hyena by its Zulu name, *impisi*, while some tribes in Zimbabwe call it *sisi*. These words literally mean 'the purifier', 'the cleaner', 'the one who makes things orderly' – a very strange name indeed for a beast which is given bad press in African fables, legends and myths!

But why was the hyena named 'the purifier'?

I shall explain. But before I go on, let me tell you that, in the language of the Tswana and the Southern Sotho, the hyena is known as *phiri*. This is another interesting name which means 'the animal of the secret'. In Setswana, a hyena is known as *sephiri*, because it moves in secret, usually in darkness and silently.

In olden days, African kings built great villages consisting of several hundred huts. Each hut was inhabited by as many as twenty people. The Batswana people in Botswana, and those in the western part of the former Transvaal, built communities of such a size that one could call them cities. One can still see pictures of these cities in books written by explorers such as Reverend Campbell, who visited the lands of the Batswana people in the early nineteenth century.

Inevitably these massive communities generated a lot of refuse: heaps of wood ash, piles of animal bones, and heaps and heaps of scraps from cereal-type foods such as sorghum, millet and maize. In fact, these villages and great city kraals, like modern communities, had a serious refuse disposal problem.

As in modern villages and towns, these communities had men and women whose sole duty was to remove refuse and to dump it as far away as possible from human habitation. This was done on an almost daily basis.

But how does one successfully dispose of heaps of wood ash, mountains of food scraps and piles of meat bones? The answer is very simple. Ancient Africans buried all of their food scraps, except meat bones, in their cornfields and maize-fields to fertilize the earth – or, as they called it, to feed the Earth Mother.

They threw the piles of meat bones into carefully selected gullies outside their villages, where large troops of hyenas assisted the village dogs in their disposal. In all ancient African communities, large packs of hyenas could be found prowling outside the perimeter fences. Their duty was to crunch the bones discarded by the villagers.

Recycling refuse was a very important part of everyday life in an African community, and the people made good use of the great and invincible forces of nature. When an animal died, it was taken out of the villages and thrown into the dongas with the meat-bones.

WHY IS THE HYENA SO UGLY?

The story goes that the Great Spirit first created the souls of people and animals, and then decided to let each animal choose its own body.

The elephant chose a powerful body. The rhinoceros chose a big body and a mighty horn on its nose because it always felt unsafe and thought that other animals would attack or provoke it. The hippopotamus chose a body that could float in water – a very big body that could take a lot of damage.

One after the other, the animals chose their bodies, but the hyena insulted the Great Spirit. The Great Spirit spoke in a very friendly way to the hyena's soul:

'Oh *impisi*, what kind of a body would you like to have?'

The hyena, being such an ill-tempered animal, replied very rudely: 'I am not going to choose my body. You are the Creator, you should choose my body for me. Don't bother me with stupid questions. You are God, not I.'

God's wife was very angry at the hyena's rudeness, so she whispered into her husband's ear that the hyena should be given a very ugly body, with high shoulders, a low back, splay feet, an ugly snout, evil-looking eyes – and a horrendous smell. Furthermore, the hyena was to be given a ridiculous stump of a tail so that it would be unable to chase away the flies.

When the hyena entered its new body, it found it very clumsy and ugly.

'Oh, now I am imprisoned in this ugly body. I am sorry for my evil words. Other animals run away from me because they are afraid of my terrible teeth; they are afraid of my smell. And the lions of the forest pursue me and want to kill me. What am I to do, oh Great Spirit?'

The Great Spirit asked, 'Hyena, are you sorry for what you said to me?'

The hyena replied, 'Oh, Great One, I am. I regret every word of rudeness. Can you find it in you to forgive me? Can you find it in you to change me and to make me beautiful? Give me, God, the grace of a dog and the speed of a cheetah.'

The Great Spirit said, 'Oh hyena, I have run out of all those things. Although you look ugly and terrible, smell evil, are shifty-eyed and have only a small tuft of a tail, I am going to create a special place in people's and other animals' hearts for you. Although you are ugly, I will make the animals love you.'

'How, Great Spirit?' asked the hyena.

'Oh hyena, have I not given you strong jaws?'

'Yes, Great One,' came the reply.

'Have I not given you secret knowledge over and above the other animals?'

'Yes, my Lord.'

'You shall help to clean the world with your powerful jaws. You shall acquire a taste for bones and for decaying meat. You shall help to remove decay from the land. People shall respect you and call you *impisi* the valiant hunter, *impisi* the purifier of the earth. Others shall call you *phiri*, the lord of all secrets, for you shall move by night, while other animals move by day. You shall see things that other animals do not see. So be cheerful, *impisi*. Be happy with your lot.'

But the Great Spirit had not only given *impisi* strong jaws and mighty teeth, he also gave him a big stomach which could not be filled easily. So the *impisi* eats and eats, but its stomach is never full.

THE HYENA THAT WANTED HORNS

One day the eland, chief of all the animals that have horns, decided to hold a great feast to celebrate the horn. A beautiful hut was built and all the animals that had horns were invited to this place.

There was much feasting, with eating, drinking and dancing, and *impisi*, being a music-lover, tried to gatecrash the party. He was promptly butted out of the village by *inkonkoni*, the wildebeest.

'Get out of here, you stinking animal!' cried the wildebeest.

But again, *impisi* tried to gatecrash the party. This time he found *inyathi*, the buffalo, waiting at the gate.

'What do you want here?' asked *inyathi*.

As the buffalo towered over him, threatening to stamp him into the ground under his tremendous hoofs, *impisi* said, 'Oh buffalo, please do not kill me!'

Inyathi replied, 'Hyena, give me one good reason why I should not stamp you into the ground? Why do you not have horns? You know that this party is only for animals that have horns.'

'Aah?' said hyena.

'Yes!' glared the buffalo, with his short-sighted eyes. 'Now get out of here before I kill you!'

The hyena ran into the bush, where he came across a pair of impala horns. The impala had been eaten by lions several days before. And then the hyena had a great idea. It was one of the best ideas he had ever had!

The hyena said, 'I am going to become an animal with horns.'

He made his way through the bush, dragging the horns along the ground in his jaws, until he came to a hollow tree where there were bees.

The hyena sang to the queen of the bees, '*Manyosi, manyosi*, mother of the bees, *manyosi, manyosi*, mother of the bees, give me your beeswax, give me your beeswax, give me . . .'

He danced around the hollow tree until the queen of the bees said, 'Who is making that racket?'

The bees said, 'Oh great one, it is a hyena asking for beeswax.'

The queen of the bees said, 'Ignore him!'

But the hyena made such a noise that eventually the queen called on her bees to throw bowls of beeswax on the hyena's head. This pleased the hyena, for when his head was covered with fresh wax, he took the two impala horns and stuck them on his head. He was so excited when he saw his reflection in water. He now possessed a noble pair of sharp horns, brightly polished with beeswax.

He boldly approached the village of the horned animals where the old buffalo stood guard.

'I am a new animal which God has created. I am called *impongopongo*.'

'Aah, get closer. Let me have a look at you,' said the buffalo. But he was so short-sighted, he could barely see beyond his nose.

'You smell like the animal I chased away from here earlier!'

'Oh buffalo, all animals smell the same!' remarked the disguised hyena.

'Do you have horns on your head?' enquired the buffalo.

'*Yebo*, I have horns on my head.'

'Go in before I change my mind!'

Hyena sat among the audience, cheering as springboks sang and impalas performed. Musical instruments were played by all the animals. It was a wonderful time. There was food by the basket-load; there were mountains of cornbread, yams and pumpkins, all cooked to perfection. The hyena really gorged himself.

All of a sudden, the weather changed. It became cold. The hyena elbowed the other animals aside and moved closer to the fire where he listened to stories, to singing, and to the playing of drums. He was really happy. As it grew colder, he moved closer to the fire. The fire heated the wax which attached the horns to his head and one of the horns dropped off!

'*Hau!*' cried queen eland, 'One of our fellow animals has lost his horn!'

She called to the great healer of the animals, the sable antelope, 'Sable antelope, *inkolongwane*, please help that animal whose horn has fallen off. He will die if we do not help him! Are you a sick animal?'

'Yes, I am sick,' replied the hyena.

When *inkolongwane* approached the hyena, he saw that the second horn was falling off. Soon all the horned animals realized that the hyena was nothing but an impostor.

'You ate our food, you listened to our music, but you are a meat-eating animal! You are not one of us!' they cried.

'Oh buffalo, come and see to this impostor!'

'I suspected that there was something false about this fellow!' said the buffalo. 'Please, my friends, do me a great favour and throw him into the air!'

The poor hyena screamed as he was thrown into the air by the other animals. The buffalo charged at him mightily and butted him right out of the village with

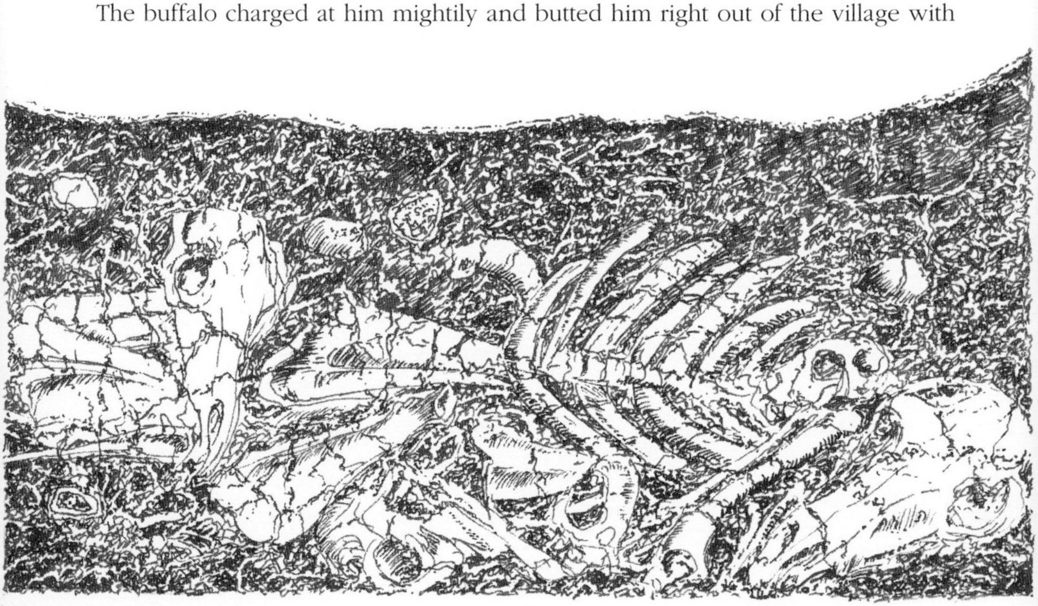

his great armoured forehead. The hyena spun through the air and screamed a tremendous scream before he fell into the soft sand of a dry river bed.

He raised a lot of dust and his ribs were painful. But the other animals heard him laughing, 'Hehehe, hehehe. You may have beaten me, but I have eaten your food and enjoyed your music! I am a hyena, the most cunning of animals. Goodbye, greedy animals! One day I will see you dead and rotting in the bush and I will chew your bones to powder, because I am the hyena, the lord of all cunning! Hehehe, hehehe!'

He disappeared into the forest, walking with a splay-footed limp.

PRAISE SONG TO THE HIPPOPOTAMUS

You, fat one who lives in the rivers
You, who get fat on mud while other cows get fat on grass
You, whose teeth are more fearsome than the battle-axes of the Zulus of old
You, whose body would put those of King Cetshwayo and Dingane to shame
You, whose eyes see everything
And whose ears can hear the smallest whisper of a lover hidden among the reeds
You are the great lazy one
The dweller in the swamps
The dweller in the mud
You are the one whose knowledge is the envy of all the gods
Your fat brings love to our huts and fertility to our loved ones
Your meat sustains heroes, for cowards can never digest it
Your feet can dance where no Zulu can ever dance
And no Venda can ever gyrate
You dance under the waters
You dance under the lakes
You rejoice among the reeds
For you are the lazy one who defied the gods themselves
You are the lazy one who chose the river as your home, whereas lesser animals chose the plains
It is said, oh *imvubu*, that when the last of your kind passes away, the land shall no longer be fat
For you are the fat of the land
You are the friendly one
You are the whisper on the river bank

You are the light that mocks me as I approach a great lake
You are the great pumpkin of Africa that walks on four legs, delighting those who see you
Oh animal of love
Oh animal of fertility
May your snorting always be heard in the great lakes and the rivers of Africa!
May you swim the rivers in the land of our forefathers until the dying of time itself!
May you hear the lion roar, the elephant trumpet and the buffalo snort, even though the forests of the land are shrinking and fading like the dreams of old men smoking dagga in a hidden village
Oh *imvubu*, oh hippopotamus
Horse that no Boers can ride!
You are the sister of the rhino
The cousin of the elephant
Though as big as the rhinoceros, you are faster than an ostrich – as many who dared to provoke your rage know very well to their cost
You are the joy of our children
You are the joy of our womenfolk
You are the darling of our old men
And the beloved of our warriors
Long may you live!
Long may you prosper!
Long may you feed upon the river banks in safety!

THE REBELLIOUS ONE

Although the hippopotamus is a mammal, it is nearly always found in water. It is called *imvubu* in Zulu, or *kubu* in Setswana and Sotho.

The Bakavubu regard the hippopotamus as their totem and are known as 'the people of the hippopotamus'. The hippopotamus is an animal admired for its great strength, its ferocious fighting qualities and its often seemingly insatiable appetite for travel.

The hippopotamus is regarded by African people as a symbol of rebellion, uncontrollability and unruliness. The Tswana name for this animal is *kubu* which means 'rebellion' or 'rebelliousness'. It also means 'sudden awakening', which in Setswana is *kubuga.*

HOW THE HIPPOPOTAMUS HINDERED THE EARTH MOTHER

A strange and beautiful story is told about three animals: the elephant, the rhinoceros and the hippopotamus.

It is said that after the great Earth Mother, God the Father and God the Son created the Earth, the moon and the sun, they found that the Earth was too rocky to grow green grass, trees and other vegetation. The soil still had to be created, and for this purpose the star gods brought three great animals to Earth to pound the rock into soil with their hooves.

The first of these animals was the elephant. The elephant had to pound the rock into powder with its great feet, and dig out water with its great tusks to form springs that would become streams, and later rivers. The elephant toiled and toiled and toiled, dancing ceaselessly, pounding the rocky plains of the new Earth into powder with its feet, and digging springs with its tusks until one of them became blunt and useless. But still the elephant carried on until it almost dropped with exhaustion. The Earth Mother ordered the elephant to rest because it still had to attend to the task of fathering other elephants.

And so the elephant rested under a great rock, happily drinking the water that bubbled from one of the springs that it had laboriously dug.

Now it was the turn of the hippopotamus to pound the earth into soil. The hippopotamus pounded and pounded, but began complaining to the Earth Mother that the work was too hard, that the earth was too rocky, and that its tusks, unlike the elephant's, were too short to dig out rivers and streams.

The beast of rebellion was getting quite tired with the task it had been given. One day, after the Earth Mother had screamed at the hippopotamus to work harder and faster, the hippopotamus decided to strike. It rebelled and ran off towards a recently formed river, where it dived underwater and refused to get out.

Then it was the turn of the rhinoceros. The rhinoceros, being a powerful, loyal and proud animal, tackled the task with great zest. It pounded and danced, it snorted and roared, it dug more springs with its horn than the elephant had with its two tusks. The rhinoceros charged against the hard rocks and pierced them with its great horn. Water spurted out to reward the beast's mighty effort.

A jealous *tokoloshe*, who resented the creation of the Earth, decided to interfere when he saw how close the rhinoceros was to completing the task that the gods had set for it. The *tokoloshe* threw dust into the rhinoceros' eyes, but the rhinoceros carried on regardless, blinking time and again to remove the dust from its eyes.

The *tokoloshe* broke the tip of the rhinoceros' horn, but the rhinoceros prayed for a new horn to grow in its place, and it did. It carried on with its work until three-quarters of the stubborn, rocky Earth had been pounded into soil. Many streams and rivers, dug by the rhinoceros' mighty horn, flowed towards the eternal sea.

Then the *tokoloshe* seized the rhinoceros' penis to prevent it from urinating, in the hope that it would be forced to stop work. But the rhinoceros carried on, while its bladder grew larger and larger, to the point of bursting.

A point was reached where the *tokoloshe* could no longer prevent the urine from being expelled. A great jet of urine surged from the rhinoceros, striking the *tokoloshe* in the face and sending it somersaulting across the rocky plain. The evil spirit struck its head against a rock, broke its neck and died. And the rhinoceros completed its task without further interference.

THE CONFUSED ONE

African people believe that the hippopotamus is not only an animal of rebellion, laziness and irresponsibility – it is also an animal of confusion. It cannot make up its mind whether it is a rhinoceros or an elephant!

The Zulu people call the hippopotamus *imvubu*. This word has several meanings, one of which has to do with mixing several things in a container (from the verb, *vuba*, which means 'to mix', 'to knit together' or 'to combine'). In this sense the word *imvubu* means 'the mixed-up creature' or 'the creature which is unable to make up its mind what it is'.

It behaves like a crocodile, but it looks like a rhinoceros and an elephant. It really is a confused, mixed-up beast and, for this reason, Zulu people sometimes refer to a person who tries to be all things to all people, and attempts to please everyone, as *imvubu*, 'the one who is mixed up'.

PRAISE SONG TO THE RHINOCEROS

U*bhejane*, you are the thunder of the valleys
You are the roar among the mountains
You are the noise upon the plains
And you are the horn that the moon loves to kiss!
You are the rhinoceros
You are the invincible one
You are the weak eye that sees into years that are yet to come
You are the sharp ear that hears a lover's whisper in the tall grass
You are the great foot that tramples everything into the ground
You are the delight of the woodcarvers
You are the joy of the painters
You are the song of those who cast in metal
You are *ubhejane*, the rhinoceros!
Together with the elephant, *indlovu*, many generations ago, you danced the world into existence, so that green things may grow upon this world.
You are the one who urinates backwards, while other animals urinate towards the ground
And it is said that those who have been covered with your urine in the forest will know the headbands of kingship!
You are *ubhejane*, the rhinoceros
You are the darling of the waxing moon
You are the lover of the waning moon
You are the thunder of the mountains
You are the vibration upon the rocky ground
You are the hard-working one, the labourer who laboured so that the Earth Mother might plant green things upon this Earth

You are *ubhejane*
You, whose dung unites the nations of Africa!
When the great kings who fought many great battles wanted to make peace between themselves and their enemies, they walked together – friend and enemy and former enemy – into a heap of your dung, *ubhejane*
And then they washed each other's feet with the milk of young cows as the sun rose early the following morning
For it was believed that your dung, *ubhejane*, which no-one dares set on fire to make a fire, can bring peace and take away enmity between people
Ubhejane, long may you roar across the plains of Africa
Long may you be seen as a mighty bulk moving between the trees – at one with the tall anthills and the great rocks, invisible to the unpractised eye
So still you stand behind a tree, watching with weak eyes, the approaching enemy unaware of your presence
Ubhejane, symbol of our greatest kings
You, whose escape from confinement is the darling of all poets
You, who are the symbol of independence of the human soul and its untameability!
They kill you for nothing, *ubhejane*, for your horn
And yet your horn is sacred to the moon and not to wife-stealing dogs!
Ubhejane, long may you urinate upon the plains of Africa
Long may you make the land wet with your urine!
For it is said that the tree upon which you urinate shall grow to become the tallest tree in the forest
And the person upon whom you urinate will become famous from one end of the world to the other
Ubhejane, animal of our forefathers
Pillar of the land of Africa
Post that supports the green world that we know
Long may you live, *ubhejane!*
May you have a thousand sons and a million daughters!
Oh beloved of the moon goddess, *bayete!*

THE MIGHTY RHINOCEROS

In olden days, Africans honoured the rhinoceros. They so respected the rhinoceros and were so much in awe of it that very few tribes named themselves after it. Throughout southern Africa, only one small tribe uses this sacred beast as its totem: the Bedla people of the land of the Xhosa (*bhele* being the Xhosa name for a rhinoceros). The Batswana people call a rhinoceros *tsukudu*, a name which means 'the struggling animal' or 'the animal of mighty effort'.

African people regarded the rhinoceros with great reverence and they regarded its horn not as an aphrodisiac, but as a weapon possessing great magical powers for annihilating and scattering enemies. If you wanted to cause confusion among your enemies and force them to scatter, and not unite against you, you took a small piece of rhinoceros horn from a rhinoceros that had died of natural causes in the bush and burnt it next to the enemy village.

In olden days, it was believed that killing a rhinoceros would result in a curse on the killer or killers of the most sacred of the big animals. The curse would extend to their wives and children, grandchildren and great-grandchildren.

To this day, when people who are friends suddenly quarrel and separate, Swazi people, especially, believe that an unknown enemy has burnt a piece of rhino horn to bring about the dispute.

BLESSED BY THE RHINOCEROS

Rain had not fallen over the land for months. The bush was dead: a brown, lifeless mass, highlighted here and there by a lifeless greyness. The grass was bleached pale gold and was brittle tinder waiting for the tiniest spark to ignite it and give birth to a bushfire.

The ground was iron-hard. The smallest pebbles were cruel to the bare soles of our feet. It was so hot that wearing boots was dangerous, because the sun heated the leather, causing our skin to blister inside.

Our bodies were covered in sweat. We were tormented by tsetsi flies which hung around our eyes, our nostrils, our ears and our mouths. A silver mist of shimmering heat covered the land, forming a barely visible curtain between us and the dead bush. There were no birds in the sky, no clouds, and even the slow-flowing river which we could see through gaps in the dense bush appeared harsh and uninviting.

Our heads were burdened with heavy cardboard boxes filled with magical equipment – canned food and other necessities of modern life. We also carried tools – picks, shovels and hammers. We were like silent zombies, moving through the bush. We were no longer talking to each other, although we were close friends – James Myombo, Peter Kiambe and I.

While we were walking in single file, I noticed something moving in the heat-veiled bush. It was huge, grey, monstrous and barely visible, but its presence did not trouble my dulled mind. I didn't even bother telling my friends about it. I didn't know what it was, and at that moment, I didn't care.

I just carried on, following my two tall companions, the hot breath rasping in my mouth, my tongue dry with thirst. All of a sudden, there was what felt like a sudden rain shower – a hot, stinking gush of liquid that soaked us from head to foot. We were startled, but our reactions were slow. We paused and looked around for the source of the deluge, and then, as fear invaded our hearts, we turned and moved on, hastily this time, hardly comprehending what had happened.

When we reached the place where the rest of our companions were preparing food, excitement erupted among all the African people present. Some hugged us, some shook our hands, and one man ran his hand through my wet hair.

'Do you realize what has happened to you?' asked the man whom we all recognized as our leader, Josiah Mporombo.

'No', I heard myself answer. 'What made us so wet?'

'Just listen to him – the stupid, ignorant, Christian fool!' cried Mporombo, laughing aloud at my ignorance. 'You don't know much about wild animals, do you? Let me tell you, son of a stupid hippopotamus cow, you and your friends have been blessed by the gods. What happened to you happens only once in a generation. You were urinated on by a rhinoceros! This means that you are all blessed by the ancestral spirits and by all the gods.'

'Yes, this is indeed so,' said the oldest member of our group, a soft-spoken man called Masungira Chiumbo. 'The three of you are going to be famous throughout the land, throughout the world. You must remember this day in days to come.'

This is how I was introduced to one of the strangest African beliefs. I learned for the first time that many African tribes, untainted by Western civilization, believe that if you walk through the bush and a rhinoceros drenches you with its urine, it is a sure sign that you are specially favoured and blessed by the gods.

In olden days, when Zulu kings sent great trading expeditions across the interior to trade with other tribes and with the Portuguese in Delagoa Bay, it was regarded as a very good sign if the expedition encountered two mating rhinoceros. It was especially lucky for an expedition to see two white rhinoceros.

It was also regarded as good luck for a raiding party to encounter a rhinoceros while setting out on a cattle-raid. It was a sign that the raiders would return with cattle, although a few would be killed or injured during the raid.

PRAISE SONG TO THE ELEPHANT

Be angry, angry one!
Be angry at the clouds and the mountains!
Be angry at the sky and the rivers!
Be angry at the sea and the trees!
You are the elephant!
You, whose loud trumpeting heralded the birth of the world
You, whose last trumpeting will herald the end of the world we know
Be angry, great elephant
You, who are hunted by those who fear you
You, who are sought by those who should respect you
You, whose tusks are the ploughs that showed our grandmothers the way
You, whose great feet pounded the earth, the hard earth into powder in ancient times, so that green things might grow
Be angry, elephant, shout at the gods of Africa
Be angry, elephant, shout at the grey ghosts of our forefathers
Be angry, elephant, and shout at the people of modern days who do not do anything to shield you from the murderer and the thief
Be angry elephant, shout at the land that no longer cares about living things
Be angry elephant, shout at the very stars themselves and demand from them justice
You are the lord of the trees
You are the master of the valleys
You are the great farmer who changes the land in which he lives
In your anger, you can dig up and cause the great marula trees to fall
In your anger, you can pierce the mighty baobab tree with one of your tusks

Great elephant, be at peace
Candle of the valleys
Herald of the dawn
King of creation
You, in whose mind shines the souls of murdered gods
Elephant, *indlovu!*
Elephant, *bayete!*
Elephant, *shwele!*
Shwele, forgive the people who kill you, not knowing whom they kill
Who destroy you, not knowing whom they destroy
Who disrespect you, not knowing to whom they are speaking
Indlovu, elephant, servant of the great Earth Mother!
It is said that it was you upon whose back the great goddess rode when she was emerging from the dungeons of the nether world
Elephant, if I had my way, you would rule the plains of Africa forever
Elephant, if I had my way, no weapon would ever be lifted against you
For you are sacred, *indlovu*
You are sacred, creature of creatures
The mighty rhinoceros bows before you
The great hippopotamus runs at the very sight of you, for you caught him on the river bank and he retreated
And he sought safety in the water which is his mother
Not only did he seek safety in the water, oh elephant,
The hippopotamus dived into the very bowels of the river and walked under the water until he emerged at the other side to escape your anger, great elephant
You are the protecting spirit of Africa
You are the whisper of our stories in the wind that has forgotten its heritage
You, whose trumpet saluted the first dawn
And you, whose trumpeting will also say farewell when the last evening ends, *sawubona*

Bayete, elephant!
Animal of our kings
You, from whom the Zulus were proud to trace their ancestry
Wena wendlovu – you of the elephant – they said to their sovereigns
Sovereigns who were nothing but weak and mortal human beings
Wena wendlovu, they said to Shaka, son of the elephant, unconquerable striker that cannot be struck
I salute you, elephant of the plains of Africa!
Wild, untamed and untameable one
Tamed only be the gods of time
Bayete!
UyiZulu, you are the thunder of the skies above
You are the trembling of the Earth below
You are the whispering of the streams and the rivers
And you are the song of the wind among the trees
You are the elephant, the greatest of your kind!
Bayete!

REINCARNATIONS OF MURDERED GODS

African people regard the elephant with a very deep reverence. It is an animal believed to be more than just a beast – it is considered a spiritual entity.

The Zulu, Tswana and Tsonga names for the elephant all mean 'the forceful one', 'the unstoppable one'. In Zulu the name for an elephant is *indlovu*, from the verb *dlovu*, which means 'to crash through', 'to pierce savagely', 'to act with extreme brute force'. The Tswana and Sotho word for elephant, *tlou*, and the Tsonga word, *njovu*, also carry this meaning.

Africans believed many strange things about elephants. They believed that elephants lived for hundreds of years and were reborn again and again in some magical way. This is why an elephant grew a new mouthful of teeth once the first set had worn out. Many tribes used the elephant as the symbol of the great belief in reincarnation and in the transmigration of souls.

African people believed that elephants were reincarnations of murdered gods; gods who had been treacherously slain by other gods in the unseen land and who were reborn on Earth as elephants.

Ivory was the purest substance known next to fire. There was the belief that ivory was neither bone nor any earthly substance, but something that proved the god-like nature of the souls inhabiting elephants – a substance that proved that elephants were really reincarnations of gods murdered in heaven.

Just before the outbreak of World War II, there roamed upon the plains of Tanzania an elephant with tremendous tusks. Africans in the area in which this particular elephant was found went to great lengths to protect the beast from white hunters and poachers. The reason that Africans were prepared to give their lives to protect this great elephant was that they believed it to be a reincarnation of Christ. They called the elephant Ishe, which is the Tanzanian word for Jesus.

I do not know what happened to this great elephant, Ishe. I sometimes hope that it lived to a ripe old age and passed on peacefully into the land of the shadows. In fact, after World War II I met a man in Dar es Salaam who claimed to have seen Ishe's skull resting in a deep valley, bleached by the Tanganyikan sun. He assured me that there was ample proof that the great beast had not fallen prey to poachers or hunters. It had died of natural causes because its great tusks, although cracked and disintegrating, were still attached to the skull, and the rest of its skeleton, although picked clean by vultures and other scavengers, was intact. When I heard that, I breathed a sigh of relief. Old Ishe had died a peaceful death.

The Bushman people of southern Africa have a complex and very beautiful mythology. One of the most colourful aspects is a belief in a great rain beast. They portray this beast either as a great elephant, with raindrops of white paint all over its body, or as a great, pregnant female rhinoceros or hippopotamus, which releases rain whenever it is about to give birth.

According to Bushman belief, and beliefs of other African nations, if the land is gripped by a great drought and people dream of stampeding elephant or rhinoceros, rain will fall on the land. Elephant, hippopotamus and rhinoceros have the magical gift of not only being able to dig for water (which elephant do very efficiently), but also of calling rain from the sky.

THE ELEPHANT WHO DID NOT FORGET OR FORGIVE

Throughout southern Africa, people believe that elephants have very long memories. And there seems to be evidence to bear this out. It is said that you must never sin against an elephant, because he will never forget.

This is the story of a man called Shungu . . .

Shungu lived in Natal during the early 1900s. At first, Shungu lived a very disreputable life, which had been forced upon him by hunger. It was after the great wars fought between the Boers and the British, which had torn the country to tatters. In many areas of Natal African people were dying of starvation. They had lost all their cattle and grazing lands, and hunger moved across the plains like a dark ghost.

At that time Shungu was a young man of sixteen years. It was his duty to ensure the survival of his ailing father and the rest of his family: his father's wives, one of whom was his mother, and his sisters, half-sisters, brothers and half-brothers. Shungu was an excellent hunter, and he kept the family alive and fairly healthy through repeated excursions into the forests to find whatever game was available.

One day, Shungu met several men who belonged to his father's clan. They told him that they were going to the north of Natal to look for elephant. They intended to bring down an elephant, rob it of its flesh, dry the flesh and bring it back in sack-loads to the starving villagers. They successfully persuaded Shungu to accompany them. They travelled for a long time until they came to the area of Natal known as Maputa, where the few surviving elephant lingered.

The hunters immediately starting digging a great hole in the ground, along an elephant trail. They worked like a team of ants, digging with heavy hoes and sharpened sticks that had been hardened by placing them in fire. The hole became deeper as they heaved out the stones they loosened from the bottom and sides. Very soon the hole was deep enough. They covered it with branches and dried grass. And then they waited . . .

They waited and waited and waited and then, two days later, they saw a group of elephant making their way towards the trap. The leading elephant suspected nothing. It was a young bull, and it moved closer and closer to the trap, leading the rest of the herd. The hidden men became very excited. In a burst of bravado, Shungu wanted to jump to his feet and throw his assegai at the elephant. But the leader of the expedition, Shongwana, restrained the impetuous young man by punching him cruelly in the ribs and whispering, 'Quiet!'

Shungu could barely contain his excitement. The next moment, there was a loud trumpeting sound, a great cloud of dust, and a long scream of agony as the leading elephant fell into the deep hole. The elephant's fate had been sealed: it could not escape the inevitable. The hole had been dug big enough for the elephant to fall into it but so that it was unable to climb out. At the bottom and at the sides of the hole, the men had planted stakes made of wild-olive and karee wood, picked dry in the bush, seasoned by the savage years, and then sharpened with axes until they were as sharp as needles.

The rest of the herd fled from the danger zone, but Shungu still wanted to hurt something with his spear. As the elephants retreated, Shungu threw his assegai at the rearmost elephant, a half-grown young calf following its mother. The assegai struck the young elephant's back, above the left leg, but it did not

penetrate very deeply. As the young elephant ran away, it managed to shake loose the assegai from its thick hide, leaving a stream of blood darkening its muddy, wrinkled skin.

From a distance, the elephants looked back to see what had happened to their leader. Shungu failed to notice the eyes of the young elephant stabbing at him like hidden arrows, as if saying, 'One day, I shall repay the wrong you have done!'

The captured elephant's meat was carried back to the villages; the people would survive. Shungu's ailing father praised his son and his friends for the life-saving meat they had brought back with them.

Several years went by until one day, Shungu met a group of white men travelling by ox wagons on the plains of Zululand. They were missionaries searching for converts and preaching the gospel to the defeated Zulu nation. Shungu, with his brilliance, agile mind and strength, soon joined the missionaries, converted to Christianity, and began spreading the gospel.

Years went by and Shungu's hair became grey. He became fat and old and was the most respected missionary in the whole of eastern Zululand.

One day, Shungu was travelling by donkey cart not far from a place which had been declared a game reserve. He was still preaching the gospel and teaching the people. He was loved and respected, but he had made a great mistake – one that no-one who sinned against a fellow human being or another living creature should ever make. He forgot what he had done in that area all those years ago.

Suddenly, Shungu heard a great commotion behind him. He turned around and saw an amazing sight. One of the elephants that had been grazing inside the game reserve was deliberately charging the fence that kept him imprisoned. The great animal charged the fence at its weakest point, broke through, and began to charge towards Shungu. The donkeys tried to bolt and swerved across the road, dragging the cart into the heart of the green bush which was elephant territory. The elephant followed in pursuit. The cart was jumping like a living thing over rocks and fallen logs and, as misfortune would have it, Shungu fell from his seat and landed on the ground with a thud.

The elephant arrived in a great cloud of dust. It picked Shungu up, looked at him, and an expression of pure disgust passed briefly across its eyes. Then, rather gently, it lifted him up and placed him in a fork of the tallest tree. Shungu was alive and unhurt, but very, very frightened. With a loud trumpet of vengeance well and truly committed, the elephant lumbered back into the game reserve, through the gap it had made in the fence, and was soon lost in the misty distance of the dust-encrusted bush.

Several days passed before a group of men travelling by ox wagon heard the loud shouting of a very frightened man, coming from the top of a tree. When they stopped their wagon to investigate the matter, they saw Shungu wedged among the high branches.

'How did you get up there?' asked one of the men in utter amazement.

Shungu was terrified. All he could say as the men created a makeshift ladder to get him down was, '*Indlovu! Indlovu!* – The elephant! The elephant!'

PRAISE SONG TO THE BABOON

Imfene, the one who looks like a man but who is not a man
Listen to me, *imfene*, you dweller among the kranses
Listen to me, oh hairy one
Old man who wears a coat stolen from a white man's farm!
Listen to me, oh long-tailed one
You of the red backside that alarms the women ploughing in the mealiefield
Lord of all the thieves!
Lord of the most cunning!
Master of all guile!
Imfene, you are the member of the Thusini tribe, the people of bronze, who, owing to their laziness, were changed into your kind by the vengeful goddess
Imfene, your wisdom is great, as great as your nostrils which look like the flutes of Venda herd-boys
Your eyes are as red as the eyes of a wizard concocting mysterious preparations in a cave
Your tail is curved like a gentle caress placed upon the shoulder of a maiden by a deceitful lover
Your eyes see very far away,
For they are sheltered under the cave which is your brow
You are ugly and beautiful, *imfene*
You are wise and far-seeing
You are the finisher of pumpkins in the cornfields and the devourer of grain in our granaries
You watch and laugh while women sweat in the fields, planting groundnuts, for you know that you shall eat them when the fools have gathered the harvest
For you are fed by the muscles of human beings

And in this world you fear neither king nor peasant, neither warrior nor coward
You fear only *ingwe*, the leopard of the mountains
Only he is your king
Only he is your equal
Around you a thousand fairy tales have been woven by snuff-taking grandmothers
Around you a thousand songs have been composed by young men herding bulls upon the mountainside
You are *imfene*, the king of the desolate land
Where the drought has devoured the trees and left nothing but empty branches
Your voice is still often heard, shouting at the world from the mountainside
Imfene, bayete!
King of all cunning!
Master of all guile!
I salute you!

THE ONE WHO RESEMBLES HUMANS

Among the many different kinds of animal that are found in Africa, there is one that has a very strange name. Its Zulu name is *imfene* and in the language spoken by the northern, western and southern Sotho people, it is known as *tswene*.

The word *imfene* comes from the verb, *fana*, which means 'to resemble'. The word *tswene* also comes from a similar verb, *tswaana*. In both Zulu and Sotho, the baboon is known as 'that which resembles'. That which resembles what? That which resembles a human being.

This animal, the baboon, is the subject of countless legends and fairy tales and hundreds of proverbs and wise sayings, and is one of the most deeply respected, feared, ridiculed and vilified animals in our motherland.

DO NOT OFFEND A BABOON

When we were young, our parents warned us never to offend a baboon because *imfene kayikhohlwa* (a baboon never forgets). We were also warned against hurling missiles at baboons. The old people said that if you missed, the baboon would take the missile and throw it back at you with its left hand – and would not miss! I never used to believe this – it was only one of many strange stories that old people told – until one day I saw a baboon score a direct hit between the eyes of a man who was chasing it, with one of the most amazing missiles I have ever seen thrown. The baboon was cornered between two high rocks and the man was closing in on it, knobkerrie in hand. The baboon defecated in terror, scooped up some of the dung and used it as a defensive weapon. Smack! Right between the man's eyes.

The man let out a hoarse cry, dropped his knobkerrie and bolted. Needless to say, my two companions and I also took to our heels, because we all believed there was nothing more unlucky than being hit with faeces thrown by a frightened baboon. It was believed that any man or woman who was struck by such a missile would die within two months.

Indeed, the man who had tried to catch the baboon was killed in a mining accident soon after this incident.

EXCELLENT CATTLEHERDS

In olden days, as today, Africans who kept livestock – cattle, sheep and goats – were plagued by gangs of stock-thieves. Many of these gangs were heavily armed with assegais, axes, bows and arrows.

They used to take a heavy toll, but very soon Africans discovered that if baboons were captured young and carefully fed and trained, they made wonderful cattle- and goatherds. One baboon that had been trained to look after a herd of cattle could see off a gang of cattle-thieves in style, barking, screaming and attacking any trespasser who dared to get too close.

There were traditional laws, however, governing the capture, taming and training of young baboons as cattleherds. You were not allowed to rob a mother of her baby; you had to wait until luck came your way. If a female baboon was killed by a leopard, leaving her baby orphaned in the bush, you were allowed to take the orphan home and carefully feed it and train it to look after livestock.

Many stories, some simple fiction and some unshakeably true, are told about loyal baboons who guarded African villagers' cattle for many years. Tales are also told of brave baboons who gave their lives defending their masters' cattle, sheep or goats against thieves.

As children, our parents warned us against stealing baby baboons from their mothers to keep as pets. It was believed that if you stole a baby baboon from its mother, the grieving female would embark on a long journey through the bush to a place where the *umdlebe* tree grew. The mother would use the blood-like sap of this tree to prepare a magical mixture with which she would cast a deadly spell on the thief who had taken her baby. It was said that anyone who stole a baby baboon from its mother, for any reason, would die a horrible death. His or her skin would erupt in watery blisters which would turn into terrible raw sores covering the entire body. The sufferer would die an agonizing death a few months later.

THE BABOON IS A SACRED ANIMAL

In South Africa there are several tribes which use the baboon as their totem. In olden days, hunting baboons for any reason was strictly forbidden and sometimes members of these tribes met with force of arms any hunter who entered the territory with the intent of hunting baboons.

Among the tribes for whom the baboon was a sacred animal and a totem were the Bahurutshe and Baklaro peoples of the Zeerust area in the North West Province. Their folklore had the baboon as the principal character in the story – either as the hero or as a wise adviser to the hero. Dreaming about baboons meant that the great totem of the tribe had extended its protection over the dreamer to shield him or her from all harm and to ensure his or her success.

Once, a young Mugarotse woke up very happy indeed. He was part of a football team that was about to play against a very powerful team – something which worried many of his teammates. The young Mugarotse dreamt that he was standing in the centre of a football field when a baboon suddenly appeared from nowhere, ran towards him on its hind legs with a football held firmly in its forepaws, and gave him the ball. Then the young man woke up. He was sure that the totem of his people had come to tell him that his team would win by a goal. His dream came true the following day. The match was a tough one. The opposing side consisted mainly of hardened veterans who ran rings around the young man's teammates. It took every effort to keep the opposing side from gaining immediate victory. When the score stood at 1–1, with the match rapidly drawing to a sweat-stained end, the young man scored the one goal that gained victory for his side.

If a member of the Baklaro tribe dreams of a baboon running away from him while he is in prison awaiting trial, he takes this to mean that his ancestors have deserted him and that he will be found guilty.

If a Bahurutshe girl dreams that she hears many baboons barking in the bush, the dream is taken to mean that she is going to be sought after by many lovers, but that she will marry none of them. If she dreams of a baboon swimming across a river, the dream is taken to mean that she is going to be married very soon and that her marriage will be a happy one, with a loyal husband and many children.

In the past, eating baboon was strictly forbidden among all tribes in southern Africa, but there are tribes in South Africa which, because of a chronic shortage of food, especially meat, have over the past century or so taken to eating baboon.

THE BABOON AND THE RAINMAKING CEREMONY

The land was dry, brittle, dying. The trees were like ghosts – ugly, grey and without a single leaf on their branches. The grass had almost vanished from the dusty veld and in the sky above, the sun shone mercilessly upon the heat-blasted and sun-browned valleys and plains of the Eastern Cape. The drought had been scourging the land for three full years and there was not a single cloud in the sky to awaken even the smallest spark of hope in the hearts of the people.

The pumpkin patches and the maizefields were dead: huge graveyards of human hopes and dreams where a few of the surviving cattle, sheep, goats and donkeys, every one of them a bony skeleton, moved listlessly, seeking nutrition and salvation where there was none.

In the yards of the trading stores scattered over the vastness of the land, long queues of people waited for gifts of food sent by relief organizations to stave off the dark demon of starvation and death. Some of these people waited for days in vain, and it was not uncommon to see someone wilting like a flower and collapsing in the long queue of misery.

The ghost of hunger was all over the land, and it was at this time that I witnessed something that I have not seen since. I watched people fighting hunger and disease, I watched as the drought grew from bad to worse. Then, one day, my host came to me with the story that a friend had successfully trapped and killed a *mbuzi-mawa* and that he had invited us to attend the ritual feast.

With great curiosity, and wondering what the creature known as *mbuzi-mawa* was, I followed my host, his wives and children to the friend's kraal. We were welcomed with open arms and smiles that masked the great suffering everyone was experiencing. It was dusk when we entered the hut in which the *mbuzi-mawa* feast was to be held. And there, inside the hut, by the light of a great cooking fire, I saw a number of people – adult men and women, and children.

There was an old man who wore a necklace of red beads and an animal-skin hat. I had seen this man before. His name was Ntunyana. He was respected as the wisest man in the district and known as a rainmaker. He was sitting bare to the waist, wearing a red blanket around his loins. Around his wrists and upper arms were metal bangles. Here and there in his necklace hung small objects – animal claws, a shark's tooth, a small, pierced stone and other objects. This was the wise man's necklace of experience which showed the places he had visited all over southern Africa.

Ntunyana greeted us. He said that we would take part in an ancient feast and that during the proceedings we were to think about nothing but rain. We were to imagine that we heard thunder in the sky. We were to imagine that the clouds had gathered and that rain was about to fall.

'You must even imagine the smell of rain, as it falls upon the dry earth,' he said in a hoarse voice. 'You must imagine the animals rejoicing, you must imagine the land happy, you must imagine rainwater cascading over rocks and dripping from the branches of the dead trees. Will you do that?'

'*Ewe* Ntunyana,' said the other people, 'we shall do that.'

'Please do. Please help me.'

Ntunyana rose to his feet and said to everyone, 'We shall now bring in the *mbuzi-mawa*. We shall bring the sacred guest upon whose holy flesh we shall feast this night.'

He went out of the hut and returned a few moments later, accompanied by a young man. The two men carried something towards the far side of the hut and sat it on a chair.

My eyes widened in astonishment. They had brought in a large, dead baboon. Its lifeless, staring eyes were dulled by the cold mists of death, and a fanged, blood-chilling grin was fixed forever upon its dead, hairy face. My heart missed a beat – so this was the *mbuzi-mawa* we had come to eat!

Ntunyana removed the pipe from the tobacco pouch which was bound to his left upper arm and pushed it into the mouth of the lifeless animal. Then his son produced an old and battered felt hat and placed it reverently on the baboon's head.

Ntunyana uttered these words: 'Greetings, great man, greetings visitor from far away, you who were born with a skin blanket, you who did not need to sew yourself any protection against the stings of winter. We greet you, oh *mbuzi-mawa*.'

Then Ntunyana's son saluted the baboon: 'Oh *mbuzi-mawa*' he said. 'We are honoured to invite you here to supper. We are pleased that you accepted our invitation. You shall eat with us and we shall also eat with you, for you are our honoured guest, for you are our friend and you are going to speak to the ancestral spirits on our behalf.'

When the young man had spoken, Ntunyana signalled to an elderly woman. She left the hut and returned a few moments later with a bowl of maize porridge, which she handed to her husband. He, in turn, placed the bowl at the feet of the seated baboon.

'*Mbuzi-mawa*,' said Ntunyana, 'we place maize porridge before you, for we have no meat with which to eat this porridge and it is my humble request that you supply us with meat.'

With one slash of a large knife, he cut off the baboon's tail, skinned it and roasted it on the cooking fire which was burning fiercely in the centre of the hut.

When the tail had been roasted to his satisfaction, he sprinkled it with salt and took it to where the baboon was sitting, and placed it on top of the stiff porridge.

He said, 'You shall eat with us, oh great man.'

He then signalled to his son and they took the baboon out of the hut. This time they were closely followed by two other men who were carrying large knives.

During their absence we were given mugs of *mahewu*, a sour drink made from maize porridge, by the kraal's women-folk. Midnight came and went. Outside the hut there were sounds of activity: the breaking of firewood, the clattering of the iron lids of three-legged pots – and the smell of cooking flesh.

When Ntunyana entered the hut again he was carrying the baboon's skin. He also carried the small wooden chair to which the baboon had been bound. He placed the chair on the ground, close to the wall of the hut, and then draped the fearsome, hairy, grey baboon's hide over the back. He saluted the skin and offered it the bowl of food that it had been offered before.

A long time passed before Ntunyana, his son and the two men brought in a large, three-legged, iron pot, which they placed on the hut's floor next to the fire.

Ntunyana said to us, 'Let us eat, my friends. But listen to me, every morsel of this meat must be eaten. Not the smallest piece must be left behind. When we have eaten, the bones must be burnt in the fire outside – every one of them. Do I make myself clear, my friends?'

'*Ewe*, Ntunyana,' said the people. 'Yes Ntunyana, we hear your voice, we hear your words.'

Then the feast began. It was the most amazing feast I have ever witnessed. It was a ritual; it was a dark sacrament of some kind and it was sanctified by the great traditions of the people of the land.

At first it was difficult for me to eat the flesh of the baboon. It had an unusual, salty taste, but I had taken part in many strange ritual feasts and I knew what was expected of me: great courage, proper behaviour and silence.

We ate every morsel of the creature's flesh, and those whose duty it was to eat the head – Ntunyana, his sons and other friends – placed the head of the baboon face-down in a large basin and began eating it from the rear, without looking at the animal's face. They pulled the flesh from under the skull without looking at it.

About an hour later, every bit of the baboon had been consumed. When the feasting ended, the bones were carefully gathered in a large enamel basin. They all had to be accounted for. Then Ntunyana's senior wife took the bones out of the hut and burnt them in the fire outside, a few paces from the entrance to the hut.

After that, we sat in the hut while the night aged. We talked in subdued voices, because it is most improper for anyone to talk in a loud voice after eating the meat of the *mbuzi-mawa*.

The dawn was a grey whisper in the eastern heavens when a large pot of frothing corn-beer was brought into the hut. We drank in silence. It was all part of the great ritual.

Then Ntunyana came into the hut carrying a small basin of sorghum. He poured it into the fire in the centre of the hut as a humble offering to the ancestral spirits; an offering of food which was in desperately short supply. It was the ultimate sacrifice demanded by tradition.

There had been enough sorghum in the basin to feed Ntunyana's four grandchildren for a week. But this precious cereal had to be sacrificed in the sacred fire in the centre of the hut. A cloud of smoke rose from the fire and soon we were all sneezing and coughing, but custom forbade any of us from getting out into the fresh air.

Ntunyana sat on his haunches close to the fire and he carefully studied the way the smoke rose from the burning sorghum. After staring at the smoke, Ntunyana uttered words that filled me with great surprise. He said, 'My friends, members of my family, on this coming day the rain shall fall.'

A murmur of astonishment burst from the people assembled in the hut. One voice said, 'We hear you, Ntunyana.'

I noticed the flames of hope lighting up many faces, but I also noticed several people exchanging sceptical glances. Rain had not fallen for several years – why should it fall tomorrow? But there was something in my heart that told me that rain would fall. Ntunyana had read the smoke, and the ancestral spirits had spoken to him.

We left the hut the following morning and returned to my host's kraal. The day grew old, sun-blasted and bleak, and then, towards early afternoon, I heard several women in the kraal ululating. I got up and went outside, where I was met by an amazing sight: rain clouds were ruling the far horizon and they were moving towards us.

When the shadows lengthened eastward, the last gaps in the sky, the last traces of blue, were obliterated. Huge, angry, rain-pregnant clouds covered the sky from horizon to horizon. I heard a growl of distant thunder – an incredible sound that sent a chill through my body.

The ululation went on and on as the first fat raindrops began to fall from the sky. Children, men and women became mad: they dashed out of their kraals into the open, and they danced and capered and leapt like springboks in the rain. It was only when the rain's fury grew such that no-one, not even the bravest, could face it, that everybody ran back to their homes and stayed there while rain, hail and thunder lashed the drought-stricken land.

That night I slept the sleep of the blessed. That night my dreams were serenaded by the roar of rain.

The following day the rain ceased, but the clouds still ruled the heavens with large gaps here and there revealing the eternal blue of the sky. But at midday, the clouds gathered and once more the watery rage of the great Earth Mother poured upon the parched land. The land would live again.

Over the years, the memory of those days still haunts me and I have many questions that have never received answers.

THE SORCERER'S FAMILIAR

Among the tribes of southern Africa, when one person calls another a baboon, he does not mean that that person resembles a baboon in his or her features or has the habits of a baboon. He means that the person is an evil-hearted, grudge-bearing, stupid lout.

In European countries, people believe that witches and sorcerers ride through the skies on broomsticks. In southern Africa, black people believe that sorcerers ride baboons at night, but they ride them facing backwards. African people say that the baboon is the sorcerer's greatest familiar.

WHERE BABOONS COME FROM

It is said that uNkulunkulu, the Great Spirit, after creating the Earth and the wild animals, decided to create human beings. He created people of many tribes, and among these tribes was the Thusini.

The Great Spirit expected all tribes to be hard-working and caring. He expected them all to start ploughing their fields in spring. He expected them to take care of the innumerable cattle, sheep and goats which he had fairly distributed among all tribes and nations. He expected human beings to look after the cats and the dogs he had given them for their protection. He expected people to build beautiful villages and to live in peace with each other, in harmony with nature around them.

The Great Spirit was pleased by what he saw many people doing. He saw how diligent they were. He saw how creative most of them were. But he saw one glaring exception: the Thusini were the laziest human beings ever created.

The Great Spirit had sent his son, the sun god, uMvelinqangi, and his mother, the great goddess Nomkhubulwane, to Earth to teach human beings many important things. The goddess taught the women how to plough the land, and how to plant corn, millet and vegetables. She taught them how to cook food.

Nomkubulwane's son, uMvelinqangi, taught the people how to smelt iron, copper and tin, and how to make bronze. He taught them how to make iron hoes for ploughing and he taught them exactly when to plough and what prayers to direct to God via the ancestral spirits, whenever they required rain, or whenever locusts or other pests devastated the grain-fields.

The Thusini were a tribe of lazy philosophers, who spent hours and days contemplating the sky, trying to read messages in stars that were not there. They had perfected the art of making necklaces and bangles out of bronze, which is why they were called *thusini*, which means 'the people of bronze' in the Zulu language. They spent days polishing their bangles, combing their hair and bathing in the streams. They did not plough the land, and built only the most ramshackle huts. They did none of the things that the Great Spirit expected human beings to do.

But the Great Spirit decided to give the Thusini people a chance. He withheld rain from their land. When they realized that no rain was falling, they were very quick to go to the summits of great mountains where they addressed very forceful prayers to God! And God sent down a lot of rain.

Do you think the Thusini did anything after the rains had fallen? No. The Great Spirit said, 'These people are a bad example to the rest of humanity. What am I going to do about them?'

Then the Great Spirit realized that there was nothing he could do to these human beings. He thought long and hard and decided he could solve the problem by changing the appearance of the Thusini people to suit the type of life they had chosen for themselves.

They saw no reason why they should waste their time making blankets from animal hides. So the Great Spirit gave each one of them a thick coat of fur. He also changed them from walking on two feet, which they found very tiresome, to walking on all fours. They did not want to keep cattle or any other animals, so the Great Spirit gave them a life which did not require them to keep animals.

They always asked why they should plough the land and plant corn when there were so many wild fruits in the bush. Furthermore, they philosophically argued that ploughing the land was wrong because it injured the earth.

Because the Thusini people loved to sit in groups staring into the sky or far into the blue distance, the Great Spirit decided to give them eyes which were deep-set, sheltered under thick bony foreheads, so that they could contemplate the distance and the faraway stars with more pleasure.

And because they were too lazy to chase away the flies that swarmed over them, the Great Spirit gave them long tails to perform this simple job.

The Great Spirit changed the Thusini people into the first baboons that the world had seen. But, after they discovered that they had changed into baboons, the Thusini people developed an instinctive distrust of human beings. Whenever they fed in the fertile bush, they posted lookouts to check for human beings. And whenever a human being appeared in the distance, the baboons on look-out duty would shout, 'Wah-goo, wah-goo' which means 'Bantu, Bantu, human beings, human beings'. The call can be heard to this very day.

WHY THE BABOON HAS RED BUTTOCKS

Once there was a baboon called Konde. He was not happy being a baboon. When he stood on the rocks high up on the mountain, he looked down on the villages and farms and said to himself, 'I wish I were a human being. Look at those wonderful animals down there. They know everything; they can do anything. I wish I could become a human being!'

One day, Konde found a cutthroat razor in the bush. The first thing Konde thought of was that he should shave his hair off and become hairless like a human being. But what does a baboon know about a cutthroat razor?

Konde tried to shave. He managed to shave a few inches of fur from his snout and then he did what any ignorant baboon would do: he cut himself! You should have heard the screams, because there is nothing that a baboon fears more than the sight of his own blood! He threw away the razor and ran. For several days he hid in his cave, refusing to come out even when his old wife, Matanazana, asked him to come out and play. When the other male baboons shouted at the human beings from the mountain top, Konde only managed a very feeble 'waaho' and crept back into his cave. The thought of becoming a human being was very strong in Konde's mind.

But Konde was also a thief. One day he decided to steal the monkey nuts which had been planted by human beings in the village. Konde painted his buttocks and tail with tree gum, and plunged his tail into the hole of a hidden, underground silo. The monkey nuts stuck to his tail, and he pulled them out and had a good feast. He did this until the owners of the monkey nuts saw him and chased him across the veld.

He ran for his life, but he fell over a cliff. Luckily, or unluckily, as fate would have it, a leopard was prowling at the bottom of the cliff. Konde landed with his glued buttocks on the back of the leopard.

'*Hau!* What is this that has fallen on my back? A stupid baboon! Come here, dinner!' cried the leopard.

But try as he might, the leopard could not get to Konde, because Konde was stuck to his back. Then the leopard had an idea.

'I am going to take this animal to my wife and children for dinner,' he thought. 'All right, here we go baboon. Hup!'

And he set off at a tremendous speed. The leopard ran through the bush with the baboon stuck to his back. He was the happiest leopard in the whole of Africa. His next meal was stuck to his back! He ran and ran and ran.

Meanwhile poor Konde was trying to escape from his predicament. What was he going to do?

'Oh brain, oh my baboon brain, work fast!'

There was a tree branch jutting directly across the path on which the leopard was running. Konde thought fast. He waited until the leopard was under the branch and then reached out and grabbed it.

Grrrrriittt!

The leopard carried on running, but only with pieces of the baboon's skin and hair stuck to his back. And there was Konde, hanging from the branch with red, raw buttocks. And this is why all baboons have red buttocks.

KONDE TRIES TO BE A HUMAN BEING

Konde never seemed to grow old. He was mischievous and a trickster. But one day Konde's dream came true. He saw a farmer searching for a lion in the bush. The farmer carried a gun and was smoking a pipe. He was a tall man, and Konde said to himself, 'Now I am going have some fun!'

He hid behind a rock and watched as the farmer found the lion and took aim at it. But the farmer did not realize that this lion was the mightiest lion of the land! The lion made short work of the farmer and ate until nothing remained except his hat, his coat, his bandoleer, his boots, his gun and his pipe, tobacco pouch and matches.

'My lucky stars shine upon me!' exclaimed Konde, 'Here's my chance to be a human being!'

When the lion left, Konde dashed down the mountainside and placed the farmer's hat on his head. He put on the farmer's coat, bandoleer and boots. Konde marched through the bush with a rifle over his shoulder and a pipe sticking out of his mouth.

'There is my farm! I am going to be the farmer today! But wait, what is this thing I am carrying? It's a gun. How does it kill? I have seen it kill.'

Konde wanted to use the gun to dispose of several baboon and hyena enemies which had been giving him a hard time. But first he had to acquire one more human vice. He loaded the pipe with tobacco, lit it with a match, put the pipe in his mouth and started smoking. That was the worst mistake he had ever made. He acquired such a terrible cough! Like a wise baboon, he gave up smoking and merely stuck the pipe in his mouth. It was too dangerous a human habit!

While he was walking he met a hyena.

'*Hau*, Konde,' said the hyena. 'What are you carrying on your shoulder? What are you wearing on your stupid head, you stinky little baboon?'

Konde did not speak. He knew which side of the gun to point at the enemy: BAH! The hyena was hit by the bullet and sent to the happy hunting grounds. And Konde was smashed by the recoil of the rifle against a rock.

Konde set out looking for another enemy to dispose of. He found an old rival who had stolen his wife, Matanazana, from him.

'Hey, you ugly baboon! You evil creature!' called Konde.

'Who are you? Why are you dressed like a human being?' replied the baboon.

'I am your master! I am now Konde, the human being!'

'Is that so? Come here. I am going to rip you to shreds, you stupid, silly thing!'

The big baboon did not realize that Konde was pointing a gun at him.

BAH!

Once more, Konde flew one way and his victim the other way. But honour was satisfied! The enemy was well and truly dead!

Konde arrived at the farm.

All the animals bowed and trembled before him. The farmer had been so ugly that the animals could not tell the difference between the baboon and the farmer. They looked alike and they were equally vicious.

But there was one animal that was not prepared to take any nonsense from Konde: the bull who lived alone in a paddock. He was in a very bad mood when Konde, who could not tell the difference between a bull and a cow, tried to milk him.

'What are you doing?' asked the bull.

'Shut up! I want you to produce milk!' said Konde.

'Hey, did you ever see a creature like me being milked?' exclaimed the bull. 'Can you not tell the difference?'

'But all animals with horns produce milk. Come on, give!'

The bull took one look at Konde. It pawed the dust with one hoof, snorted like the thunder of heaven and the dust flew in waves. The bull lifted Konde with one horn and hurled him head-over-heels across the grass. And then it went after him. Konde's gun was trampled to matchwood and scrap metal. Konde fled for his life, with the bull thundering behind him. When he glanced over his shoulder, he saw the red eyes, the wide-open nostrils, and the triumphant, needle-sharp horns close to his red backside. Konde prayed to his ancestors: 'Help me, oh ghosts of my forefathers!'

He ran until he came to the barbed-wire fence and threw himself at it. He was covered in scratches, which cured him of all his desires to become a human being! He ran as he had never run before. The bull crashed through the barbed-wire fence, and continued chasing Konde.

Eventually, Konde managed to escape. He reached the cave where Matanazana was waiting for him, a very sorry-looking baboon indeed. Poor apes should not try to imitate human beings. They do not know what we have to put up with!

PRAISE SONG TO THE MONKEY

Greetings, oh tasty one!
Dinner of the cannibals!
Delight of the gourmands of old Zululand!
Greetings, oh monkey – you, whose flesh is delicious when cold!
Greetings, you of the silly-looking little face – a face which hides great wisdom!
It is said that your ancestors danced upon the great river of milk when the universe itself was born
It is said that they wove their tails together into a great rope, down which the gods themselves descended
Oh monkey – you, whose little snout carries a hidden smile
Oh monkey, whose little hands are so weak and fragile but, if the stories are true, once lifted a great mountain which had fallen over the world
Oh monkey, warrior of warriors!
You, whose great magic laid low the proud Kgogo-modomo monster, which had farted upon the Earth and destroyed nearly all life with a terrible stench!
But you defeated him, oh monkey, and you hurled him out of the sky!
You are praised
You are hailed
But you are fried and you are boiled!
For that is the destiny of a god!
Monkey, how many stories have been woven around your little head?
Monkey, how many songs have been sung about you?
Monkey, how many fables do grandmothers tell us about you?
Oh monkey, may you leap from tree to tree and, even though the years come and go, the centuries pass away, may you still climb the tall tree and still eat the gum of eternal life!

THE IMPRESSIVE ONE

In the North West Province, there is a very large tribe that consists of two divisions. The larger and the older of the two is in Botswana. This tribe is known as the Bakgatla. At one time, the Bakgatlas were one of the most powerful Tswana-speaking tribes in southern Africa. They regard the monkey as their totem and call it by two strange names: *kgathla* or *kgabu*. When the Bakgatla speak to their kings or chiefs, they also refer to them as *kgabu*.

The monkey's name comes from the verb *kgathla* or *go-kgathla* which means 'to dazzle', 'to outshine' or 'to impress very deeply'. The monkey is known as the 'impressive one' or 'the one who outshines all'. *Kgabu* comes from the verb *kgaba* or *kgabesa*, which means 'to decorate richly'. When Bakgatla people wish the king or chief a long and prosperous life, they use the following words: 'May it climb the tallest tree and eat the gum of long life, the monkey.'

In many ceremonies and festivities held in the villages of Bakgatla kings and chieftains, I have heard girls singing:

'The monkey, let it climb that tall tree and eat the gum of life,
Oh let it climb the tallest tree and eat the gum of life,
Let it climb the tallest tree and eat the gum of life,
Let it climb the tallest tree and eat the gum of life.'

THE MONKEY AND THE DREADED HATER OF LIFE

The following story was told to me many years ago by an old Bakgatla woman. It is the story of the first monkey, Kgabu, and his wife, Kgabu-nyana.

It is said that after Modimo, the great god, had created the Earth and every living thing upon it, he found that of all the creatures he had created, the wisest and gentlest was Kgabu the monkey. Modimo made friends with Kgabu and often asked him and his wife, Kgabu-nyana, to visit him in his great village at the end of the rainbow in the sky. Kgabu-nyana often gave important advice to Modimo, which was gladly accepted by the mightiest of the mighty ones.

One day, Modimo called Kgabu, and when the wise little monkey reached the gate of the great shining village of the gods he found Modimo sitting outside, drinking beer from a golden pot. Modimo offered Kgabu a drink from the pot and as Kgabu took a tiny sip Modimo said to him, 'Oh Kgabu, for reasons that I cannot reveal even to you, my greatest friend, my wife, my son and I must go far away to visit my wife's relatives at the very end of creation. We shall be gone for many days and, for this reason, I am going to ask you, Kgabu, to do a very important thing for me. Are you willing to do this?'

'Great one,' said Kgabu, 'if it is possible for one as small and as weak as I am to do the task that you request, I shall do it to the best of my ability.'

God laughed and scratched his scraggy grey beard and, as he did so, a million shining lice fell out of his beard to become the stars in the sky. God smiled at the wise little monkey and said:

'Kgabu, while I am gone, it must be your duty to see that no harm befalls the Earth below us. It must be your duty to warn all animals, and those impossible creatures who call themselves human beings, of any approaching danger. Here – take the great horn of warning.'

Modimo unhooked a *tsasabi* horn from his waist and gave it to Kgabu. The horn had to be blown to warn every living thing on Earth of any danger.

'You must blow this horn, Kgabu, and shout a warning from the very clouds to the Earth below. And if danger comes, you shall do your utmost to combat it and drive it away, whatever it may be. Will you do that?'

Kgabu said, 'Great grandfather of the skies, I shall do that. Give me a little of your magic power, give me a little of your strength, and I shall confront any enemy that may threaten the Earth and all that you have created.'

Modimo smiled and called for his wife, Nemagulo, the mother of the world. Nemagulo came waddling towards her husband. She was huge and fat, as big as an elephant. Her breasts, belly and thighs were huge, and her legs were like those of a rhinoceros. She had a tremendous bottom and a beautiful, round, plump, smiling face with the gentlest eyes Kgabu had ever seen.

'Mother of the world,' said Modimo, 'I wish you to give a little of your magical power to Kgabu so that he may look after the Earth while we are gone.'

She smiled and said, 'Come to me, Kgabu.'

The little monkey approached the great Earth Mother and she knelt down on the ground and placed her forefinger in the centre of Kgabu's forehead. When she took her finger away, there was a glowing spot on Kgabu's furry forehead.

'Now, Kgabu,' said the great Earth Mother, 'you have the power of the Gods. You have the strength to repel any danger that may threaten humanity, the animals and all living things on the Earth. Modimo, our son, Ntswana-tsadsi, and I must leave now. Stay well little monkey.'

Some time later, the little monkey watched as Modimo, Nemagulo and Ntswana-tsadsi left the village of the gods. Modimo walked in front, wearing a great kaross and carrying his staff in his right hand. In the other hand he carried a leather bag which contained the water of life. Behind him was Nemagulo, bearing a great bundle of golden firewood on her head. She carried a leather bag in her right hand containing the corn bread of eternal life, which the gods eat and which makes them live forever.

Behind Nemagulo walked the tall, young sun god, Ntswana-tsadsi. He was armed with a great cowhide shield and twelve assegais with blades of pure light. On his head he wore a sheepskin hat with a leopard-skin belt, in which were three great, dark blue feathers, for he was the lord of all the heavenly warriors. The gods walked away from the village of heaven until they became one with the distant blue skies and vanished from view.

Kgabu had been so busy watching the gods leaving the great village, he did not see the monstrous shape creeping up on him from behind. He was brought out of his reverie by a terrible snarl: 'Grrrrrrr . . . !'

An awful voice that shook the very ground underfoot said, 'What are you doing here you hairy little monkey? Who invited you?'

Kgabu fearfully glanced over his shoulder and he saw that the speaker was the dreaded Nchamogodu, the four-headed dog that guards the village of the gods. Kgabu did what all monkeys have done since then: he jumped up and bolted up the trunk of a great tree which grew just outside the village gates. From one of the tree's topmost branches, he watched as the furious four-headed dog prowled the dusty ground at the foot of the great tree.

'I asked you a question, you silly-faced monkey,' demanded the dog, working itself into a fury. 'Who invited you here? What are you looking for? Do you have any relatives in the village of the gods? Do you have any friends?'

'Oh great dog,' replied Kgabu, 'it was Modimo himself who invited me here. He gave me the duty of watching over the Earth while he, his wife and his son are away.'

'Is that so!' roared the dog. 'Is that really so? Why would Modimo ignore me, his most trusted watchdog and faithful companion for these many, many, many millions of years, and choose you, a silly-faced, scrawny little monkey to watch over the Earth. Why? Tell me that!'

'I do not know, great dog,' replied Kgabu. Every hair on his body stood on end. 'I do not know!'

'I think you do know,' said the angry dog. 'I think you do. You wormed your way into the almighty's favour. You curried favour with Modimo and his wife and son, you cunning, back-biting little lickspittle! I am going to kill you today! I promise you by your father, your grandfather and your great-grandfather, today I will kill you!'

The dog continued, 'Are you going to stay on that branch forever? Are you going to stay up there for ten years, for a hundred years, for a thousand? Are you not going to get thirsty and come down to find water? Are you not going to get hungry and come down to look for food? And what will you find when you do that monkey? You will find *me*, Nchamogodu, the dog of the sun. You will find my fangs as sharp as needles, ready to tear you to pieces. You will find my rage and my fury. You will find Nchamogodu, the dog of all dogs!'

With that, the terrible Nchamogodu sat down at the foot of the tree, waiting for Kgabu to come down. Long, weary moments passed and Kgabu suddenly felt himself weaken. He was hungry, his little stomach rumbled and he was thirsty. His throat was parched.

In the middle distance, halfway between the Earth below and the village of the gods, was a silvery stream that tumbled over great rocks before it wound its way into the distance like a bright, silvery serpent snaking through the lush greenery. And close to the village of the gods was a large patch of succulent, sweet-smelling green *dinawana* beans – Kgabu's favourite food. Seeing the water and the beans made his thirst and hunger grow from bad to worse, but the tree was his refuge.

At the foot of the tree, Nchamogodu lay on his belly, his four heads resting on his massive paws. He was also feeling drowsy and he lay still with his eyes half closed. Suddenly, Nchamogodu felt something strike his broad back – bah! The great dog jumped up in time to see Kgabu spring to his feet and start running for dear life. Kgabu had fallen asleep and tumbled onto the great dog's back like a ripe fruit. But he was not going to get away that easily. With a great roar, Nchamogodu was after Kgabu, and he caught and pinned him to the ground with one of his great forepaws.

Kgabu screamed – a lonely, piercing sound in the vastness of the land of the gods: 'Yaaaaaaaaaa . . . !'

'Be quiet, monkey,' snarled the dog. 'Stop screaming in the face of the inevitable! I have caught you and you are going to die. Do you have anything to say? Anything intelligible, that is! Any last requests?'

'No, great dog,' whispered Kgabu, 'I have nothing to say.'

'But you must!' said Nchamogodu, with four great smiles on his four heads. 'Every creature that is about to die is entitled to say something, even if it is only a feeble, whispered goodbye. Are you going to say goodbye to the Earth and farewell to life?'

'I do not want to die,' whispered Kgabu. 'I am too young to die!'

'Well, well, well,' said the great dog. 'Listen, stupid one, no-one is ever too young to die. Death comes to all living things, except me, Nchamogodu. And when death comes, mortal beings must accept it with grace, must greet it like a friend, and embrace it like a lover. You are not going to be a coward in your last moments of life, are you? Try to die bravely, like a good monkey.'

As the dog spoke, a shadow fell upon the land of the gods and upon the Earth below. The great dog looked up at the sky and its eyes widened in horror and astonishment.

'By my mother's tails,' swore the dog, 'will you look at that!'

'What is it, Nchamogodu? What do you see?' asked Kgabu, who was lying flat on the ground, pinned down by one of the dog's great paws.

'By the face of Modimo!' the dog swore again.

'What is it?' asked Kgabu. 'What do you see?'

'I see Kgogo-modomo, the bird of all evil, the enemy of all living things. Kgogo-modomo has just flown overhead,' cried the dog.

'Oh no, oh no,' whispered the monkey. 'Modimo warned me against this monstrous bird. He told me about it! Let me go, great dog. Only I can save heaven and Earth from that terrible beast!'

'Why should I let you go?' questioned the dog. 'I have caught you. You are my legitimate prey and I must devour you.'

'Great dog,' said little Kgabu, 'release me! For the sake of all creation, release me and I give you my word as a monkey and as a servant of Modimo that when this danger passes, I shall come back to you. I shall surrender myself to you, because I am your prey. I will not run away. I promise.'

'Very well,' said the great dog, 'I will hold you to your word. But remember, you are a tricky creature and I do not trust you!'

'But you have to trust me, great dog,' said Kgabu. 'For the sake of all living things, you have to.'

Nchamogodu released Kgabu. He sprang to his feet and dashed into the village of the gods.

He brought out the great horn, placed it to his lips, and blew with all his might.

'Abuuuuuuuuuuuu, abuuuuuuuuuu!'

The sound of the great horn echoed and re-echoed throughout the world. The lesser gods heard it in heaven and living things heard it on Earth. Then, through the great horn, Kgabu shouted, 'Pinch your nostrils shut, all living things, pinch your nostrils shut! The Hater of Life is in the skies above you, pinch your nostrils shut, do not inhale the poison that the Hater of Life is going to release! Abuuuuuuuuuuuuuuuuuuuu, abuuuuuuuuuuuuu!'

The heavens shook with the blast of Modimo's horn. The piping voice of the little monkey was heard by all living things. In the great forests, the rivers and the dense jungles, and on the desert plains, animals responded to the monkey's voice. Giraffe went down on their knees and pressed their nostrils firmly against the ground. Impala and eland did the same. Birds of all kinds blocked their nostrils with their wings. The fish in the rivers and the streams dived to the very bottom. Hippopotamus and crocodile did the same.

'Do not inhale the poison that Kgogo-modomo, the Hater of Life, is going to release! Block your nostrils!'

Again and again, Kgabu's voice rang out from the heavens. Every animal on Earth obeyed, but human beings in their villages and kraals ignored his words.

'Ha, that monkey is mad,' said the people, laughing. 'Who will believe a little monkey like Kgabu – a silly, cowardly creature that dwells in the forest.'

The people went about their daily tasks and ignored Kgabu's words. They were oblivious to the dread-warning that rang out from the skies. While the people were laughing and enjoying themselves, Kgogo-modomo's malevolent silhouette appeared in the skies above.

Kgogo-modomo was a monstrous flying creature. He had a head like a great grasshopper's, a long neck like a python's, a body like that of an ostrich and legs very similar to a bird's. He had a long, scaly tail like a crocodile has and huge wings like a bat's, but many times larger than those of that delicate creature. His wings were so large that they covered almost half the sky, and under his tail, between his legs, he had a huge, red anus, which was opening to release poison over the Earth.

As he passed across the sky from north to south, Kgogo-modomo released a great fart. The sound was like no sound any human or animal ears had heard before. It shook the heavens, it caused the Earth to tremble, and great landslides to thunder down the sides of mighty mountains. It broke branches off great trees and caused rivers and streams to shudder.

Agbuuu, buuuuuu, ba barabababbbabababa . . . ! It was like thunder that tore the very skies apart. Both Kgabu and Nchamogodu saw a huge cloud of poisonous vapour jet out of the monstrous creature's anus. They saw the cloud fall like a stone to the ground and cover the whole Earth.

Once more, little Kgabu shouted through Modimo's great horn, 'All living animals, hear the words of the monkey, pinch your nostrils shut, do not inhale the vapour of death!'

As Kgabu spoke, Kgogo-modomo swung around in a great arc in the sky. Its wings beat steadily and propelled the monstrous creature across the skies. There was a red malevolence in Kgogo-modomo's eyes. His intention of destroying the Earth and every living thing on it was obvious. He was planning to release yet another burst of flatus on the Earth. Nchamogodu and the monkey realized that this had to be prevented at all costs.

'Now foolish monkey,' said Nchamogodu, 'what did Modimo tell you to do in an emergency such as this?'

'I . . . I . . . don't know,' quivered the monkey, 'I am confused.'

'You are confused? You don't know?', howled the dog. 'You don't know?'

'Wait, wait, let me think,' cried Kgabu.

'Think fast, or the gods will find no Earth left by the time they return.'

Suddenly Kgabu vanished. The dog's four mouths opened in amazement.

'Where has he gone, the cowardly little wretch?' cried the dog. 'Has he fled from danger, like the craven being that he is?'

'I have not fled, great dog,' said a voice from above Nchamogodu's heads. 'I have turned myself into a bee and I am going to try to sting Kgogo-modomo.'

Nchamogodu saw a tiny, golden bee streak heavenwards, towards the great, flying shape. Nchamogodu waited, his four paws wide apart and his long tail stiff behind him. He was quivering with excitement and expectation. Something was going to happen: something great, something brave, something important.

Suddenly, the great dog of the gods heard a terrible, hoarse, reptilian scream which tore the heavens apart. It was a scream of terror. It came again and again and again. Then Nchamogodu saw the huge, flying monstrosity that was Kgogo-modumo fold its wings and dive head-first towards the Earth below.

'Whaaaaaaaaaaaa wha wha wha whaaaaaaaa . . . !'

Nchamogodu watched in amazement as Kgogo-modomo flew into the side of a mountain and fell to the ground with a great crash that splintered every rock and tree on the slope. The monstrous beast gave one convulsive twitch, then was still and silent. Nchamogodu heard a wind rising, one which howled across the face of the world, driving away the great cloud of vapour that was covering every mountain, valley and plain like mist. The Earth smiled again. Kgogo-modomo had fallen from the sky and lay senseless, but not dead, on the mountain.

Kgabu reappeared at Nchamogodu's side.

'What did you do?' asked the dog.

'It was easy,' replied the little monkey. 'I changed myself into a bee and I flew up and stung Kgogo-modomo's anus until it swelled shut. He couldn't release any more poisonous vapour on the Earth. The pain I gave him was so great that he lost consciousness and fell out of the sky.

'Then I summoned one of the four great winds to blow the poison away from the Earth, towards the edge of creation and beyond. Oh great dog, Earth is saved, living things are saved. I have returned for you to eat me.'

'Ah-ah, ah-ah, no, no, no,' said the great dog, 'I am not going to eat Modimo's favoured servant. What do you think I am? In any case, your job is not finished, monkey. Don't you think you should go down to the Earth and find out how things are? Come on, I will give you a lift on my back and you shall ride to the land of human beings in style.'

When the monkey arrived on Earth, he found that every animal had obeyed his instructions. They had pinched their nostrils shut and escaped the effects of the poisonous vapour released by Kgogo-modomo. But the nostrils of many animals never returned to their original shape, and that is why sheep, goats, impalas and other antelope have pinched-looking nostrils.

Although the animals, the birds and the fishes had been saved, the same could not be said for human beings. When Nchamogodu and Kgabu arrived at the human villages, they found tragedy and disaster. Many human beings had died after inhaling the green vapour from Kgogo-modomo's bowels. The survivors looked sick: their skins were covered with an awful rash, blood streamed from their nostrils and their eyes were runny. Many of them were so weak that they could barely stand.

'Why did you not listen to my warning?' asked Kgabu. 'Why did you not pinch your nostrils shut?'

'What warning?' asked some of the human beings. 'What warning? We never heard a warning, just the thin, reedy voice of a crazy monkey telling us to do something impossible and not telling us why. Why did you not warn us?'

'But I did warn you,' said the little monkey, 'I sounded the great horn of Modimo and I warned you!'

'You did not warn us often enough. You did not sound serious enough,' cried the angry, dying people. 'Leave here and let us die in peace.'

Kgabu's heart was broken. The sight of so much suffering and misery stung the very core of his sensitive soul. What was he going to do? How was he going to fulfil the duty laid upon him by Modimo, and save humanity from its own stubbornness and folly?

'I think I can help you,' said Nchamogodu. 'We must return to the village of the gods. A tree grows in the centre of the village of heaven, planted there by God many generations ago. It is the great tree of life which often exudes a thick gum that can heal any illness. Get on my back and let us return immediately. Hurry!'

The monkey did as the dog commanded and the impossible pair dashed towards the village of the gods. The dog sped through the open gate and headed straight for the tree in the centre of the village.

'Can you get up that tree, Kgabu?' asked the dog.

'I think I can.'

'Look up there, among those branches, do you see those shining things? Those big lumps?'

'Yes, yes, yes,' replied the monkey.

'That is the gum of life. You must get up there and prise the lumps off the tree. I will wait down here with a leather bag, and I will fill the bag with them as you release them. Now get to work!'

The monkey went up the tree like a bolt of lightning. He was soon high above the ground, prising lumps of amber-coloured gum from the tree's trunk.

'More!' demanded the dog from below. 'The bag is not full! Get more!'

The dog drove the monkey mercilessly until the bag was filled to the top with nodules of life-giving gum. Then Kgabu gladly climbed down; his arms were sore, his hands were numb, but his job was done.

'Get on my back,' cried the dog, 'and hold this bag. Hold on tight with your other paw.'

The dog ran like the wind towards the Earth below, and within a few moments they had arrived at the first village of human beings. Here, Kgabu the monkey filled a large, clay pot with water and lit a fire under it. When the water boiled, he dissolved in it a handful of the life-giving gum, and forced every human being to drink some of the brew. The moment the people swallowed the life-giving fluid, the rash disappeared from their skins and the blood from their nostrils, and their weakness vanished.

The monkey and the dog went to the second village, the third village, the fourth village and the fifth village, and more. Wherever they went they saved hundreds of people. For many days they travelled the length and breadth of the Earth, saving human lives, making the sick well and the weak able to walk.

'There is one more thing to do,' said the great dog.

'What is it, my friend?' asked the monkey.

'Hagh! Whom are you calling your friend? I am still your enemy!' snarled the dog. 'But, honoured enemy, we have one more task to perform. Get on my back!'

The dog ran towards the mountain where Kgogo-modomo had fallen. The heroes found the monster lying unconscious. Kgogo-modomo was more fearsome close up than he was from a distance: he was huge, ugly, the essence of evil.

'What are we going to do, great dog?' asked the monkey.

'What are we going to do?' the dog echoed, its eyes widening in mockery. 'Listen to this!'

The dog howled will all four heads: 'Ahwooooo ahwooooo, wowowo wah-woooo . . . '

In response to the terrible howling, the dense forest at the foot of the mountain came alive as hundreds of animals answered Nchamogodu's summons. Lion, leopard, cheetah, rhinoceros, elephant, insects of all kinds, snakes, monkeys, baboons – every animal on Earth responded. Every animal brought a piece of firewood. Every bird brought dry leaves and twigs. At Nchamogodu's signal, the animals began piling the combustible matter in a heap over Kgogo-modomo.

It took ten full days to cover the monster, which began to show signs of regaining consciousness. Half the mountainside was covered with firewood. A great mountain of dry wood, grass, leaves and branches covered the Hater of all Life. Then Nchamogodu called on Tswene, the baboon, to produce firesticks and light a fire. Tswene did this with great pleasure. He twirled the firestick on the flat piece of wood, held firmly with one hind paw on the ground. He twirled and twirled until smoke spiralled skywards. Mmutla, the hare, poured his own powdered droppings onto the wood and blew a tiny flame to life.

'Ahaaa! That is good, Mmutla,' said the baboon.

'You have lit a fire. Stop talking and hurry up!' snarled Nchamogodu from the mountaintop. 'Come on monkey, help your cousin before I lose my temper! Make a torch from dry grass, light it in the fire and throw it onto this pile of wood.'

Kgabu did as the great dog commanded. A torch was prepared, lit and thrown on the heap of wood that covered Kgogo-modomo from the tip of his evil tail to the point of his ugly snout. Flames roared and smoke poured skywards in a huge, grey cloud. Sparks flew towards the heavens and Nchamogodu summoned two of the great winds to fan the fire into white-hot life.

When Kgogo-modomo felt the searing heat, he regained consciousness and tried to escape. He uttered a series of blood-curdling, reptilian screams. He tried to release his fearsome, deadly flatus, but his anus was swollen shut and nothing came out. The flames roared and the smoke bellowed towards the stars.

Thrashing wildly, Kgogo-modomo freed his head, which was burnt black and blistering. Great lumps of flesh fell off his scaly neck and from the top of his evil head. He screamed a scream of awful pain that threatened to tear the skies to tatters, and shouted, 'I am going to put a terrible curse on you all!'

Then a gust of wind blew a cloud of smoke between his open jaws and deep into his throat. The curse he was about to utter died unborn in fearsome choking.

His head fell back onto the flames, sending a storm of sparks and burning wood to the heavens.

'Die, Kgogo-modomo, enemy of all living things!' shouted a lion.

'Perish, you monster, destroyer of worlds!' trumpeted an elephant.

'Die, beast of no mercy that for centuries has ruined God's work!' roared a hippopotamus and a rhinoceros in unison. 'Die!'

The winds howled and the flames roared, while the smoke bellowed in a dense column. Such was the intensity of the heat that some of the rocks next to the monster's funeral pyre began to melt, releasing the hidden metals within them in gleaming rivulets of silver and white-hot copper. The fire roared and roared. Kgogo-modomo's funeral pyre blazed for three days. His monstrous body was burnt to a skeleton, which was reduced to fine, white ash within minutes.

The excited animals scattered, seeking their distant homes as rain roared down on the landscape, sweeping Kgogo-modomo's ashes to oblivion over the cliffs and into the gulleys choked with greenery. The great task of destroying the monstrous Kgogo-modomo was complete.

Several days later, Modimo returned with his wife and son. They listened and smiled at the exploits of the monkey and their great dog. God shook Kgabu's hand as the little monkey prepared himself to return to Earth.

'You must avoid human beings, oh monkey,' said Nemagulo. 'Do not expect them to be grateful to you for what you did. Human beings are not like that. Remember my words.'

'Go well, my friend,' said God, taking a deep draught from his golden beer-pot. 'I shall watch over you always and save you from any threatening danger. Go well. I hope to see you again soon.'

Kgabu left the land of the gods and travelled to Earth without incident. When he reached Earth, his mind was filled with thoughts of his beautiful wife, Kgabu-nyana, the mother of his four children.

As he walked through the bush, he suddenly felt quite

hungry and went into a field of sorghum, where he began feasting on the ripening corn. While he was eating, loud voices rang out in the cornfield.

'There is the monkey. He thinks that because he saved our lives, we should be grateful to him and allow him to eat our corn. No! kill him!'

A rain of assegais, battle axes, knobkerries and stones fell around the terrified monkey as a force of men erupted from the corn and made their way towards him. Only his agility saved his life. Several hours later, a little the worse for wear with his body battered, bruised and aching all over, Kgabu reached his home and the welcoming arms of Kgabu-nyana.

PRAISE SONG TO THE LEOPARD

I*ngwe mabala*
Oh great spotted cat of the high mountains of our country
Oh protector of the human race
And defender of the just
Oh leopard, joy of our kings
Revered and loved by great ones
Such as Shaka
Such as Dingiswayo
Such as Punga
And Mageba
Who told their sons and the sons of their sons, and the sons of their sons, always to respect the leopard and to wear his skin with honour
You are the shield that guards our mothers' fields against the hairy sons of the baboon
Where you cough, the baboons do not shout
Where you snarl, all the hairy ones must flee
For you are the devourer of the ape
You delight in sucking the marrow of the *imfene*, the baboon
And all the animals are afraid of you
You are the one who sits upon the tree and challenges the gods
You are the thunderstorm of fire
You are the whirlwind
You are the hailstorm
You are the cold mountain air
You are the *ingwe*, protector of warriors
You are the *ingwe*, joy of our kings

You are the *ingwe*, totem of our sangomas
You are the *ingwe*, symbol of our nation
When the time comes for me to visit the grey ones of Kokonjame
When the time comes for me to go down into the dark womb of the Earth
Never to come back as a human being again,
I pray to the grey gods that live under the earth to grant me this:
That I return to this Earth as an *ingwe*, protector of the nations
The leopard, master of all the apes.

THE COURAGEOUS, NOBLE LEOPARD

All African tribes regard the leopard as an animal which symbolizes all that is noble, courageous and honourable. It is called *ingwe* by the Zulus and *nkwe* by the Basutos. These are very ancient words which originally meant 'pure sovereignty' or 'pure kingship'. In very ancient times, a king who ruled over other kings among the Botswana tribes was called *nkwetona.*

Africans rightly believe that a leopard is not a wanton killer. If a leopard kills, it only does so out of hunger or fright. They believe that if you walk through the bush and you see a leopard sitting peacefully in a tree, and you show no fear, the leopard, being an animal of deep understanding, will not harm you and will allow you to pass in peace.

It is believed that fear smells terrible in a leopard's nostrils and that is why a leopard will attack a coward.

In olden days, King Shaka of the Zulus taught his warriors loyalty and courage by sending a troop into the forest to catch a leopard alive, bring it to him to touch, and then take it back into the bush and release it unharmed. It was regarded as very important for a warrior who felt his courage in battle ebbing, or who felt nervous before going into battle, to touch the head of a living leopard and so re-energize his courage.

Not everyone was allowed to wear a leopard skin – only those warriors who had fought nobly in a minimum of six battles. Only those men and women who had proved their loyalty to the king and their courage in battle beyond all doubt were allowed to wear a leopard skin. Africans believed that if you wore the skin of a particular animal, the characteristics of that animal became part of you. For this reason, kings wore leopard-skin breastplates and headdresses.

For an ordinary person to dream of a leopard meant that that person would soon be promoted by the king for meritorious service. If a person dreamt of being savaged by a leopard, this was taken to mean that that person was about to undergo a deep process of spiritual rebirth.

African people believed that the leopard, like domestic cats and like other wild cats found in the wilderness, was specially brought to this world by the gods. Their purpose was to protect the Earth and all living things against destructive demonic entities that wanted to corrupt creation from within. They believed that if the leopard and other cat-like animals disappeared from the face of the planet, a great spiritual darkness would descend upon all life. The trees and grass would perish and the rivers would turn into stinking pools of mud and sand. The oceans would turn into stretches of boiling, sulphurous mud in which nothing could live.

We are told that the gods sent the leopard to Earth specially to guard against one particularly vicious race of demonic entities known as the *Chitawouli*, which means 'the whisperers of death'. The *Chitawouli* are behind every war that has ever been fought on Earth and will be behind every war in the future. They are nurtured by the negative forces which are generated when nations or tribes are at war. The whirlwind of fear, hatred and terror which covers a nation during war is like food to these demonic entities, and the only beasts they fear on Earth are the leopard, its mighty cousin the lion, and its noble brother the cheetah, animals which are believed to be reincarnations of the souls of minor deities.

LENGAU, THE GREAT LEOPARD

In the land of the Batswana lived a great leopard called Lengau. Lengau was the biggest leopard in the land. He knew how to look after himself and feed himself – the land was full of baboons on which he fed, and laden with goats and sheep, which were wonderful snacks whenever he was bored with baboon flesh. He grew big, sleek and fat, and people in faraway villages heard him when he coughed in the forest. Other leopards were very envious. He preened himself in the sunlight, and sat on a rock, licking his paws after a healthy meal.

But there is an ancient proverb which states, 'The fattest leopards always attract the sharpest spears', and it was not long before Lengau found himself the object of unwelcome attention from the king of the local tribe.

The king was old, tired and rheumatic. He was fond of sleep, although he was always troubled by insomnia. One day he met a *ngaka*, a wise old healer who told him that the best cure for insomnia was a good skin blanket. The king asked the *ngaka* what kind of skin the blanket should be made of.

The *ngaka* answered, 'Oh, king, the skin must be that of a leopard, trimmed with jackal and dassie skin at the edges. The blanket must be carefully made and it must be able to cover you from your chin to your toes on a cold winter's night.'

'It is important,' went on the *ngaka*, 'that a great king like you sleep under a blanket of leopard skin so that you are protected against the *tokoloshes* that your enemies send every night, and that your dreams are fitting for a king: beautiful dreams filled with great victories and joy!'

'I shall make myself the best leopard-skin blanket in the land!' cried the old king. 'And when I die and enter the land of my ancestors, I shall be wrapped in this blanket and not with any old cowhide.

'Warriors,' said the king to his men. 'Go into the forest and the bush, and find me the biggest leopard there is. Bring me his skin and the skins of twenty jackal and thirty dassies within ten days. Hurry!'

The warriors saluted their king, put on their headdresses and their leopard-claw necklaces, and had their wives and sisters rub leopard fat between their eyes so that they would see the biggest leopard as quickly as possible. Armed with their bows, arrows, spears, battle axes and skinning knives, they set out to hunt.

It was not long before the warriors came across an old Bushman.

'Tell us, oh Bushman, is there a leopard in this valley?'

The Bushman said, 'Tsk, tsk, tsk, tsk . . . '

They asked again, 'Is there a leopard in this valley?'

The Bushman said, '*Ncha!* (which is Bushman for 'Don't bother me! Get out of my sight!').

One of the warriors had an idea. He took out his snuff box, opened it and studied the contents very tantalizingly. He then took out a pinch of snuff and carelessly threw it on the ground. The Bushman's eyes lit up. There is nothing Bushmen love more than snuff. So the snuff box was exchanged for information. The Bushman snatched the snuff box from the warrior and took three pinches. Then he sat down and sneezed: 'Yetchow! Aw!'

Then he squatted on his haunches and said, 'Poor, stupid warriors. You are looking for the biggest leopard in the land?'

'Yes, yes, we are!' they replied.

'Is that so? Well, you see that mountain you passed two days ago?'

'*Eya, eya,* we see it!' chorused the warriors.

'Well, on that mountain lives Lengau, the biggest leopard in the land. If you had been wise like me, son of Okohoyi, grandson of San, you would have seen the spoor of that leopard. But you are big, stupid Tswana warriors, and you could not see because your bellies are so heavy, they obstruct your view of the ground.

'If you eat less,' said the Bushman, 'you will see all the leopards in the land. Now, go back two days until you reach the mountain.'

The warriors were tired, but news of the great leopard gave them fresh strength. They retraced their footsteps, through the unfriendly thorn bush, through dongas, past great rocks and past great trees. At one place, a warrior was unfortunately caught and eaten by a pride of lions.

The surviving warriors continued. Early one morning, they saw a sight which warmed the cockles of their hearts. There, on all fours at the edge of a crystal-clear waterhole, was the biggest leopard they had ever seen. The great beast was crouching at the edge of the waterhole, lapping up the water. Smack, smack, smack went the leopard's tongue on the surface of the water. The warriors could not believe their eyes. The leopard was big, fat and sleek. Its eyes gleamed like living gold and its whiskers were as white as the snow on the Waterberg. The warriors watched spellbound. Then one of them snatched an assegai from behind his shield, drew back his arm and threw it with all his might.

Whizzzzzzzzzzzzzz.

The assegai sped through the air like a bolt from the thunder god. How the assegai missed its target, Lengau the leopard never knew. The next thing he heard was a fearsome 'tugg! thud!' close to his right forepaw. He jerked up his head and saw the menacing assegai, its point buried deep in the moist earth at the edge of the waterhole, the flexible shaft quivering like a mamba's tail.

Lengau yelled with fear and ran off as a veritable shower of assegais fell around him. One of the assegais nicked him as he disappeared behind a tree: 'Ahhhowww!'

To make matters worse for poor Lengau, the warriors had brought along two dogs. They made Lengau's life a misery because wherever he fled to, the dogs arrived a few moments later. Lengau climbed a tree and the dogs gathered around its base, snarling. When the warriors appeared with their bows at the ready, Lengau leapt from one tree to the next.

He never knew how he managed to escape from the dogs and the warriors, but escape he did. He sat high up on a rock, on his favourite mountain, surveying the landscape below with fear-misted eyes. There they were, the relentless hunters. They and their dogs were combing the bush for him. Lengau decided to disappear as fast as he could.

The deadly game of hide and seek went on for many days, with the warriors getting closer and closer, and Lengau becoming more and more exhausted by the minute. What was he going to do?

He began to think, 'What animals can help me out of my dilemma? Somebody has got to help me, or I will be a skin in a chief's home!'

He thought and thought and then an idea came to him. He needed advice.

A dark night fell, which shielded him from the hunters. It was a night filled with familiar sounds. Then, far away in the darkness, Lengau heard a hateful, disgusting sound, made by a creature he despised.

'Ahoooooooowohooo ya haha ya haha!' A hyena was laughing in the darkness.

'If there is one animal that can help me, it is the hyena,' thought Lengau. He decided to swallow his pride and ask the hyena for advice. He found the hyena, sitting inside his small cave, surrounded by his wives and several children.

'Greetings, oh hyenas!' said Lengau.

'Look who is here! Greetings, leopard Lengau. Greetings, my enemy and my friend. Greetings! Why are you looking so sorry for yourself? You are covered with scratches. Did you lose an argument with the king of all the vultures?'

'No,' said Lengau proudly, 'I would never be afraid of the vulture. I am being pursued by human beings.'

'Human beings?' laughed the hyena. 'What do they want with you?'

'They want my skin!'

'Is that so?' said the hyena. 'They want your skin?'

'Yes! Can you help me?'

'I can help you,' said hyena, relaxing, with a big smile on his ugly face. 'But I would advise you to keep a civil tongue in your head. You need my help. So please, don't be rude!'

'How can you help me?' demanded Lengau.

'Well,' said the hyena. 'We have to work together. We must fool the old chief!'

'How?' asked Lengau.

'Well, let me tell you what we are going to do.'

The hyena whispered into the leopard's ear exactly what they had to do, but the leopard became so angry at the suggestion that he cuffed the hyena with his large forepaw.

'How dare you suggest things like that! You want me to risk my life!'

'Listen, coward,' said the hyena. 'There is no risk.'

'You say that we must raid the sheep folds of the king whose warriors are hunting me! You say that you need the skins of several sheep! Why?'

'You will see,' said the hyena. 'So, are you going to help me?'

'But the king is looking for me!' replied the leopard.

'Correction,' said the hyena. 'The king's warriors are looking for you. The king would never imagine that you would dare to appear in or near his village, would he? He doesn't expect you to turn up there, so you are quite safe, my cowardly friend. Come on, follow me!'

The poor leopard had no choice but to obey. He followed the hyena, and during the night the two raided the king's sheep folds, killing some of the sheep.

'Now what?' said the leopard.

'Well,' said the hyena. 'My wives and I will take all of these carcasses to our cave and we are going to skin each one. Of course, we are also going to enjoy the meat, but what you need are the skins.'

'Yes! Yes!' said the leopard impatiently. 'Then what are you going to do?

'Be patient, my friend. Be patient!'

Several days later, the hyena went to Lengau's hiding place. The hyena's belly was huge and full of good meat. His eyes were bright with mischief and a roll of something was tied to his back. He approached Lengau.

'Look, Lengau!'

When the hyena unrolled the bundle that had been tied to his back, Lengau's golden eyes widened with astonishment. Spread before him was the skin of a huge leopard – one that looked bigger than Lengau.

'What is this?' cried Lengau. 'How can there be a leopard bigger than me living in the bush?'

The hyena laughed. 'This is not a leopard skin, stupid. This is a skin which my wives, who are very powerful sorcerers, have made from the sheep skins, which they carefully shaved, dyed and then painted with spots. Well, my old friend, if this fake leopard skin has successfully fooled you, the biggest and wisest leopard in the bush, it will definitely fool a silly old human king!'

'What are we going to do?' asked Lengau with great excitement.

'The answer is very simple,' said the hyena. 'I am going to ask my friend the owl to bring his friends and carry this fake leopard-skin through the night to the warriors' camp. The warriors are not going to ask any questions when they wake up and find a nice, big leopard skin lying in a tidy bundle next to them!'

That night a number of large owls could be seen flying together, their wings whispering under the light of the stars. They carried a large bundle in their claws and dropped it, noiselessly, next to the sleeping warriors.

When the warriors woke up the next morning, they were amazed to find a huge leopard skin spread out in front of them. It did not occur to them it was made up of a number of sheep skins which had been sewn together. It did not occur to them that the hyena's wives had used magical dyes to make the so-called leopard skin a convincing golden colour with black spots. The warriors seized the skin, rolled it up and took it straight to the chief's village. Lengau the great leopard was forgotten, although the same could not be said for the jackal that the warriors encountered, or for the unfortunate dassies that lost arguments with spears and battle axes.

Some days later, the chief could be seen sleeping and snoring to high heaven under a very large blanket of 'leopard skin', trimmed with jackal and dassie skins. Those who knew about leopard skins expressed amazement that the skin smelt more like a sheep than a leopard.

And Lengau the leopard lives in a safe, isolated valley, with six wives and just as many cubs. He is happy and content, and knows that for the rest of his spotted life, no-one will hunt him for his skin.

PRAISE SONG TO THE LION

Ngonyama, lion, lord of the forests!
Creature that puzzled our forefathers, who did not know what to make of you!
And they called you *ngonyama*, the creature with two fleshes
They called you *ngonyama*, the creature of two shapes
They said that your tail was that of the bull of the skies, of the bull of heaven
They said that your mane was that of the great baboon of the wilds
And they said that your head was nobler than that of *ingwe*, the leopard
They said you were three animals in one like God Omnipotent on high!
Ngonyama, symbol of the kings of the Zulu people!
Ngonyama, thunder of the valleys!
You, whose roar frightens the dreams out of the heads of sleeping warriors!
Ngonyama, you, whose footprint is never erased by the passing winds!
Ngonyama, where your roar is heard, there is life to be found!
Ngonyama, where you are smelt, there is no evil,
And where you are heard, there is no ill,
And where you are seen, there is no fear!
Ngonyama, long may you walk the plains of this land!
Bayete!

KING OF THE BEASTS

The lion is an animal which African people believe to be, like the hippopotamus, a mixed animal which combines the characteristics of a number of different animals. It is believed that the lion is not an absolute carnivore, but that it has the gentle characteristics of a herbivore. Anyone who has encountered lions close up will agree with this strange belief. Left to themselves, lions will not harm human beings unless they are first harmed. I can vouch for the fact that you can pass close to a tree under which a pride of lions is resting, without being harmed. They will allow you to pass by in peace. This happened to me several times, especially while I was working in Kenya and Tanzania. Walking through the bush, too tired to be on the lookout for whatever dangers there might be, you may find to your surprise that you have passed a tree under which a number of lions are resting.

Because a lion's tail ends in a tuft of dark-coloured hair, African people believe that the lion has the gentle characteristics of a cow. And because the lion is such a powerful animal, the Zulu people call the lion *ingonyama*, which means 'the master of all flesh'. The name consists of two words: *ngo*, an ancient term meaning 'very, very high', and *nyama*, which means 'flesh' or 'power'. Another Zulu term for a lion is *ibhubesi*, which comes from the verb *bhubeza*, meaning 'to make the final decision', supporting the belief that the lion is the king of all beasts.

The Basotho and the Tsonga peoples call the lion by an interesting name: *tau* or *ndau*. This means 'the star creature' or 'creature that came from the stars'. The Mashona people call a lion *shumba*. This means 'the royal beast'. *Mumba* means 'a king of kings' in ancient Shona, so *shumba* means 'the greatest ruler of all'.

In ancient times, kings of the Zulu people – and of some other tribes – embarked on a ritual hunt every five years. The law of the hunt required the king to kill a lion on his own to prove his power of kingship, and to fill his people with respect for him. A great lion, usually the oldest in the area, was driven out of hiding by a force of warriors beating their weapons on their shields and shouting at the tops of their voices. The lion was driven towards the king, who would challenge it with his shield and spear and kill it single-handedly. The lion's body was then slit open and the king had to grasp the heart while it was still beating. When this was done, he was entitled to be called *silo*, a euphemism for a great lion.

While the lion is living in the bush, it is regarded as a symbol of all that is good and noble. But if the lion turns into a man-eater it symbolizes all that is negative and destructive. The lion is therefore used as a symbol for both good and bad.

KING MAGEBA AND THE LION

Many years ago, in the land of the Zulus, there was a young king called Mageba. Mageba was a great warrior; he was a man of great courage and without fear. He was also a man of great wisdom and knowledge.

One day, it is said, a group of warriors came to Mageba's village. They brought him the skin of a great lion they had hunted. The skin was to be tanned and made into a blanket for the coronation of Mageba who, at this time, was still a prince.

The wise men of the Zulus had studied the omens – they had looked at the birds which flew across the heavens, and, by night, they had studied the stars and learnt what the gods wished them to do. The gods wished that King Mageba be crowned wearing the skin of a lion, rather than a leopard. The warriors brought Mageba the skin of a lion and a fat little lion cub which they had captured during the hunt. Mageba fell in love with the beautiful animal and had his people look after it. He cared for it and it became part of him. Wherever he went, the lion accompanied him. It grew powerful and strong, and when it was about to grow a mane, Mageba said that the lion had to be set free to find other lions in the wilderness.

'I cannot keep another king slave in my village,' said Mageba to his warriors. 'The lion has grown. Very soon it will be a fully matured male. It must go into the forest and enjoy life as uNkulunkulu has decreed.' The warriors took the young lion into the forest, where they released it, then returned to Mageba.

Several years went by and then, one day, a terrible war broke out between the Zulu people and the Mangwani people. It was a long war resulting from Mangwani raids on Zulu caravans which traded with the Portuguese. Whenever the Zulus went up the coast, the Mangwani would leave them alone. But they would attack them viciously and suddenly when they returned, knowing that they were laden with trade goods, tobacco leaves and shining trinkets.

One day, while leading his army into battle against the Mangwani raiders, King Mageba was separated from his men by a regiment of enemy warriors. He fought bravely and savagely. He was wounded, but he was not about to give in to his murdering enemies. He fought until his shield was shred to tatters by Mangwani battle axes, until his body was covered with blood of the enemy as well as his own.

As the young king was about to be overcome, out of the forest there exploded, like a thunderstorm, a great pride of lions. The lions were led by a large, young male, and leapt upon the Mangwani warriors like demons of the dark. Men screamed as they were torn by the angry lions, and scattered in all directions following this sudden and unexpected attack. Men who feared no human enemy ran screaming like children from the presence and fury of the great carnivores.

The lions disappeared as suddenly as they had attacked. As Mageba recovered from the surprise, he looked around and saw a familiar sight – the lion which had led the attack was limping because one of its front paws was slightly deformed.

'Only one animal has such a deformity,' thought Mageba. 'It was the lion I kept many years ago. Could it have saved my life?'

When Mageba led his victorious army home, he turned and looked behind him. In the blue distance, a lion and its females were following the group, ensuring that the king had a safe journey home. This incredible beast, it is said, later guarded King Mageba on many trading expeditions, the great king of the wild protecting the human king. To this day, Zulu people honour and respect the lion, the monarch of the wild, and call their king *Ingonyama.*

PRAISE SONG TO THE SPRINGBOK

Oh shining tassel
You, whose beauty surpasses all that I know
You, whose hooves are as swift as the wind
You, whose hide is the envy of the other animals
Even the angry lions are ashamed to devour you
Even the furious leopard is afraid to pursue you
Oh springbok
Animal of the sun
Guardian of our forefathers' dreams
Oh springbok, you, who at one time in your millions scarred this ancient land
From place to place you migrated
From valley to valley you travelled – bringing fertility to the waiting land
Bringing rain upon the valleys
When you passed by in your thousands, the clouds sweated gentle rain
  and the droplets of rain fell, fertilizing the land
Oh *insephe*, bright ray of the sun – so our forefathers called you
Oh *insephe*, animal of great sanctity
Long may you continue running across the plains of our country
Long may you continue jumping from bush to bush
Oh *insephe*, *oqobolwayo*, the very one, the springbok!
Oqobolwayo! shouted the old warriors when they saw you
Oqobolwayo! shouted Shaka's Zulus when they saw you running across
  the veld
Inyamazane, the animal of animals!
They say, oh springbok, that you can smell water many, many paces
  under the earth

They say, oh springbok, that you can smell if the rain is going to fall
They say, oh springbok, that if war is going to come to the land, you can
tell by the way your little horns crack
Oh springbok, long may you be the guardian of our land
Long may you be the fertilizer of our plains
Long may your beautiful skin – white, gold and dark brown – be seen upon
the plains of our fatherland
Sister of the zebra
Beloved of the white hawk
Friend of the giraffe
We salute you!

THE BEAUTIFUL AND GENTLE SPRINGBOK

It is said that many years ago, during the magic time of *Imbabajani*, when the rocks were so soft they could be shaped as a potter shapes moist clay, the great god of light, uMvelinqangi, the son of uNkulunkulu, looked down on the people on Earth from the summit of the great Qudeni mountains in the west of the land of the Zulus.

The sun god saw how greatly humanity suffered on Earth. At that time, humans lived like wild animals – in the tops of trees, in caves and in holes in the ground. They had no laws or medicines; and they had no knowledge of melting metal or building huts. They led a savage existence in which every person was a law unto him- or herself. Parents sometimes ate their own children, and spouses killed each other for food, or sometimes simply for pleasure. They did not know anything about bathing and keeping themselves clean. People ran around naked, like baboons, because they did not know how to tan animal skins and use them as clothes to keep warm during winter and to hide their modesty during summer.

The sun god, being a compassionate god, decided to go down to Earth and help human beings by bringing them laws, knowledge and light. He made his intention known to his mother, Nomkhubulwane, the great Earth Mother, who told her son to leave the human race alone. She told him that human beings were the most dangerous and ungrateful creatures on the face of the Earth and that he should forget about trying to help them. But the sun god quarrelled with his mother and defiantly left the golden village.

When the sun god first appeared among human beings in the full blaze of his godly glory, they stood up and ran for their lives. He shone like the sun; his countenance was brighter than the moon and, faced with such beauty, the human beings reacted typically by running away.

One day the sun god, close to despair, was walking through the bush when he came across a young man dying alone in the forest. The young man had been attacked by a warthog which had torn his right thigh open with one of its tusks. He was bleeding to death.

The sun god allowed the young man's soul to leave his body. Immediately, the god of light entered the body and healed the terrible injury. He stood up and walked, although he had a noticeable limp.

The young man's family and friends were amazed to see him alive, for they had seen the warthog gore him. They gathered around him when he called them and he began teaching things that, at first, filled them with deep puzzlement, then with annoyance and, finally, with great amazement.

We are told that the first thing the sun god showed the people was the secret of making fire. He asked them to gather a pile of twigs and small logs and arrange them in a pile near the entrance of the cave in which they lived. Then he rubbed two sticks together until there was a puff of smoke and little flames danced in the pile of grass packed close to the logs. To the people's horror, fire erupted from the grass and climbed onto the logs and twigs. Very soon, the first campfire ever was seen on Earth, dancing and crackling and sending a great pillar of smoke skywards. Again, the people reacted to this spectacle by running away, leaving the sun god alone at the fire.

However, one woman found the courage to return, carrying her child on her back. She sat next to the sun god and was warmed by the great fire he had lit. Gradually, other people came back to the entrance of the cave and they were soon sitting in a circle around the fire, looking at the crippled young man with amazement and admiration. It was around this fire that the sun god began teaching the people many useful things.

He taught the men how to make spears with bits of stone and shards of splintered animal bone attached to long shafts. These were followed by maces with stone heads, and bows and arrows. The band of people began building huts of mud and grass, creating the first village on Earth, and left the caves which had been their homes for generations.

Other groups and families came out of the bush to learn from the sun god. One man wanted to know how to cross a river, and the sun god taught him how to make a dugout canoe. He also taught the people how to catch fish in the streams, the lakes and the rivers. He also taught them simple laws to live by, and, most importantly, he taught them about the gods who lived in the unseen world.

Within a few years, human beings became a lively race of intelligent creatures, with laws, proper homes, chiefs, elders and healers. The sun god also taught them how to dance and sing. He showed the women which herbs were edible, which were medicinal, and which were poisonous. He taught a group of men how to melt copper, iron and tin, and how to create bronze by mixing copper and tin. He taught them how to make tongs, hammers and ploughs.

But as the years went by, disturbing things began to reveal themselves to the sun god. Some of the people whom he had taught were misusing the knowledge he had given them. He had taught them how to make harpoons to catch fish in the river, but they turned the harpoons on each other. He had taught people how to capture wild goats in the forest, show them love and keep them in special pens. But he also saw that some people stole other people's goats. He had taught people how to keep cattle, but some had turned into cattle-thieves.

One day, the sun god was heartbroken by a particularly ugly act committed by a group of people. He told his followers that the time had come for him to leave and return to the land of the gods.

'No!' cried the people. 'We cannot allow you to return to the land of the gods. If you leave us now, your knowledge will leave with you.'

'You do not understand,' said the sun god to the people. 'The knowledge that I have brought is forever enshrined in your minds. It will never leave. In fact, like a beautiful tree, it will grow through the generations. I am tired and I must return to my mother and father.'

Some of the people decided to murder the young sun god, cut up his body and eat it, in the belief that, by eating him, they would become as great and as strong and as knowledgeable as he was. They tied the sun god to a tree and murdered him, using nine spears. They cut up his body and ate it. But instead of becoming great and wise, the stupid people became mad. They shouted at the tops of their voices for no reason, they danced and capered and spoke what they thought were words of great wisdom, when in fact the words they uttered were nonsense. As they danced and screeched, they developed funny little faces and their bodies became covered with fur. They turned into monkeys.

They had eaten the flesh of the sun god, but they found that his bones could not be broken or cracked because they were made of gold. In their madness, they ran hither and thither through the bush, scattering the bones in all directions.

After this terrible deed, the sun died in the sky, the moon passed away and darkness fell upon the Earth, a darkness which was to last for many generations. We are told that the land turned into ice, the rivers froze, and the trees became white ghosts, forever frozen.

In a lonely cave on the slope of a mountain, a little springbok prayed to the great gods not to destroy the Earth because of the sinfulness of a few human beings. The springbok crouched in the cave, praying and chanting and singing for many months, and, at long last, the gods heard the prayers.

The Earth Mother came down from the sacred mountain, bringing with her a glow of warmth that warmed the forests and the mountains, the rivers and the valleys. She called out to the animals in the bush and told them to go into the frozen forest and find her son's bones. The animals did as the goddess commanded and brought the bones to a particular rock.

The bones of the sun god were placed on the rock with a heap of firewood. The Earth Mother lit a pile of wood with one of her fingernails, and the bones started to melt in the great blaze. The Earth Mother floated in the air above the fire and the smoke entered her womb. With the help of lions, baboons and hyenas, the great Earth Mother, in great pain, gave birth to the sun god once more.

When warmth had returned to the world – when the sun had been rekindled and the moon had been reborn – the Earth Mother rewarded the little springbok, saying, 'From now on, you, springbok, will be known as the animal of light, faith and reliability. You, springbok, are going to be called *insephe*, "the shining tassel". Others will call you *tsete*, which means "the faithful one", "the reliable one".'

To this day, Zulu people call the springbok *insephe*, because of the fringe of hair near the springbok's rump, which gives the animal a strange, glowing appearance as it leaps in front of the sun.

Botswanans and other Sotho-speaking people call the springbok *tsepe*, which means 'the one who is reliable', 'the trustworthy one'. This word has given birth to another word in the Sotho and Tswana languages, *tsepo*, which means 'hope' or 'faith' and *tsepega* which means 'to be trustworthy', 'to be unshakeably faithful'.

There is a belief, long held by many black tribes in Zambia, Angola, Namibia and Botswana, that on the day the last springbok dies, the world will end. With the death of the springbok, the sun and moon will die in the land of the shadows. For this reason, the springbok is held in great esteem, and people rejoiced whenever a springbok migration passed through their land.

Although these little animals of great beauty devastated cornfields, crushing the growing corn with their sharp hooves, the people did not grieve or rage, for they knew that the following year there would be good harvests. As the springboks migrated across the land, they left behind heaps of dung. The dung decomposed, filling every nook and cranny, and when the rains came, the land was fertile, beautiful and green. It was believed that all migrating animals were the blood in the arteries of the Earth Mother, for they only followed certain routes and this is where the trees grew tallest and the grass the greenest.

PRAISE SONG TO THE ELAND

In the days of our ancestors, you chose to be the one that goes deep
into the bowels of the Earth
To the land of Nomhoyi you went
To the land of the old goddess you went
To bring back the mother of the stars
To the surface of the Earth
Oh, eland, *impofu*
Oh, golden one
Mighty animal of the forests
You, whose footprints are sacred
You, whose horns frighten the lightning away
You, whose ears hear the music of life itself
You, whose nostrils can smell the souls of those as yet unborn!
Oh, eland
You are in my dreams, just as you are in my eyes
You are the one I can touch and the one I can see
You are the one I cannot see in the valleys of my own mind
Eland, *impofu*
You are the one who lifts up the souls of the dead warriors to the land
of the gods!
Eland, *impofu*
You are the one who is the subject of the songs that the Bushmen sing
in the forests!
They who dream of you are blessed twice by the dark gods of the land
They who dream of you are the loved children of the great Earth Mother
They who dream of you are the healers who heal illnesses

They who touch you with their hands
And remove the pain in your heart
Eland
May you live long upon the surface of this land!
May your children's children's children's children still drink the rivers of our motherland long after we are gone!
Eland
May I continue seeing you in the bush
May your kind never disappear from the face of the Earth!
For you are the light of our ancestors
You are the light of the old ones of many years ago
You are the joy of the gods
The delight of the mountains
And even the whales greet you as they pass across the wide seas!
Impofu, beast of the sun
Eland, carrier of light between your horns
You are the one who pointed the way that people should live for others
Not for themselves
You are the one
And yet you are two
And yet you are three
And yet you are four
For you are the eland
The one who has four souls
You are the eland, the one who knows all.

THE ELAND

There is an animal that Africans believe possesses the same magical power as the elephant: the eland. The eland is an animal which Bushmen revered and whose likeness they painted inside their caves. It is quite common to find more than twenty eland depicted in one Bushman cave. It was believed that the eland was the antelope of the sun.

One fable tells us how the eland went on a very hazardous journey to the underworld to fetch the sun which had been stolen by the great cannibal goddess of darkness. The eland returned with the sun between its horns and borrowed wings from a great flamingo to fly to the sky, taking the sun to safety, far out of reach of the cannibal goddess. When the eland had completed its sacred task of rescuing the sun, it tried to fly back to Earth, but its wings failed it because it forgot the magic words that kept the wings attached to its body. The wings tore off the eland's body and flew back to Earth on their own, and the eland fell out of the sky and died in a valley, far below.

The eland appears in hundreds of fables and legends. Zulu-speaking people call the eland *impofu*, which is a word with several meanings. One is 'the golden-skinned one' or 'the tawny-skinned one'; another is 'the poor one' or 'the humble one'. In Zulu, to be poor is *mpofu*, and a poor person is regarded as *mpofana*. Poverty was equated with humility in ancient times. The Batswanas and Sothos called the eland *pofu* which means exactly the same thing.

If an African dreams of a eland while caught in a web of deep personal troubles, it is regarded as a sure sign that that person will become free of pain and able to solve all his or her problems.

The eland is an animal which symbolizes spiritual enlightenment as well as deep piety and humility. An eland was the one animal that people of all tribes protected vigorously, regardless of whether or not it was their tribal totem.

If someone found a dead eland in the bush, they had to immediately skin it and remove its fat. This was then used in some of the oldest rituals. Eland fat mixed with powdered herbs is used in rituals where the spirit or spirits of dead people are called up by spirit mediums. The mixture is burnt, filling the interior of the hut with a sweet fragrance, and the spirit medium repeatedly calls the name of the deceased person while gently tapping the skin of the spirit drum. When the spirit responds to the summons, it announces its presence by making its own tapping sounds on the spirit drum. Any questions put to the spirit by the spirit medium will be answered by a series of tapping sounds.

Eland fat mixed with powdered, luck-bringing bark, herbs and roots is carried in small containers by people setting out to seek their fortunes, either by working or by facing enemies in a court of law.

If an African woman who has been tormented for years by miscarriages or stillbirths dreams of an eland which bleeds through its nostrils, this is taken to mean that the gods will show mercy and give this woman one living child.

If a man who has lost his wife and children to an epidemic disease, a war, or a tragic accident has a similar dream, it is taken to mean that God will give him a new family and that his joy will be as great as his sorrow.

HOW THE ELAND SAVED HUMANS FROM EXTINCTION

One time there was a great epidemic in the land: people were dying in large numbers and many villages were emptied of all human life. When the great king called together the sangomas and *inyangas*, and asked them to ask the spirits why they had been visited by disease, the healers threw the bones of divination and spoke with one voice. They said that the great Earth Mother had cursed the land with the epidemic because, on the day the king's only son had been born, the baby's mother boasted that her baby was twenty times more beautiful than the Earth Mother's baby, the sun god. They went on to say that if the disease was to be banished from the land, the young prince had to be sacrificed to the grandmother of the underworld.

It was with a heavy heart that the king prepared to sacrifice his son. When the boy had been laid on the rock of sacrifice, a voice was heard calling from the bush, telling the king to stop what he was doing. The king turned and saw an eland with its horns entangled in a bush. The eland told the king not to sacrifice his son, but to sacrifice him instead, so that the boy and the people of the land could live.

'The great goddess, Nomhoyi, is blind,' said the eland. 'She will not be able to tell the difference between my blood and the blood of your son. She will come to the rock of sacrifice, lick the blood with her long tongue and find it delicious. And she will spare your people and your land.'

With an aching heart, the king killed the eland with a polished bronze knife. He took its blood and spilled it on the great rock of sacrifice. That night, the terrible queen of darkness came out of her cave in the underworld and crept up to the rock to taste the blood. In her blindness, she assumed the blood was that of the young prince and she ordered the bringer of illness to leave the land and let the people live their lives in peace.

HOW THE ELAND RESCUED THE EARTH MOTHER

The bony hand of winter had the world in its grip. Everything was covered with ice and it was bitterly cold. Under a thick blanket of frost the trees were dead and the grass was dead; even the rocks were dead. The streams and the rivers had been reduced to ice. The mountains were covered with snow and the sky was a grey, wet misery, across which a frozen wind blew mercilessly. There was ice on the shores of the sea, and the waves were frozen, unmoving, lifeless.

The Earth was dead because the goddess of life, Ninawato, also known as Nomkhubulwane, had been sentenced by seven judges to spend three months in the underworld. She had been sentenced at her own request because she had looked down from the mountain of the gods and had seen the terrible things that human beings were doing to each other and to the animals and birds on Earth. She had seen the slaughter of senseless wars. There was no peace on Earth; there was no rejoicing.

The great Earth Mother looked around and asked herself, 'Who is responsible for the carnage? Who is responsible for the misery?'

The answer that came back to the loving goddess was, 'I am! I am the one who gave birth to the evil race, those restless creatures. I am the one who gave birth to all that pain and misery! Justice demands that I, the great mother of the stars, the great Mother of the Earth, suffer for my crimes. I should have created human beings who were devoid of fear, anger, greed and all the vices to which human beings are prone. I should have learnt from my mistakes, from the many worlds I have created that destroyed themselves through meaningless wars. But I did not! So I must suffer!'

The Earth Mother sent messengers to the dark land on the very edge of the world, where Radamu, the pitiless judge and his six brothers and sisters live in silence. Summoned by the goddess, the judges sat on the summit of a great mountain to try the Earth Mother. They found her guilty and passed a fearsome sentence. The Earth Mother languished deep in the bowels of the Earth in a land whose existence we may not even acknowledge. She was beaten and tortured by the hag, Nomhoyi; she was tortured and ravished by Nomhoyi's son, the monster Sondokati. She suffered for the transgressions of human beings, but hoped that her suffering would make them change their ways. But they did not.

After three months, Imbube, the lion, called a gathering of all the animals, deep in the bowels of a cave where there was warmth from a blazing fire. The animals came out of the cold. Immediately the ice melted off their skins. They looked at Imbube, the great judge of the animals, surrounded by his wives and cubs, with their golden skins shining and their eyes blazing like precious stones in the bright firelight.

Standing on either side of Imbube was a mighty elephant and a rhinoceros, and there was a giraffe on its knees near the judge. One of Imbube's advisers was a fat, comfortable-looking hippopotamus.

'I have called you, my brothers and sisters,' said the lion, shaking his great black mane, 'to discuss a serious matter. It is my intention to send one of you to the underworld on a long and perilous journey to rescue the mother of the world from the clutches of the dark ones in the land with no name. The great sangoma, Imfene, the baboon, has thrown the bones of divination and the bones have indicated that Impofu, the eland, must make this dangerous journey.'

When he heard his name mentioned, Impofu was visibly startled. His big, gentle eyes widened and grew brighter and brighter as tears flowed, one after the other. He felt something warm and moist pushing against the side of his neck, and he turned to find his wife, the beautiful Impofuzana, nudging him. Her eyes too were brimming with tears and her belly was swollen with future life.

'My love,' she whispered, 'you are the one who has been chosen. What will I do if you do not return? What will happen to me and to our unborn calf?'

'Be courageous, Impofuzana,' said Impofu. 'This is the time to be brave. I too am filled with great fear, but a brave person conquers fear. Be brave, my wife!'

'Are you willing to go on this journey, eland?' the lion's voice whiplashed in the silence of the cave.

Impofu stepped forward and as he nodded his head, a gasp rose from the assembled animals.

'Answer me, Impofu,' said the lion. 'Are you willing to go on this journey?'

'I am willing,' said Impofu.

'Then go! There is not a moment to lose!'

At that moment the rhinoceros and the elephant moved as one. They pushed aside a great rock at the far end of the cave, to reveal another huge, dark, yawning cave. A terrible, hot smell came from the cave – one which no animal on Earth had ever smelt.

'All of you must flank the path that leads to the entrance!' said the lion.

Impofu walked the path to the underworld with his head held high, his horns proud and gleaming, and his tail gently swishing as he fought for courage that he did not feel. He disappeared into the yawning mouth and the great rock was repositioned with a fearsome thundering sound.

'A brave hero has gone to do his duty,' said Imbube. 'Let us wait here for his return . . . if he returns . . .'

Impofu entered a world of darkness; a world so hot and with air so poisoned that he could barely breathe. He relied on his sharp sense of hearing and on his even sharper sense of smell to find his way through the brooding underworld.

He journeyed for what seemed like an eternity, and then, all of a sudden, there was a fearsome red glow ahead of him. In a huge cavern, a mighty volcano exploded, spewing smoke and boiling lava high into the air. By the light of the red malevolence, Impofu made his way deeper and deeper into the underworld.

He crossed a stream known by storytellers as the Incinega, the 'grinning skull river'. It was not water that thundered through its gorges or swirled around its rocks, but the blood of the millions of people butchered in senseless wars since the birth of time. The stench was awful. Impofu saw human skulls floating in the red flood; he saw skeletons of animals and human beings borne away in the red tide. His heart was filled with fear which lent speed to his limbs.

He then reached the awful forest of fear, where all kinds of evil spirits had their homes. A demonic being seized Impofu by the tail, but he furiously kicked it away and freed himself. Another demonic creature leapt on Impofu's back – a dark and ugly shadow which stank of all the evil in creation – but Impofu shook it off and galloped on.

Ahead of him, among leafless, dead trees which had turned into stone, he saw an ugly, dirty village basking in the glow of the volcano's fires. Outside the gate of the village, Impofu started to sing.

Eventually, a faint voice drifted from one of the huts, saying, 'I am here. Who are you?'

'I am Impofu, the eland, mother of the worlds. I have come to get you out of this place. Are you alone?'

'Yes, great eland, I am alone. My tormentors are drinking beer in the neighbouring village.'

'Where are you, Great Mother,' asked the eland. 'Direct me with you mind.'

The goddess directed the eland to where she was. When the eland burst into the hut, he found the goddess lying bound hand and foot on the unswept floor; a beautiful form, a mighty image, an unconquerable source of eternal light.

The eland freed the Earth Mother and asked her to jump on his back. Exerting every ounce of his strength, Impofu bolted out of the evil village. He bolted across the ugly land and through the forest of fear, but this time the demonic beings that lived there were frightened by the light that shone around the head of the mother of all life.

'Give me strength, Great Goddess. Add strength to my limbs,' cried the eland.

He ran like the wind and at times appeared to be flying, carrying the beautiful Nomkhubulwane on his back. They crossed the red river of Incinega and plunged into darkness. As the eland began to think that it had reached safety, the goddess screamed with fear. He glanced over his shoulder and there, riding a fearsome monster serpent in the dark and murky skies of the underworld, was a terrible, one-eyed monster, brandishing a great bow and many arrows.

'Come back, my wife!' roared the monster. 'I, Sondokati, command that you come back!'

But the eland ran even faster. The monstrous creature riding the flying serpent let loose an arrow from his bow. The arrow only grazed the eland's rump, but it was a poisonous one. The eland felt its strength ebbing, but continued running.

'Hold on to my mane, Goddess,' said the eland. 'Hold on! My strength is failing, but you must not be captured by that monster!'

The goddess was angered at the injury inflicted on the noble eland. She turned on the animal's back and, with her hand extended, sent a lightning bolt lancing skywards. It struck the huge serpent, which died in mid-air and fell to the ground, while Sondokati fell like a ripe pumpkin onto the rocks below. He was stunned, but not hurt, because he was an immortal being.

The eland ran on and on, no longer caring whether he was alive or dead. And then, ahead of him, he saw a gentle yellow light which grew brighter and brighter. It was the exit from the underworld! Exerting his last ounce of strength, Impofu ran and ran, but before he could reach the exit, his heart failed and he fell onto his knees and died.

As she felt the eland faltering under her, the great goddess jumped off. As the eland's spirit left him, the great Earth Mother briefly cradled the dying Impofu on her silvery lap and then, with crystal tears cascading down her cheeks, she made a number of magical gestures with her hands, and turned the carcass into a swarm of stars which flowed out of the dark cavern of the underworld. To this day there is a group of stars that African people call the Impofu constellation.

The great goddess walked the short distance to the exit from the underworld and stepped into the huge cavern where hundreds of animals were awaiting her return. She stood there, the blameless mother of all life, with her silver skin, golden lips, burning golden eyes and her chest heavy with three great breasts. She accepted the welcome from the lion, his wives and all the animals. They created a pathway for her in the great cavern and she walked through it towards the frozen land.

As she emerged from the cave, the mists of cold and ice vanished for ever, and the clouds parted, no longer angry and threatening snowstorms. The ice and snow melted off the summits of the mountains, and in the grinning forests and smiling wilderness innumerable birds began to sing.

The eland is one of the many animals that African people use to symbolize love and dedication to duty, diligence and strength in the face of adversity. The eland is regarded as sacred because it rescued the goddess from the underworld, with humility, love, self-sacrifice and unmatched courage.

THE SABLE ANTELOPE

DOOMED TO EXTINCTION...?

One of the most beautiful and rare animals in Africa, which for generations has been viewed with great reverence, is the sable antelope. It is a beautiful beast with a jet-black body, a snow-white belly, and long, curved horns that look as if they are made from polished ebony. There are white patches on the sides of its face, and its tail is long, with hair like that of the wildebeest. Its neck curves gracefully, and when the creature moves, it is a poem – a hymn in graceful movement.

In olden days, whenever a sable antelope appeared, Africans would ululate and show great joy. It is said that anyone who saw sable antelopes mating in the bush was truly a blessed person. African people believed the sable antelope to be a symbol of the unity of nature: of the fierce and the strong, the graceful and the delicate, of darkness and light, united in perfect harmony. It was a symbol of grace and strength welded together to create breathtaking beauty.

In olden days, only kings were allowed to have blankets made from the skin of this most sacred animal. Only those who were capable of seeing into the future were allowed to own the horns of a sable antelope. So jealously protected was this animal by many kings in southern Africa that it was hunted only once every five years and, even then, only one animal – an old bull – could be killed.

The Zulus call this animal *inkolongwane*, which means 'the ululating'. In Sesotho it is called *mugulukwane*, and in old Setswana and Sesotho *gulukwane*, which means 'the one over whom people ululate'.

Animals similar to the sable antelope once existed in the Cape. Their skins were blueish, like the blue wildebeest, instead of black, and they were known as *bloubok* (blue buck). Large numbers of bloubok were exterminated by white settlers and hunters, shot out of sheer bloodlust, and not for food. These people did not know that the Xhosa looked upon the bloubok and its cousin, the sable antelope, with great reverence. Xhosa people believed that anyone who wantonly shed the blood of a bloubok or a sable antelope would bring a curse of drought upon the entire land. Killing these noble animals angered the Xhosa.

Another creature, one of the strangest creatures ever to walk the southern African plains, but now existing only in folklore, was known as an *ingebevane*, or pug-faced lion, by the Zulu people. It died out so quickly that only faint memories of it survive in legends and songs. The *ingebevane* was a rare animal, and an impressive monster when seen alive.

Unfortunately, the *ingebevane* and the *bloubok* are now extinct. Will the fate of the sable antelope be the same?

PRAISE SONG TO THE WATERBUCK

Toyi, toyi, toyi, toyi, serwala bothloko!
You, who carry the pain of people between your horns
You, who remove the illness from the ailing chieftain so that he may once more rise and lead his people
You, who are the darling of the blacksmiths
You, who are the friend of all healers
You, who show us the way and tell us how we should live
That we may not quarrel with the trees
That we may not argue with the forests
That we may not be enemies of the grass
That we may not be foes of the rocks!
Run, waterbuck
Take my illness away!
Run, waterbuck
Take my bad luck away!
Run, beautiful one
And bring health to my little babies, to my wife and my grandmother!
You were blessed many, many, many years ago by Modimo
You were blessed many generations ago by Mmamogolo, the mother of all life
Run, run, waterbuck
May you run for the next thirty generations
May you run for the next ten thousand years
May your kind exist even though the mountains have become like little hills
And the hills have become as small as anthills
And the anthills have disappeared
May you be there, waterbuck, when the sun no longer sets, but sits above the

western mountains, dying of old age
May you be there, waterbuck, when the human race no longer walks upon
this world
And the huts and the villages have become ruins upon the forgotten valleys!
May you be there
You, who carry within you the sacred stone of life which your first ancestor
swallowed in the village of the great god
Look upon me with your smiling eyes, oh *serwala bothloko*
Taker-away of pain
Hear my plea with your beautiful ears
And show me the white mark on your backside
As you take away my misfortune and dump it in the bush, never to be
seen again!
Hay-ee! Hay-ee! Serwala bothloko!
Hay-ee! Taker-away of pain!
You, beloved of birds and people and reptiles and rocks and rivers
The streams smile when you come
And the rivers weep when you go

THE CARRIER OF PAIN

In days gone by, people healed their loved ones and themselves by faith alone. African people used to go to a lake or a river and carefully capture a special antelope believed to possess magical healing powers. This antelope was a waterbuck – one of the strangest deer-like animals in Africa. The Batswana people called a waterbuck *serwala botloko* – 'he who carries our pain' or 'the carrier of pain'. It was firmly believed that if a sick person touched a living waterbuck, especially on the rump, the waterbuck would take away pain and sickness. When a waterbuck was captured for the purpose of healing a sick person, great care had to be taken not to injure it in any way. If it was injured, it was believed that the patient would die of his or her illness.

Equally great care was taken when the waterbuck was released, to ensure that it was not harmed in any way, and its movements through the bush were carefully observed.

If the waterbuck ran into a dense clump of bush, this indicated that the sick person would recover slowly. If the waterbuck crossed a river, this was an extremely good sign that the animal was taking away the patient's illness and that recovery would be rapid. If the waterbuck began grazing, this signified that the patient would recover, but would die soon thereafter from another illness.

Why did African people believe that a waterbuck possessed healing powers? Firstly, a waterbuck's horns, when viewed from the front, form a perfect crescent – the symbol of the healing moon. And, a waterbuck's rump has a strange marking which looks like an open wound. It is formed by white fur and is clearly visible as the creature runs away. The mark is lozenge-shaped, and symbolizes the sacred wound or the sacred organ of the Earth Mother.

African people told the story of how a waterbuck nursed the Earth Mother back to health after she had suffered great pain giving birth to the first people. The waterbuck comforted her and licked the tears from her eyes as she wept in pain. It brought her flowers from the bush and even brought Gobiyayi, the clowning monkey, to amuse the goddess with his antics.

For its good work, the gods rewarded the waterbuck with the white fur mark, in the form of the Earth Mother's sacred organ, painted on its rump.

NO ORDINARY HORNS

In olden days, waterbuck were greatly respected by our people, and their horns were used as the snouts for bellows which were used by blacksmiths to pump air into metal-smelting furnaces. They were used to smelt copper and tin to make bronze – the sacred metal of kings. Bellows for smelting ordinary iron for ordinary tools were made from cattle horns.

When a waterbuck was killed for its horns, a ceremony of apology was performed over the carcass. The horns were removed but its flesh was not eaten. The animal was ceremonially buried, like a human being, in a special grave, and when the grave was filled in, songs were sung to speed the reincarnation of the waterbuck's soul.

PRAISE SONG TO THE WILDEBEEST

You are the sangoma of the forests
You are the *inyanga* of the tall trees
You are the hidden one in the long grass
You are ugly, yet you are beautiful
You are strong, and yet you are weak
Your tail is filled with magic, and when you flick it, all the *tokoloshes* run away!
You are the wildebeest, *inkonkoni*
The champion of all the animals, the healer of all the animals!
You are the one we all swear by, you are the one we all sing about
You are the one who adorns the hearts of sangomas
You are the one who decorates the headdresses of mighty chiefs!
Your horns no sorcerer may touch
Your ears no witch may fondle
Your tail makes even the strongest *tokoloshe* run home to its mother!
Inkonkoni, wildebeest
Trampler of the valleys, plougher of the plains of our fatherland
You are a friend of the zebra, her guardian and her protector
You are the one with the red eyes that see deep into the darkest night
You are the one who knows tomorrow
Who knows yesterday, and who knows today
You are the one, you are the *inkonkoni*, the champion of all the animals!
You cross rivers that even the elephant dare not cross
You pass across valleys where even the lion may not tread
For you eat the right herbs in the bush and are protected against all evil
And the sangomas of the land swear by your sacredness

THE UGLY WILDEBEEST

One of the ugliest animals in the African bush is the *inkonkoni* or wildebeest. African people believe that the wildebeest leads the antelope-like animals that are thought to possess great magical powers. Ugly as it may be, the wildebeest is regarded with great reverence as there is the belief that the long hairs on its tail have magical powers to exorcize evil spirits and to heal people suffering from nervous conditions.

African people hold the wildebeest in such reverence that its Zulu name, *inkonkoni*, is also used to denote a champion or a leader in any field. The wisest and greatest traditional healer in any community is always called 'the *inkonkoni*'. The best football player in any township, especially in KwaZulu-Natal, is always nicknamed '*inkonkoni*', in tribute to his football skills.

Africans remove the tail from a dead wildebeest and secure it to a short, thick wooden handle, making an instrument which is wrongly called a fly-switch. However, it is not made to swat flies, but to spray magical preparations – mixtures of water and powdered bark or herbs – which are believed to possess the power to expel demons from people and huts.

When an initiate healer explodes into hysterical fits, the teacher uses a switch to strike a number of carefully calculated blows on the pupil's back. The purpose of the blows is not to cause pain but to stimulate nerves along the initiate's spine to his or her benefit.

Some of the great African leaders carried switches in public, to indicate that they were spiritual as well as political and temporal leaders, in control of the physical bodies and souls of the people they ruled.

Only those people who have been initiated into the deepest of African mystique and mystery are allowed to carry switches. If an impostor carries a wildebeest's tail, he does so at the risk of having an awful curse placed on him.

If a poltergeist makes a nuisance of itself in an African kraal, the sangoma who has been summoned to deal with it burns wildebeest neck-hairs in a fire, specially lit for the purpose, inside the hut. The hairs are believed to be very effective in getting rid of even the most stubborn poltergeist.

HOW THE WILDEBEEST SAVED THE ANIMALS

It is said that Nomhoyi, the goddess of destruction, which is one of the three aspects of the great Earth Mother, was very hungry and invaded the Earth. She started eating all the animals and human beings she could lay her hands on. She ate for several months, feasting until her belly was distended. She ate most of the world's animals, leaving only a few survivors, among which was a wildebeest.

The wildebeest decided to set the animals in the goddess's belly free by tricking her. He bewitched Nomhoyi so that she fell in love with him and, when the goddess wanted the *inkonkoni* to make love to her, he refused, saying he could not make love to someone whose belly was so big. He tricked the lovelorn Nomhoyi into having her belly sliced open so that some of the animals she had eaten could be set free.

After this, however, the wildebeest still protested that her belly was too full. He cast a spell over her so that she became unconscious and then he sliced her belly open, releasing all the animals. The *inkonkoni*, assisted by the baboons and other animals, filled the space with great rocks.

When the goddess regained consciousness, she realized that she had been tricked and vented her rage on the wildebeest by devouring him and leaving only his tail, which she threw angrily into the bush.

The other animals recovered the wildebeest's tail and used it to bring him back to life. And we are told that from that day on, the wildebeest's tail was possessed of magical powers.

PRAISE SONG TO THE ZEBRA

Cele, Cele, Cele, Cele, Cele, Dube!
You, who are day and night in one body
You, who are dark and light in one form
You, who are good and evil in one shape!
Animal of two colours, animal of perfect harmony
Beautiful beast, whose fragrance perfumes the forests of Africa and the plains
Cele, animal of our grandmothers
Cele, animal of the kings that are long gone!
You, whose little hooves edge waxing moons upon the dust of the land
You, whose dung blesses the plains with fertility
You, whose courage is greater than that of the lion, your sworn enemy
You, gentle and soft, but braver than a thousand lions
You, who are stronger than the elephants and wiser than the cunning little monkeys
Dube, animal of mixed colours!
Dube, animal beloved of the Earth Mother!
Dube, luck-bringer of the plains!
Dube, urinator of the rivers and creator of the lakes!
It is said that the fishes in the rivers of Africa sing your praises
It is said that the birds in the sky chant your love song
It is said that the luckiest man is he who, in his travels through the bush, sees two zebra making love under the marula tree
You are the soft in the strong
You are the weak in the might
You are the hoof that runs faster than the wind in August
Dube, zebra of our forefathers!

AN ANIMAL SACRED TO WOMEN

The zebra is known by the Zulu-speaking people of South Africa as *idube*. It is regarded as one of the holiest animals, for when the zebra moves through the bush, it leaves tracks like little crescent moons on the ground. These tracks are also regarded as sacred.

African people believe that the zebra is an animal sacred to darkness and to light because it has black and white stripes on its body. It is also believed that the zebra is particularly sacred to women because the shape of its ears resembles female reproductive organs.

After undergoing herbal treatment, African women who suffered from menstruation pains often went into the bush and crouched over the track of a zebra. It was believed that even the tracks had the power to heal human illnesses.

Zebra dung was held to be very effective in driving away negative spirits that harmed women and children. To this day, traditional healers will burn a concoction of certain animal fats mixed with dried and powdered zebra dung to chase ghosts and other negative entities from huts and even from caves which people use for sacred ceremonies.

The zebra is also the symbol of musicians. One of the best compliments one person can pay another is, 'You are a zebra at music' – in other words, 'You are the best singer there is.' And I remember, in the earliest years of my youth, at mission schools, young soccer players called themselves zebras.

In the bush, the zebra is rarely seen alone. A herd of zebra is often accompanied by wildebeest. Anyone who regarded the zebra as his or her totem was honour-bound to protect not only the zebra, but also the wildebeest. It is believed that these two animals protect each other in the dangerous African bush. During the day, the wildebeest has very poor eyesight, whereas the zebra's eyesight is excellent. At night, these roles are reversed.

There are many southern African tribes and clans which claim the zebra as their totem, including the KwaZulu-Natal families or clans called *Cele* and *Dube*. Among the Tswana people in Botswana and in the North West Province, the Bahaduba regard the zebra as their totem.

PRAISE SONG TO THE BUFFALO

You are the buffalo
You are the one who shakes the trees and makes the bush tremble
You are the dust in the earth and the bellow that challenges
the guns of thieves
You are the one whose horns defy the spears of those who hunt you
and whose hide smiles at the edges of their shields
You are the buffalo
The one our forefathers said was the nourisher of the earth
The one who feeds the earth with your dung
May you never vanish, dark shadow of the greenery!
May you never vanish, thunder of the hillside!
May you never vanish, oh dusk that greets the setting sun!
May you still be here in the days that are yet to come!

INYATHI: THE BUFFALO

Anyone who has travelled by foot through the timeless valleys and eternal plains of Africa will, at one time or another, have come across the formidable beast that Zulu people call *inyathi* and which the Sotho-speaking people know as *nari.*

The Cape buffalo is one of the mightiest beasts to roam the African subcontinent. Zulu praise-singers hail the Cape buffalo as the wild ox which defied taming by generations of kings. These wild cattle can only be fenced in by the rocks and mountains of the land. The buffalo is hailed as the mighty one, the defiant one, who only fears the waves of the ocean, and who does not shrink or tremble, even when lightning strikes the land. The Zulu people believed that Cape buffalo were specially created by the great Earth Mother and God the Father to keep the earth fertile. In olden days, when vast herds filled the land, these mighty beasts migrated and grazed their way across the plains and through the valleys, leaving behind huge quantities of dung.

Inyathi literally means 'fertilizer of the earth'. Baca sewerage workers refer to human waste by the same name, and when they spread the waste to dry in the sun, they say they are 'stabbing the buffalo', *sigwata inyatsi.* The name used to refer to the buffalo is the same as the name for human excrement or cow dung when it is used as a fertilizer to benefit cornfields and vegetable gardens. *Inyathi* is a very fitting name indeed for the great beast; the herd brought about the degradation of the environment throughout Africa. These and many other animals which roamed the African subcontinent did, in fact, fertilize the land.

When a Zulu parent blesses a newborn baby, he says, 'Oh my child, may you grow as big and as powerful as the buffalo of the wilderness. May you grow as wise as the giraffe of the plains, and as gentle as the zebra of the valleys.'

Africans believe that if a person dreams of Cape buffalo grazing peacefully, it means that that person will soon acquire a powerful friend who will bring peace to his or her life. However, if a person dreams about a charging buffalo, this is taken to mean either that the person will face a formidable enemy or that ancestral spirits are furious. The dreamer must mend his or her ways as quickly as possible so as to avoid being punished.

According to Zulu storytellers, a few weeks before the great battle of Isandhlwana, King Cetshwayo had a dream in which he saw a herd of buffalo moving through a great rainstorm, and his adviser told him this dream meant that he would win a great military victory over a powerful enemy. He would descend on the enemy like the rainstorm descended upon the buffalo. This was indeed so: King Cetshwayo won the battle of Isandhlwana, defeating a well-armed and highly trained British military force.

In olden days, African hunters left buffalo alone because there was very little need for anyone to hunt this mighty beast. The animal is one of the bravest, most cunning animals that one can meet in the great wilds of Africa. While I was working in Kenya, I saw many tourists in search of big-game hunting trophies either seriously injured or mauled by these ferocious creatures. When a buffalo is hunted it becomes as dangerous as a human being. It is aware of a hunter's intention and takes several defensive measures to meet the threat. It can either flee quietly or ambush the hunter. It is also capable of successfully faking death.

The Zulu and Ndebele people have a very brutal saying, 'Never provoke a Cape buffalo, otherwise on that day you shall see your own mother.'

THE KUDU

A BLUNDERING AGGRESSOR

There is a large antelope, known as a kudu, which is sacred to African people for a very strange reason. The Batswana people's name for a kudu means 'the blundering aggressor', while the Zulu term recalls the horn of an animal smashing against the horns of another.

The kudu is used to instruct young sons and daughters about the futility of conflict. Very often, when two male kudus fight during the mating season, their horns get so interlocked that they are unable to free themselves. Both will eventually die of hunger or thirst with their horns inextricably locked together.

When hunters found two dead kudus with interlocked horns, they would take the two skulls to the chief who would put them in his house to show young people the price that living things pay for indulging in senseless strife.

African people believed that if you dreamt of a kudu it meant that you were going to be promoted to a high position in the tribe. However, you had to be careful not to indulge in quarrels, because your subsequent downfall would be swift. Zulus regard the kudu as a symbol of senseless pride which brings about a person's demise.

There is a tribe in the North West Province known as the Barolong that was once known far and wide for its metal-smelting talents. The Barolong's totem and symbol was the kudu, and they call it 'the father of iron'. The reason for this is that the kudu's horns are easily detached once the animal is dead, and make excellent blowpipes for cow-hide bellows.

The horns are also used as trumpets at ceremonial occasions by tribal praise-singers and rainmakers. In major rainmaking ceremonies, fourteen kudu-horn trumpets were used to call the rain. They were sounded repeatedly while the rain-makers sprayed the congregation with switches dipped in bowls of fresh water.

PRAISE SONG TO THE ANT BEAR (AARDVARK)

Oh diligent digger, who digs many holes
Oh diligent miner, who mines deeply into the earth
What are you looking for, ant bear?
Why do you dig so many holes, but spend your nights in only one?
What are you looking for, what magic secret?
It is said that you are the king of all the sangomas, the lord of all the healers
It is said that you are looking for the great medicine that lies hidden in the bowels of the earth
It is said that you are looking for the ultimate herb with which to help humanity
That is why all the sangomas, all the healers, call you their father
Oh animal, with the long nose that can smell into the future
You, whose bones are used to foretell things which are yet to come
Oh animal, whose mysterious behaviour has for many years excited the curiosity of our forefathers
Long may you live!
Long may you crawl!
Long may you dig!
Isambane, the digger of holes
You were the inspiration of our miners of old as they dug into the land, seeking the iron
As they dug into the land, seeking the copper
As they dug into the land, seeking the tin
Bayete!

SYMBOL OF ALL HEALERS

Throughout southern Africa, the ant bear (aardvark) is the symbol of all healers because it digs up roots, sometimes from deep underground, to make the holes in which it lives. An ant bear is a very strange animal. It digs a hole deep into the ground, abandons it, digs another hole some distance away, abandons that one too, and then digs yet another . . . After digging five or six holes, only one will please the ant bear in some way, and it will make this hole its home.

This appears to be very puzzling behaviour, and some people believed that by digging and abandoning so many holes, the ant bear was trying to protect itself from predators who would look in all the wrong holes while it slept safely.

Some wise men believe that the ant bear is very sensitive to the presence of secret energies under the earth and that it digs the holes in search of them. It abandons a hole when it does not find the energies to give it peace, health and wellbeing. Others believe that the ant bear is very knowledgeable in healing roots and herbs, and that any root dug up by this animal has the power to heal any kind of illness. The ant bear is also the symbol of a person who toils for others while gaining very little in return. The abandoned holes often become homes to snakes, such as pythons, and other creatures that live in the bush.

Every association of traditional healers in South Africa today uses the ant bear as its symbol. It is an animal sacred to all rainmakers and healers. And according to tradition, no-one is allowed to harm an ant bear, whether or not it is the family totem. All ant bears, whether ordinary or sacred totem animals, were protected by meaningful taboos. If you killed an ant bear, it was believed that great misfortune would befall your family and disease would attack the community. The ant bear has the power to keep illness away simply by being alive in the bush.

In the land of the Rain Queen, near Duiwelskloof in Mpumalanga, one may come across another ant-eating animal, the scaly ant-eater, or pangolin. Anyone finding this animal in the bush must take it unharmed and alive to the Rain Queen who will then release it in the bush, according to custom.

MAKIWANE AND THE ANT BEAR

Many years ago, there was a young man called Makiwane, who lived to the east of the land of the Zulus. Makiwane was a very friendly, sensitive young man. He befriended the animals he found in the bush and he did not like to see any animal in distress. He loved to carry little goats in his arms, and he called the birds to sing to them and feed them.

Makiwane was walking through the bush, playing his bow harp, on his way to court a girl whom he loved, when he saw something moving in the undergrowth.

Being curious, he went to investigate. The creature was creating a little cloud of dust under the stunted thorn trees.

'What is going on?' said Makiwane to himself.

He found an ant bear caught in a cruel snare. Some mischievous herdboy had made the snare from a woven rope of zebra tail-hairs and the ant bear was struggling desperately to be free, but was being strangled.

Makiwane knew that he had to help this animal. He took out his knife and cut the ant bear free from the snare. It was a strange-looking animal with a long snout, two pointed ears, and a large body which reminded Makiwane of a big rat.

Makiwane and the ant bear looked at each other for a long time, then Makiwane said, 'Ant bear, go away, run away!'

But the ant bear sat just there, its flanks heaving.

Then Makiwane realized that it couldn't breathe properly.

He took the ant bear in his arms and he pumped its chest, in an attempt to get air into it. He rubbed the creature's hairy stomach. At first, the ant bear struggled, but it soon discovered that Makiwane was a friend and not an enemy.

Makiwane noticed that the animal's neck was swollen where the snare had tightened around it. What was he to do? He rummaged in his bag, brought out his firesticks and took out his clay pot, which he filled with water from the river.

The ant bear lay on its side, watching Makiwane with suspicion. Makiwane boiled some water, tore off part of his loinskin, dipped it into the hot water and made a compress to take away the pain caused by the swelling.

He stayed with the ant bear and missed the appointment he had made with his girlfriend. He didn't leave until he saw the ant bear moving sluggishly away, with a look of gratitude in its eyes.

Makiwane walked for several days to the place where his girlfriend lived. It was a long journey, but for Makiwane no journey was too long. There were birds to serenade him and wild animals to amuse him. People greeted him when he passed their villages and animals saluted him. The goodness of his heart shone like a newly born star.

Makiwane's wedding took place on a beautiful day. Makiwane was so happy, as was his young bride, Nomaza. They thought they would live happily for a long time, but he who hopes is not the one who has gained; he who dreams is not the one whose dreams have come true.

Soon thereafter, the village was attacked by a hostile tribe of cannibals and Makiwane was injured in a terrible battle. To make matters worse, his young wife was carried off by the king of the cannibals.

Leering, snarling and proud of the evil thing he had done, proud of the people he had killed and eaten, and the village he had burnt to the ground, he laughed at Makiwane as he lay in the dust, 'I have taken your wife and you shall never see her again, stupid young man!'

Makiwane lay there, very ill. Friendly tribespeople picked him up and took him to their village where they tried their best to nurse him back to health, but his heart had been broken and he no longer wanted to live. The people said, 'You have to live, Makiwane. You have to recover; we want you to live. Without you, who will bring us the laughter? Who will dance? Who will sing? Who will sing the songs you sing to our children? You have to survive, Makiwane!'

But Makiwane said, 'I do not want to live. I have nothing to live for. My wife has been taken away and I don't know where she is. I know I will never see her again.'

One day, while Makiwane lay in his hut, he heard a noise at the entrance. There, entering the hut, like a squat, long-eared, furry shadow, was a big ant bear. Makiwane wondered what the animal was doing there.

The ant bear moved ridiculously and clumsily. It approached Makiwane and looked closely at him. Makiwane was surprised: *hau*, there was recognition and laughter in the ant bear's eyes. And, on its back, the ant bear was carrying a bundle of herbs and roots. It placed the bundle close to Makiwane and then sat and looked at him.

Makiwane called out to the people and, when they heard his voice, they came running. They entered the hut where they found the ant bear squatting close to him, 'Ha, Makiwane, do you know what has happened?'

'No, I don't!' replied Makiwane.

'The ant bear, *isambane*, the digger of herbs, has brought herbs to heal you!'

'I do not want to be healed!' said Makiwane. 'I do not want to live. What do I have to live for?'

The ant bear spun round, reared up on its hindquarters and smacked Makiwane on the chest with its tail! It hit him again and again, until he sat up. Then the ant bear stood up, looked at Makiwane, and used its long snout to push the bundle of roots and herbs towards him.

'What am I supposed to do?' asked Makiwane.

The ant bear looked at him with utter contempt, then urinated on the hut's floor to show him exactly what he thought of him. After that, the ant bear simply walked out of the hut.

'Makiwane,' said the headman of the village, 'the sacred ant bear has brought you medicine. But who knows how to mix such medicine?'

There was no-one who could prepare the medicine for Makiwane.

Then the headman's wife said to the people and her husband, 'I think there is someone in another village, far away, who knows about herbs. Let us go there!'

Two women left with the headman's wife and they were gone for several days.

When they returned, they were accompanied by a very wrinkled old woman called Namuteya. Namuteya took one look at the bundle of herbs and roots that the ant bear had left and said, 'I recognize these herbs. The ant bear is the wisest animal in the bush. It knows all the herbs of healing. I can mix these herbs and heal this young man.'

'Oh,' said the people. 'Please help him, old one. Namuteya, please help him!'

'No, no, no, no, huh uh, huh uh, *hayi*,' replied Namuteya. 'In this world there is a price for everything. Before I heal this young man, he must promise me that, when I have healed him, he will become my husband!'

Makiwane did not know what to say. He had no choice but to agree as his illness suddenly grew worse.

Namuteya prepared several herbal brews for him. She pounded the roots and herbs; she used some as poultices to heal his aching body, she gave some of them to him to drink and others to use as enemas to clean his bowels.

Within ten days Makiwane's illness had disappeared. Only his broken heart remained. One moonlit night, Namuteya said to Makiwane, 'Oh, Makiwane, I want to help you to forget your wife. Marry me! Let us be happy together.'

'But you are so old! You are old enough to be my great-great-grandmother! How can I marry you?' asked Makiwane.

The old woman said, 'Ah, do you not understand, silly young man, that the oldest beer in the village is the one that tastes the best?'

And so it was that Makiwane and Namuteya became man and wife, joined in sacred wedlock by the headman of the village. At the wedding, squatting under a tree and listening to music, was *isambane*, the ant bear. He listened and rejoiced, and then quietly departed to carry on with his daily life.

Makiwane never saw his young wife again, but it is said that he became a very happy and wise man with old Namuteya at his side.

To this day, African people laugh at the story of Makiwane and they say that he who loses the day star must content himself with marrying the old moon.

PRAISE SONG TO THE PYTHON

You are the light of the long grass
You are the rainbow of the tall trees
You are the great-grandmother of wisdom
You are the mother of all magic
You are the python, the snake of all snakes!
You are the python, the mother of all reptiles!
You are the python, the queen of all the witches!
You are the python, the one who rules the rivers!
You are the one whose eyes are friendly, but whose coils are the deadliest of death
You are the wood, you are the trees
You are the tall grass, you are the mountains
You are the one who has all the knowledge of our forefathers
You are the great snake that we all revere
You are the drum to whose rhythm we all dance
You are the *domba* in whose honour the maidens of Venda dance the night away
You are the python, the queen of all snakes!
You are the one who opened to us the fragrant door of the village of love!
Oh python
Snake of snakes, bringer of wisdom
Ruler over the souls of the sangomas!
Oh python, queen of the rivers
When you cross a river, all the warriors must tremble
Where you hide yourself in the tall grass between the thorn bushes, there will be a fragrance that the nose will never forget
Python, great snake, it is said that while you exist, so long shall the rivers flow

but when the last of your kind dies, Africa shall dry up.
Oh snake, oh great serpent
Mama nyoka, mother of all serpents!
They honoured you
They cheered you as you crept like a living river among the green bushes
They saw the rainbow sheen of your scales and they praised it
They saw the brightness of your eyes and they feared
They call you the symbol of eternity, of rebirth, because every year you shake away the old scaly hide and you adopt a new one in rebirth.
Inyoka, mother of the serpents!
Inyoka, light of the forests of Africa!
Inyoka, omen of our kings!
Inyoka, in whose body one day we all shall reside!
Bayete!

SNAKES ARE REVERED CREATURES

African people do not regard the snake as an evil creature; they regard it rather with at least the same reverence as with which they regard large land animals such as the elephant, rhinoceros and others. The people believe that the first creatures created by God on this Earth were reptiles and fishes. This belief is supported in many African legends where the snake is shown to be much more intelligent than a human being.

Among some African tribes, being called a snake is not taken as an insult, but rather as a compliment, because to these tribes the name 'snake' also means a very clever person. It is only among Christians that being called a snake is the worst insult, because the Bible tells us that the snake is an evil and deceitful creature.

Today, however, dreaming of a snake is often taken to mean that an ancestor urgently seeks to communicate with the dreamer – especially if the snake is seen swimming in water. But for an African to dream of a snake biting him or her means that this person is going to face a powerful enemy who might do him or her serious injury in the very near future.

By far the most revered and respected snake in Africa was the python, around which well over two thousand legends, myths and fables have been woven. Our people believed in many different kinds of python. They knew about the ordinary python, the *inhlwathi*, a name which means 'the one who makes you unconscious', a name which is also born of another word, *isihlwathi*, which means 'a brief loss of consciousness'. The python is so named because of its ability to hypnotize its victims before crushing them to death, rendering them incapable of resisting while the snake arranges it coils around them. African people also believed in python-like snakes which were imaginary, and one of these is a huge snake known as the *nyandezulu* or 'the great bundle of the heavens', which is said to live in many lakes, rivers and dams. The snake sometimes takes to the air as it moves from lake to lake, giving birth to a tornado which devastates the land.

Many years ago, Albertina's Villa, a shanty town south of Johannesburg, was destroyed by a tornado, a very rare phenomenon in South Africa. The destruction of this shanty town resulted in heavy loss of human life, with several hundred people killed or injured. African people believed that the destruction was brought about because a *nyandezulu*, or, as some call it, a *nkanyamba* had been angered by a nameless man who had insulted the great serpent's daughters, who were mermaids on the Transkei coast.

There is no lake or dam or great river anywhere in southern Africa which African people do not believe is inhabited by a monstrous snake. Many sangomas claim to have captured or tamed such gigantic reptiles, and many more have drowned while diving into lakes and rivers in search of the great serpent, which is said to have the ability to supply any sangoma with great knowledge.

There is another very interesting mythical reptile: a fabulous, feathered serpent – a great reptile, bigger than the biggest python, which is said to have a crest of green feathers on its head. What I found interesting about this African belief is that the Aztecs and Toltecs of Central and South America also believed in this feathered serpent which they held to be the symbol of their hero god Quetzalcoatl.

The Venda, Tsonga and Batsonga peoples hold the unusual belief that it was a python that taught the first men and women on Earth about the mysteries of sex. This is why Venda maidens perform their famous python dance in honour of the great snake which was once held to be the symbol of the Earth Mother.

There is a snake, also of a shadowy and mythical nature, which Xhosas believe can be captured and tamed by women and used to gain dominance over men. It is called the *ichanti*, and is said to be a long, thin, silvery snake with dark red and dark green spots along its back. It is said that a woman can tie the *ichanti* around her waist, like a string, underneath her skirt.

Myth has it that Xhosa women use the *ichanti* to call back wayward husbands who have left home to take mistresses. The Xhosa woman puts the *ichanti* under the sleeping mat in her husband's hut and then softly calls her husband's name, kneeling close to the snake under the mat. As she calls her husband, the snake will crawl out from under the mat and join her, swaying in rhythm to her chanting, ordering him to return home. It is said that if a woman uses the *ichanti* snake on her husband, he will fail miserably each time he tries to have intercourse with a strange woman, until he sheepishly returns home to the wife he has deserted.

When one is studying African culture, one often encounters that shadowy realm where the real and the unreal merge into each other and become one, where it is no longer easy to distinguish between what actually exists and what is a figment of some long-dead person's imagination.

In African culture, magical beings are often seen to be more real than flesh and blood, for Africa is a continent of myth and legend, where fable and fact walk hand in hand like immortal lovers across the emerald plains of the land of the gods.

In the land of the Xhosa there is a snake which is known as the *majola.* This snake is said to be reddish in colour, and the Xhosa people accord it the same reverence that the Zulu people accord to the mamba. When a *majola* enters a Xhosa village, it is left strictly alone.

But there is an unusual twist to the story of this snake. If a Xhosa wife has given birth to a child whose paternity is doubted by both her husband and her mother-in-law, the woman's reputation is saved if a *majola* snake enters the home a few days or weeks after the birth of the baby. The appearance of the *majola* at the kraal is taken as positive proof that the newborn baby is the offspring of the woman's husband and not the fruit of an adulterous affair.

The Xhosa people, like the Bushmen of the Kalahari, believe in a long, thin snake which is made entirely of some kind of electrical energy, and which the Xhosa call *umbilini.* We are told that the snake lives in every one of us and is brought to life by certain vigorous dances. When a sangoma dances, she reaches a certain stage during the dance when she goes into a trance-like state, when she no longer feels her legs moving. When she sings she feels as if she is floating in mid-air, or swimming in a warm ocean of unseen water. It is at this time that the *umbilini*, which supposedly lives at the bottom of the spine, is unleashed, uncoils like a fiery spring and races up the sangoma*'s* spine to explode through the top of her head, and flies skywards towards the dark reaches of the unseen world.

It is said that once the *umbilini* has become unleashed, the person develops intense psychic power and is able to see and cure illness in other people. I can vouch for this. In my younger days, I took part in several healing dances, with groups of Bushmen and Xhosa sangomas. I felt the *umbilini* energy serpent, which the Bushmen call *ncum.* I felt the serpent tearing up my spine like a jet of scalding water. I have felt it burst out of the top of my head, leaving me with the feeling of having a hole on the top of my skull, through which a cold breeze blows to the bottom of my spine. Once the new moon has risen, you feel like a completely new person. Your vision, both spiritual and physical, becomes intense, your sense of hearing unbelievably acute, and you are able to see illness and even old injuries in the people around you. These illnesses or injuries look like dark patches in the glow that is the aura of the person you are observing.

Our traditional village in Mafikeng stands next to the Lotlamoreng dam, which was built by Botswana tribesmen in the 1930s. It is just an ordinary dam, not even remotely as big as some of the other dams in South Africa. But the local people firmly believe that a great reptile lives in this dam – a monster which sometimes seizes people and drowns them in the polluted waters of Lotlamoreng.

The tribespeople call this monster *senoamadi*, 'the blood-drinker'. I have often seen people making offerings to this beast, especially at night, in the light of the moon. They throw coins – five- and ten-cent pieces – far into the centre of the dam as offerings to the *senoamadi*. If it becomes known that you doubt the existence of this mythical reptile, the local people will shout you down, for fear that you might bring the wrath of *senoamadi* on their heads by denying its existence.

Why do people believe in such things?

The answer is very simple. In many cases, belief in the existence of such monsters is triggered by strange and seemingly inexplicable incidents in and around a stretch of water. And, believe me, many strange things happen near some lakes, rivers, and even marshes in southern Africa.

A news report claimed that a strange animal had killed three men near a marsh south of Johannesburg. It was said that the beast had mutilated these men, and when the authorities examined the corpses, they could not identify the type of animal that could have caused these terrible injuries.

Many, many times, near South Africa's great dams and rivers and lakes, the great lakes in Central Africa, and near rivers such as the Kafue and Okavango, simple, honest and reliable men and women claim to have seen creatures of a monstrous reptilian nature emerging from the water at night or on misty days. Often the creature is seen by more than one witness.

To the east of Johannesburg, *en route* to the Kruger National Park, is a dam called the Loskop dam. Groups of black people, some of them unknown to each other, have on various occasions reported to sangomas in Soweto and other townships that they have seen a strange beast emerge from the dam and crawl onto dry land, evidently in some pain. It is said that the beast stays on the land for ten or fifteen minutes before struggling back into the water.

People who have seen this beast describe it as having a very long neck like a python, a barrel-shaped body, four great flippers and a long tail. But most amazing of all is that all the people who claim to have seen it give identical descriptions.

What kind of creature is this monster? And where does it come from?

PRAISE SONG TO THE CROCODILE

I saw a shadow in the green womb of the waters
I saw a shape
I heard movement
I felt a song
I saw a log that was alive, moving in the waters
I saw two eyes, two nostrils
And it was you, *ingwenya*, the devourer of the rivers!
Our fathers say that when the gods created the first living things in this world, they created the fish and then they created you, oh *ingwenya*
And because the gods had not had experience creating, they created you without lips
With the teeth that smile on the outside!
You are the one
You are the one who devours your prey with a smile, oh crocodile
You are the feared one whom our forefathers used to think of with dread
You are the invincible one
The shadow in the water
The movement
The song
You are the drumbeat, you are the sound
You are the swell of water, you are the silence
You are the crocodile, the sangoma of the waters!
You are the crocodile, the first-born of all reptiles!
You are the crocodile, the wisest one of the waters!
You have few friends in the river except the hamerkop
You have few friends in the river except the little birds that clean your teeth

Many fear you, many dream about you
And they say that he who dreams of a crocodile must know that he will face
a powerful enemy tomorrow
You are the sweeper of the dead
The devourer of those things that are no longer alive
That the waters may live and be clean
You keep the streams pure
You keep the rivers pure
You keep the ocean smiling
You keep the clouds singing
You are the crocodile
The symbol of our kings!
You are the crocodile, the daughter of the sun!
It is said that at one time, when the sun was angry with all living things
You, crocodile, sang to him and he calmed his rage and cooled his fire
You sit upon the mud bank, there I see you
And when you are seen, the old women keep the young women away from
the river banks
And when your egg is found, it is good luck for the newly-married virgin
For they say that she who finds a crocodile's egg shall mother many sons
and daughters!
Oh, crocodile
You are the feared shadow in the deepest waters
You are the whisper of rushing water as you seize your prey
You are the slashing tail that beats the river into foam
You are the song
The movement
You are the thunder
The silence
You are *ingwenya*, the crocodile
Bayete!

THE HONOURED SCAVENGER

The crocodile, like the hyena, has an unsavoury reputation as a vicious scavenger, but it is honoured, and became the totem of one of the greatest African tribes.

In Africa there existed a very ancient tribe of highly cultured people, people who reached great heights of achievement in many fields. These people called themselves the Bakwena, 'the people of the crocodile'. And there was in the land now known as Zimbabwe a small offshoot of these people, a nomadic tribe known as the Tangwena. The Bakwena were one of the oldest tribes in southern Africa, having been founded, we are told, well over two thousand years ago. Upon them, the gods of knowledge appear to have smiled very early on in their long history. They were the best metal-workers in southern Africa and it was they, or so legend tells us, who discovered iron. They were the best bronze casters and tin and copper miners in southern Africa and the best astronomers and astrologers in Africa.

The Bakwena people regarded the crocodile with almost god-like awe. They never harmed a crocodile in any way and, if they found a dead one on the banks of a river, they always gave it a solemn burial, as if it had been a human being. To them, the ability of a crocodile to creep up on its prey underwater and grab it in its great jaws was a sign of the crocodile's greatness and invincible magical power.

To the Bakwena, a crocodile was a beautiful, strong and noble animal. A crocodile symbolized all that was holy, powerful and purifying. The Bakwena built sacred huts and the entrances were shaped rather like the snout of a crocodile.

The crocodile is a much-hated reptile in other parts of Africa, because it is one of the most notorious killers of human beings. However, it brought about great advances in surgery among African people: crocodiles tore off the legs of many tribespeople and, as a result of this, traditional surgeons developed techniques of amputation which were quite advanced. A man or a woman whose leg had been seized by a crocodile stood on the very shores of death and would die if he or she did not immediately receive the attention of a good surgeon.

In Johannesburg, I saw one of the strangest collections of African artefacts. It comprised a number of artificial legs – some wooden, two made of ivory and others of metal – all of which had been created by black traditional surgeons between the mid-1700s and the early years of the nineteenth century, to help people who had been mutilated by crocodiles. As part of this great art of life-saving, traditional healers developed powerful oral anaesthetics which could kill pain so that a patient's leg or arm could be amputated. These amputations took place on high mountains, and many, many lives that would otherwise have been lost through infection were saved by the skilled men and women who made the artificial limbs.

African people believe that the fat of a crocodile, when rubbed upon the gums, would help stop the gums bleeding. And sometimes, in those parts of Africa where crocodiles are plentiful, women would stuff fresh crocodile fat into the cavity of an aching tooth in the belief that it lessens the throbbing of toothache.

Some people in southern and East Africa believe that the best protection a man has against impotence and venereal disease is a special walking stick made of ebony or some other hard wood into which a crocodile's penis has been pushed and allowed to dry. And a crocodile's tooth is a powerful protection against murderers, assassins, and other malignant forces, whether physical or spiritual. There were tribes in West Africa, Nigeria and southern and Central Africa whose warriors would go to battle wearing heavy necklaces of crocodiles' teeth as protection against enemy weapons. Our people believed that inside the skull of every crocodile was a special stone which, if you found it, would make you the wisest person on Earth. And when Africans came across a dead crocodile, the first thing they would do was split its skull open with an axe, in search of this fabulous stone of eternal wisdom.

In many parts of Africa, where crocodiles are eaten (like parts of Uganda, Sudan and Tanzania) you are encouraged to eat crocodile meat if you suffer from fear of any kind. If you are scared of being knifed by thieves and are afraid to venture out of your home at night, you are advised to eat well-cooked crocodile steak, which will fill you with courage. The right foot of a dead crocodile is said to have great protective powers against murderers and spirits of the night.

I remember one day in Soweto when I assisted in the exorcism of a ghost from a haunted house, I met a sangoma from Mozambique who had also been summoned by the owners of the house. The man had a massive dried crocodile's foot, which he waved around in a very impressive way. We worked for several hours trying to get rid of the ghost. We burnt herbs and chanted incantations, and then, just when we were about to leave, my friend from Mozambique started waving his crocodile's foot with its string of beads. Suddenly, a loud blow smacked the man's face and he flung the crocodile's foot down on the ground and fled.

Around the crocodile, many fables have been told and many proverbs spoken. There is a proverb that says, 'Never insult a crocodile until you have crossed the river.' This means that you should never criticize people until you have left their territory. Another states: 'No matter how smoothly the canoe of love may glide over the waters of the lake, the crocodile of discord is never far beneath the surface.'

MAKENDE, THE TRICKSTER

Many years ago there lived in the land of the Shangani people a cunning young man called Makende. Makende was a trickster; he loved to play jokes on people. He lived by his wits and created trouble wherever he was. He stole chickens, goats and cattle, but he stole them in such a way that nobody could blame him.

One day, Makende met an old man in the bush. The old man said, 'I see you, Makende.' And Makende said, 'Old man, I also see you. Where are you going and where do you come from?'

The old man replied, 'I am travelling. I have been travelling for a long time. I have been travelling since the very beginning of the world. I am known by many names in many places. And I am prepared to reward those who are good of heart and to punish those who are bad.'

When Makende looked into the eyes of the old man, he was filled with an unknown fear and he quickly tried to move away. But the old man held him by the arm and said, 'Tell me Makende, are you a good person or a bad one?'

'Old man, I am a good person,' replied Makende.

The old man said, 'Are you sure, are you quite sure you are a good person? Well, I would like you to prove to me that you are a good person by answering a few questions. Tell me, when you see that someone has lost something in the forest, what do you do?

'Well, sir, I would call out to that person and point out to him or her the thing that had fallen.'

'Would you?' said the old man, 'Really?'

'Yes!'

But once Makende had said that, all the hair on his head turned white, and the old man said, 'Makende, look at you! You are telling me an untruth. See how your hair is turning white. If you continue telling me lies, you are going to be as old as I am, or even older. Tell me again, what would you do if somebody dropped something precious in the bush. Now, telling lies is like falling into a pot of sticky gum – once you tell one lie, you must tell many more.'

Makende continued lying to the old man. And the more he lied, the older he became. He told seven lies to the old man and he became as old as the old man.

Then the old man said to Makende, 'Makende, listen to me. Do you want me to reverse the spell that I have put on you?'

'Yes! Yes! Yes! Please, yes!' pleaded Makende.

'Makende, far away in the forest there is a great lake. You must dive under the water and find me the pot of magic that lies at the bottom.'

To get rid of the terrible spell that was cast on him, Makende hobbled in haste to the lake. He found a long reed, put it in his mouth, and dived under the water. He found nothing and surfaced again. Then he dived again. For two days he searched the lake, finding nothing until at long last, among tall reeds, he saw in the mud at the very bottom something shining, glowing under water. When he swam towards it, he found a magic pot. The pot was full of beads and bangles – everything that Makende had ever collected. It was filled with great treasure and wealth.

Makende immediately became true to type. He took the pot and, instead of taking it to the old man to whom it belonged, he tried to steal it. But as he hobbled away with the golden pot in his hands, he fell. The pot fell to the ground, spilling its treasure. As Makende fell upon his stomach he felt himself changing. His body grew long, he grew a tremendous tail, and when he cast a glance behind him, he nearly fainted at the sight that befell him.

'I am changing,' he screamed, 'I am becoming a crocodile! No!' When he tried to scream, he could only make the ugly sounds that a crocodile makes through its throat, and hurried into the water.

To this day, people say that in that lake you will still see a lonely crocodile skulking among the reeds. It is the biggest crocodile in the land and there is a strange fear and sadness in its eyes.

It is said that after Makende became a crocodile, he was swimming among the reeds when he saw a young man. The young man stood looking down at Makende and there was a sad smile upon his face. The young man said, 'Makende, I thank you for what you have done. You removed an old curse that had been on my shoulders for many generations.

'By trying to steal my pot, you have broken the spell. Here is my pot on my shoulder; I am taking it home with all its treasure, knowledge and power, and I say to you, oh Makende, thank you very much. May you remain a crocodile for as long as the world shall endure.'

That is the story of Makende. In the land of the Shangani, when people encounter a particularly large crocodile in the river, they often joke about it, saying that it is probably Makende, the trickster and liar.

THE MONITOR LIZARD

The monitor lizard, or leguaan, is a large lizard which may be found in some of Africa's rivers. In the language of the Zulu people, the monitor lizard is called *uxamu,* and African people believe that the skin of this lizard has curative powers. It is said to take away rheumatism when strips of its fresh, moist skin are worn as bangles and as anklets.

This is why, in rural areas, you sometimes find tribespeople wearing strips of monitor lizard skin around their wrists and even around their legs. These people suffer from chronic rheumatism in their limbs and they use strips of monitor lizard skin to ease the pain.

In olden days, when African youths came across a dead monitor lizard in the bush, they took it home, gutted it, dried it and then stuffed it with grass and sewed it up. This stuffed lizard would be used in a very fierce game played by two or more teams over a stretch of land. This game resembled European rugby or soccer. The stuffed lizard was tossed from player to player and the team whose member brought the lizard to the home of the local sangoma was declared the winning team.

The teams chased each other over the marked land, fighting and struggling and kicking and sometimes gouging to gain possession of the stuffed lizard as the whole melée ran towards the home of the local healer. The prize for the winning team in this rather dangerous game was usually a fat ox which was immediately slaughtered and barbecued by the victors, who would then graciously share some of the meat with the losing team.

But there was a ritual punishment in store for the leader of the team that lost. He was seized and smeared with dung from head to foot, and the horns of the slaughtered ox were tied to his head while its tail was tied to the small of his back. He was then forced to dance around, shouting: 'I am an ox! I am an ox! I lost the game! I am an ox!'

Today, of course, most Zulus call a football by a name which is a corruption of the English for 'football', namely *ibhola,* but you will sometimes find some Zulu people in KwaZulu-Natal calling a football by a strange name. The proper Zulu term is *uxamu,* the monitor lizard.

THE IMBEDLE LIZARD

Among the many different types of lizard which may be found in South Africa, there is a lizard, known by the Zulu people as *imbedle*, which looks remarkably like the dinosaurs of old. The *imbedle* lizard is small and fat, and it has sharp spines all over its body, like a miniature dragon.

Zulu, Baca and Xhosa women who find this type of lizard in the bush take it home uninjured, because they believe that it possesses powers to subdue wayward and stubborn husbands. If a woman finds that she is married to a wayward husband who leaves home to wander around in search of other women, she uses the *imbedle* to bring him to heel.

She keeps this little lizard in a basket, holding it in her hands, and she whispers her husband's name repeatedly into the basket. Sometimes she will burn a sweet-smelling herb, and the man will suddenly feel an irresistible urge to return home, no matter where he may happen to be. After that he never leaves his home again, but is always seen sitting either inside his hut or just outside its entrance.

When a man is devoted to his wife and doesn't like to leave his home, even to go to parties with friends, people soon start believing that he has been bewitched by his wife and an *imbedle* lizard.

PRAISE SONG TO THE CHAMELEON

You, of whom the warriors of old were afraid
And you, of whom the men of today are also afraid
Little chameleon, what is the secret of your magic?
Why do the children of Africa hold you in such dread?
Even the bravest will quail at your touch
Even the mightiest will shrink from handling you
Only little children, secure in their innocence, dare hold you in their hands
What is your story, chameleon?
There are those who say that at night, when you are angered, you can swell and swell and grow until you are bigger than an elephant
And that in that guise, as a fearful dragon, you will come to the offender's village and wreak horrible vengeance
There are those who say, chameleon, that you exude a poison, and that if you bite somebody you hate, you inflict a wound that never heals
That is healed only by death
Chameleon, the slow one, *unwabu!*
Chameleon, the beautiful one who changes his colours
Chameleon, the symbol of the *sanusis*, keepers of the hidden wisdom
They taught us in the great huts of grass
They taught us in the caves and in the holes in the ground
They taught us that we should be like chameleons, invisible to our enemies
They taught us to seek the knowledge of long ago and to see both into the future and into the past
To see both into the visible world and into the invisible world
Just as you swing your eyes, one looking forward and one looking backward
So we are taught to be like you

You are an object lesson to all the wise people
You are the totem of all those who keep the ancient knowledge secure
You are the silent one who has never uttered a sound
But about whom so many sounds have been made, so many songs sung
Slow one, weak one, feared by countless kings
I wish I knew your real story!
They say that you bring great luck to the land
They say that when you are seen upon the trees, it is a sign that
  rain will fall – it is true
They say that only those who are chosen by the gods can handle you
  without fear
And those who are pure of spirit can hold you in their hands without dread
They say that the very touch of you can heal many illnesses because you are
  the chameleon – the slowest of the slow
There were those who used to say that a chameleon never dies
Who believed that a chameleon lived for a million years, as they believed the
  tortoise, the turtle, did
Bayete, slow one!
Bayete, chameleon!

THE TERRIFYING CHAMELEON

Africans in South Africa have great fear for a lizard that is nothing more and nothing less than our dear little friend the chameleon. I have never quite understood why many African people are terrified of this harmless reptile.

But perhaps a clue can be found in the names by which this creature is known in various languages in southern Africa. The Zulu people call the chameleon *unwabu*, which means 'the one who moves very lazily', a name which is born of the verb *nwabuluka*, which means 'to move in a very, very slow fashion'. The Botswana people call the chameleon *lebodu*, a strange term which has to do with decay: *bubodu*, 'the rotting one' or 'the one who causes decay'.

It is said that after God had created the Earth, after the great Earth Mother had given birth to human beings, God decided that people should be deathless, unageing and immortal like the gods themselves.

He sent a chameleon to take this message from heaven to the human beings on Earth below. The chameleon left the great golden village of the gods, moving very slowly, each step a sluggish one. It moved from tree to tree and its journey to Earth took many hours and many days. It often stopped on its journey to seek food in the eternal forest and, for the sluggish chameleon, this was a very difficult task indeed. It would sit on a branch for many hours until a gleaming insect flew by on wings of light, and then its tongue would dart out and strike the insect, and it would swallow it. The chameleon could wait many hours for the next insect.

Meanwhile, in the land of the gods, God had changed his mind; he had suddenly realized that if he allowed people to become immortal on Earth, disaster would follow. He realized that death was necessary, otherwise, within a very short space of time, the world would be overcrowded with people and there would be no food and no water left to feed them all.

So God decided to withdraw his gift of immortality from the human race, and sent a second messenger to Earth with his decision. He chose the *indula* lizard, a fast-moving little reptile, to take the message to Earth and the *indula* sped out of the great kraal of the gods. It hurried along the mystic footpaths of heaven, leaping from rock to rock and from tree to tree, and on the way it passed the sluggish chameleon which was filling its belly with insects.

'You have not reached Earth yet, oh stupid and sluggish one,' cried the *indula*, sneering at the chameleon. I shall reach Earth long before you do!'

It was indeed so. The *indula* lizard arrived on Earth and told human beings that all their lives would end in death. It explained to the people why death was necessary for all living things on Earth. The people, hearing the message, accepted God's words and cheered the *indula* lizard as it returned to heaven to report that it had handed the message to the human beings.

By the time the chameleon arrived on Earth with God's first message, the people met it with much ridicule.

'You stupid, scaly little creature,' cried the people, 'you must have slept on the way. We have no time for your words now, for we are following the words of the *indula* lizard. We understand why death is necessary for us and for all flesh-and-blood creatures on this Earth. Now please go away! Leave us! Lose yourself in the bush and fill your belly with flies!'

So the poor chameleon, weeping a flood of tears, slunk away into the bush, not even daring to return to heaven to tell God how it had delayed giving the people the first message. To this day, when African people see their relatives dying, they always blame the chameleon for having been lax in bringing the message from God to human beings.

PRAISE SONG TO THE TORTOISE

Hail, *fudwazana*!
Hail, little tortoise!
You who walk so slowly that a whole year can pass before you reach your grandmother's village!
And yet you who showed the hare
You who showed the jackals
You who showed the elephant
Who is the wisest one of all!
You are the one who carries your own hut on your back
The rain and the wind do not frighten you
The sea and the sand do not frighten you!
You are the one who is always moving
You are the one who lives forever
You are the one who is blessed by the ancestors
You are the one who teaches us about the stars
Ufudu, tortoise
You are in the heavens as the sky above us
You are in the sea as the depths of the terrible waters
You are the one who, our grandmothers say, supports the world as it swims round and round the sun!
You are the one who is the friend of the musician
You are the one who is the friend of the gambling man
They say that if you are kept alive in a place, there is great luck that shall follow that place!
You are the one who dies and awakens
Telling us the meaninglessness of death

Teaching us that the shadow is not to be feared and that the night is
nothing to flee from
You sleep when winter sings her marriage song to the trees
And you waken when spring dances among the mealies in the mealiefield
You are the one who was there before the world began
You are the one who will be there when the world has passed away
You are the one who tells us how long the world has been
You are the one who tells us what will happen in the years to come
You are the perfect one who was blessed by God the Father
many years ago
When you brought sacred snuff to cure the eternal headache of
the All Highest
You are the one who is the darling of the ants
You are the beloved of the grasshoppers
You are the beloved of the sparrows and the swallows and the pigeons
You are admired by the maidens
You are the dear one of the warriors
You are *ufudu*, the one who is always on the move!
You teach us a great lesson, oh tortoise
You teach us a great lesson, oh *fudwazana*
You teach us that no matter how hard the burden of life may be and
how painful
The human being should keep moving
The human being should keep moving!
The witches fear you
The warriors admire you
The young lovers smile at you
For you bring good luck when you cross the path of a wedding procession!
The thieves fear you
For where you are, the thief is afraid to enter
Oh, *fudwazana*
Light of the sangomas

Oh, *fudwazana*
Sun that never sets
Oh, *fudwazana*
Stone that moves
You saw the wagons of the white men trundling over the land
You heard the whistles of the trains as they sped along rails past you
The world moves around you like a whirlwind, a wind gone totally mad
But you are the island of calm in the great turbulence of life
You heard the war-cries of the warriors of Kings Malandela and Shaka
You heard the thunder of the cannons outside the towns of Mafikeng and Kimberley
You hear the sound of the flying machines as they pass through the heavens
And you know that all that will also pass away and be forgotten
For the past is yours
The present is yours
The future is also yours!
May you be blessed, oh tortoise
No matter where you may hide!
They say, they who tell the stories of our father's father's fathers, that you were born of a rock
That your mother was a stone
And because you move so slowly, carrying your terrible burden
The merciful, loving gods, gave you a long life, a life that never ends
Bayete fudu!
Bayete, fudwazana!
Hail, oh little tortoise!

THE ANCIENT ONE

Some ordinary mountain tortoises grow quite big over a number of years and are respected by Africans because they believe that the tortoise, like the snake, the frog and the lizard, were the animals that God first created in this world.

The tortoise is the symbol of longevity, because many tribes in southern and central Africa believe that a tortoise lives for several hundred years. Some of our traditional astrologers believe that the entire universe is in the shape of a tortoise. These people believe that we are all the dreams of this cosmic tortoise, and should the tortoise wake up one day, all creation will fade away.

Wise men and women call this great cosmic tortoise the 'great sleeper' or the 'eternal dreamer'. Some say that the eternal dreamer is not a tortoise at all, but rather a goddess who fell asleep thousands of millions of years ago and who sustains all of creation by dreaming.

Africans believe that the studs on the shell of a tortoise represent the many different worlds that exist somewhere in space.

The small geometric tortoise, called so by scientists, is found in places like the Cape. For years it was used by African fortune-tellers who would study the marks on the tortoise and tell fortunes.

Some African tribes believe that the flesh of a tortoise is an excellent medicine when boiled with certain herbs, and old men and women who suffer from urinary problems are often advised by their sangomas to eat the flesh of a tortoise.

In olden days, African people regarded the tortoise as a symbol of resurrection, because tortoises hibernate during the winter months and then rise from the dark sleep the moment the weather starts getting warm and the trees show signs of awakening.

In ancient times, a number of tortoises were kept by *sanusi* priests in sacred huts which were also used as observatories and in which horoscopes were plotted. These tortoises were always well treated, fed and watered daily while they were still active and then carefully watched and protected while they hibernated during the long winter months.

When the tortoises awoke from hibernation, the rebirth of spring was celebrated. People believed that the great Earth Mother had risen from the underworld and had returned to her golden village in the sky, signalling the coming of the first spring rains.

In traditional African symbol-writing the word for rebirth or resurrection is always represented by a tortoise.

PRAISE SONG TO THE WHALE

I have seen you play, oh whale, upon the waves of the sea
I have heard your mournful song directed at the gods of long ago
Your cornfield is the waves
And your village is the eternal sea
I have seen the waving of your great tail as you dive beneath the waves
Only to rise and surface again
You are the untiring player who plays to delight the gods, the gods that are of old Africa
You are the one who knows all
Our forefathers called you *umkhoma*, the one who knows everything
If only your mouth could speak with human speech, what knowledge we would gain from you!
If only I could shake your hand, what medicines I would learn from you!
You are the lord of the mermaids
The commander of the sharks
You lead the choir of the fishes that dwell under the waters
It is said that many, many years ago your kind were human beings
A noble race of demigods that fought against the dark ones at the birth of creation
Oh whale, may I hear your song before I pass away from this world
May I hear your mournful singing before I return to the grey darkness from which I came
The birds of the sea sing when you appear
The fishes are delighted
And the waves leap high to accompany you as you play to the delight of the sun and the gods of long ago

May you survive for a thousand years and a hundred thousand years more!
May it be that when the last human being upon this Earth has passed into oblivion the song of your kind is still heard upon this world!
Great fish of salvation
Great singer of the oceans
Great dancer of the waves
Oh drinker of the spray that no human mouth can drink
May your road be long, your life be long
And may it never come to an end!

THE MIGHTY WHALE

Africans throughout southern Africa believed that the whale was a supernatural creature. They believed that, like the elephant, the whale was the reincarnation of a dead god. Some tribes believed that whales had been brought to Earth, together with their cousins the dolphins, by the great sea god, Mpangu, to protect the Earth against negative beings and forces.

Africans in KwaZulu-Natal call the whale *umkhoma*, which comes from the ancient Nguni verb *khomo*, which means 'to overcome' and 'to conquer'. Thus, the whale is called 'the conqueror' or 'the all-conquering one'. Our people believed – and modern science has since proven – that whales possess almost supernatural intelligence and are capable of speech. Our people believed, quite correctly, that whales were once land-dwelling animals but were banished and sent to live in the sea by a jealous god.

There is a story which says that whales were originally members of a highly developed race of human beings which inhabited this Earth long before we lesser human beings existed. It is said that these all-conquering people reached great heights of development during their thousands of years on Earth – they even invented immortality. They mastered the deepest secrets of the universe. They could travel from place to place without moving their feet. Simply by thinking of where they wanted to go, they would immediately find themselves there. It was said that these great people, the Mkhomo people, the conquerors of everything, became embroiled in the last centuries of their existence on Earth in a terrible war between themselves and a race of evil entities that had come from the outer darkness. In that war, we are told, the Mkhomo people were unconquerable.

They could snatch streams of fire out of the sun and use them as whips to clear the land of demonic armies. They could use the very ocean, the mighty tidal waves from the sea, to whip away enemy armies within the twinkling of an eye.

It is said that after many years of fighting, the Mkhomo people eventually destroyed the demons which had been threatening their existence. So few were left alive after that great war that the few surviving Mkhomo people asked God to turn them into whales so that they would live in the sea in peace.

Whales still recall the years of greatness they enjoyed while living on land, and sometimes suffer from such a deep depression that they beach themselves on the seashore and die.

Among the Zulu people of days gone by, it was regarded as very unlucky for a school of whales to beach themselves in the territory of a tribe. Whenever Zulus saw a whale trying to beach itself, rolling onto the shore and seeking the dark embrace of death, they would do everything in their power to persuade the animal to return to sea.

Warriors formed long chains with calabashes and clay pots, throwing pots of sea water on the beached whale again and again, while *sanusis* and sangomas sang and played music with rattles and stringed instruments to persuade the suicidal whale to go back to sea and not die on the beach.

When they saw a whale swimming close to shore – peacefully and in good spirits – the Zulu people would beat drums and sing, and try to communicate with the great creature, for they believed that whales are the possessors of the greatest wisdom any living creature may possess.

THE DOLPHIN

THE REDEEMER

The Zulus call a dolphin an *ihlengethwa*, which comes from the verb *hlenga* which means 'to redeem', 'to ransom' or 'to save'. Thus the translation of the Zulu word *hlengeto* is 'the fish of salvation' or 'the redeemer fish'.

The Zulu people believed, as did other nations in other parts of the world, that if a human being fell into the ocean, or was stolen from the seashore by waves and swept far out to sea, he could be saved from drowning, or from being mauled by sharks, by schools of dolphins which nudged the victim towards the shore.

The people also believed that, like the whale, the dolphin is gifted with speech and great telepathic power. When you are undergoing training as a high *sanusi*, you are taught to communicate with dolphins. You are taught the clicks and the grunts which we are told are the language of the dolphin.

It is said that Bushmen could communicate with dolphins with amazing accuracy.

Bushman medicine men and women had the ability to summon a school of dolphins close to shore from far away in the ocean, simply by uttering a long series of clicks and other sounds to which the dolphins never failed to respond.

When I was a young man undergoing training as a sangoma I met an old Bushman on the Wild Coast who worked as a cattleherd for a wealthy Xhosa businessman. This wrinkled old man, who had come to the Wild Coast from the northern Cape, amazed me and my fellow apprentices by sitting for about two hours near the seashore, telepathically communicating with dolphins in the sea.

We watched as dolphins responded to the old man's silent calling. Among these dolphins was a large one with a scar on its dorsal fin. We noticed how this particular dolphin, which the old man called Ximba, never failed to appear in response to a call.

Our people believe that on the day we start communicating with dolphins and whales, great doors of knowledge and wisdom will be opened to us because these marine animals, the *umkhoma* and the *ihlengethwa*, are custodians of knowledge that we wretched human beings have not even dreamt about.

THE SEAL

THE SHEEP OF THE OCEANS

The Zulu people call the seal *imvuyamanzi*, the goat, or rather the sheep, of the oceans. Our people believe that a seal possesses great powers of prophesy, that it can foretell the future with great accuracy. They also believe that it is very unlucky for one to hear a baby seal squealing on the seashore, because it is a sure sign that the person hearing that sound will soon meet with a terrible and sometimes fatal accident. However, it is also said that if you see a seal resting on the seashore, you must offer it a raw fish, and if the seal accepts, you will become a very wealthy person.

THE GIANT SEA TURTLE

The majority of South Africa's people do not realize how close the country once came to an unusual disaster. One of the country's big mining houses planned to mine the sand dunes of St Lucia in KwaZulu-Natal for the metal known as titanium. This plan was bitterly resisted by groups of concerned South Africans, among them the great environmentalist Ian Player.

The mining house explained repeatedly that if mining were allowed to take place in St Lucia it would create many jobs for unemployed people. But the outspoken opposition achieved a turn-about by the mining company. There were those who pointed out that mining would cause irreparable damage to the plant and animal life of the area.

Had the mining operation taken place, a terrible war would have broken out in KwaZulu-Natal between those people who favoured the mining and those who were bitterly against it. For the time being, the threat of mining has been averted and the fragile dune ecosystems on the eastern shores are safe.

But there was another reason why Zulu people in particular bitterly opposed the scheme. The Zulus were told that it was here at St Lucia that the great Earth Mother arrived in *isihlenga*, a large raft made of reeds, bringing with her cattle, sheep and goats, as well as a knowledge of how to heal illnesses in human beings and domestic animals by means of plants and other methods.

At St Lucia there are great sea turtles which Africans call *isixaxa*, which come out of the sea occasionally and crawl over the sand, breathing heavily and with great difficulty, to lay eggs.

These great turtles are sacred to many Africans. It is said that if they were to disappear from the face of the Earth, the seas would dry up, the rivers would fade away and rain would no longer fall from the skies. There is the belief that the *isixaxa* turtle, the large sea turtle, is a custodian of the clouds and guardian of the rain and wind.

Wise African men and women believe that the Earth is contained in a great clay basin which is stuck by some miraculous means to the back of a very great sea turtle. This turtle swims around and around the roaring cooking fire of the gods, which we call the sun. It is said that the sun is a fire, lit by the Earth Mother, which burns eternally in the centre of a small island entirely surrounded by ocean.

A story is told that the gods have, in the past, created and destroyed the Earth many times, and that the Earth in which we live is the sixth Earth that the Earth Mother created. On the day that the Earth Mother completed the creation of the Earth, she placed it in a large clay basin and called out to the great *isixaxa* of the universe, Ngununu, to come out of the sea of eternity and carry the Earth on his back around and around the sun.

But old Ngununu fiercely refused. He told the great goddess that he was sick and tired of gods who created worlds, destroyed them and created them again and again, expecting him, Ngununu, to work day and night carrying the world around the sun.

'You stupid, fat, old witch,' Ngununu is said to have hissed to the goddess from the depths of the ocean. 'You can jump into the ocean of eternity yourself, carry the Earth in your hands, and swim around the sun. I am tired of being ordered around by you.'

The great goddess just smiled at her rebellious subject and sent for her son, uMvelinqangi, who came with his great four-headed dog, Mboneni. When uMvelinqangi asked the turtle to come out of the ocean and was met with an angry refusal, he simply sent Mboneni into the sea to chase the big, stubborn turtle out of the water.

It is said that Mboneni dived into the sea with great pleasure, and when he came out he was dragging the great turtle by the tail. The turtle wept a flood of tears when uMvelinqangi applied a thick layer of gum to its shell and then gently lowered the clay basin, which contained the Earth, onto his back.

'Oh Ngununu', said uMvelinqangi. 'In this world, we are all born to perform certain tasks and no-one should ever try to escape carrying out the duty for which he or she was born.'

We are told that the reason why sea turtles shed such tears when they crawl over the seashore is because they still weep for their ancestor, Ngununu, who was forced to carry the Earth on his back.

THE CRAB

I, Credo Mutwa, am a member of the Mutwa clan which is part of the Msimango tribe, and our totem is a very strange one: a crab, any crab. We are not allowed to harm a crab in any way, whether it is an ordinary freshwater crab, a lobster, or any such creature. If your surname is Mutwa, even if a crab attacks you, you are not allowed to kill it. You must rather avoid the animal by running away.

When I was young, I did not know this. One day I fell victim to a prank played by the boys at boarding school. These boys would tease and torment all new boys in particularly vicious and heartless ways. They tormented me, but I decided that I had to fight back. I fought and kicked and punched until the crowd of young thugs turned tail. I assumed that they would leave me alone, but I was wrong. A number of boys pounced on me, slapped my face, kicked my stomach and one of them shoved a live crab into one of my trouser pockets. I screamed with fear and terror; I ran like a thing gone wild, trying to get rid of the creature in my pocket. I ran into a plantation of poplar trees, removed my trousers, and struck them against a tree trunk, squashing the crab in the pocket to a pulp.

Shortly afterwards I became haunted by strange nightmares in which the dead crab figured again and again. These dreams were so frightening that I woke up screaming with terror, night after night, until I became so ill that the missionaries wrote to my relatives and asked them to fetch me from the boarding school.

The illness haunted me for two years until my father's brother, against my father's wishes, took me to see a sangoma. (My father had, by this time, joined the Christian Science Church, which strictly forbids the use of all medicinal preparations and any contact with doctors and traditional healers.)

The sangoma threw the bones of divination and told my father's brother that the reason I was sick was because I had unwittingly brought about the death of an animal which was very sacred to me. The sangoma wanted to know what type of animal it was that I had killed. I told my father's brother about the crab I had killed before I became sick, and the sangoma said: 'Yes, that is it!'

She asked me whether or not I had known that the crab was my family totem. I told the sangoma that I had no such knowledge as no-one had told me about the crab being the totem of the Mutwa family.

In the years I have been a traditional healer I have come across many cases similar to mine – where an African had killed an animal which he had not known was his family totem, and had thus, sooner or later, brought disaster upon himself and members of his family. Even now, I do not really know why this happens.

Life is truly a strange thing.

Love, Sex, and Democracy in Japan during the American Occupation

Mark McLelland

palgrave
macmillan

Love, Sex, and Democracy in Japan during the American Occupation

First published in 2012 by
PALGRAVE MACMILLAN® in the United States – a division of
St. Martin's Press LLC, 175 Fifth Avenue, New York, NY 10010.

Where this book is distributed in the UK, Europe and the rest of the world, this is by Palgrave Macmillan, a division of Macmillan Publishers Limited, registered in England, company number 785998, of Houndmills, Basingstoke, Hampshire RG21 6XS.

Palgrave Macmillan is the global academic imprint of the above companies and has companies and representatives throughout the world.

Palgrave® and Macmillan® are registered trademarks in the United States, the United Kingdom, Europe and other countries.

ISBN 978–0–230–12059–4

Library of Congress Cataloging-in-Publication Data

McLelland, Mark, 1966–
Love, sex, and democracy in Japan during the American Occupation / Mark McLelland.
p. cm.
Includes bibliographical references.
ISBN 978–0–230–12059–4 (alk. paper)
1. Sex—Japan—History—20th century—Sources. 2. Sex customs—Japan—History—20th century—Sources. 3. Sex role—Japan—History—20th century—Sources. 4. Social change—Japan—History—20th century—Sources. 5. Japan—Social conditions—20th century—Sources. 6. Japan—History—Allied occupation, 1945–1952. I. Title.
HQ18.J3M39 2012
306.70952'0904—dc23 2011032116

A catalogue record of the book is available from the British Library.

Design by MPS Limited, A Macmillan Company

First edition: January 2012

10 9 8 7 6 5 4 3 2 1

Printed and bound in Great Britain by
CPI Antony Rowe, Chippenham and Eastbourne

Contents

Illustrations

A Note on Japanese Names and Sources

The bulk of primary sources for this book reside in the Gordon W. Prange Collection, the originals of which are housed in the library of the University of Maryland. The Prange collection contains virtually everything that passed across the desks of the Civil Censorship Detachment set up by the Occupation authorities to ensure that materials published in Japan during the first three years of the Occupation met with Occupation guidelines. There was very little published at the time that did not go through this precensorship process and the Prange collection houses the vast bulk of all material published in Japan between 1945 and 1949. Microfiche of the collection are available at the University of Michigan and also at the National Diet Library in Tokyo. Material for the book was sourced from both these locations. The collection *Kasutori shimbun: Shōwa 20-nendai no sesō to shakai*, edited by the Kanshū shimbun shiryō raiburarī, and published by Ôzorasha in 1995, is also an excellent source for pulp periodicals of the time. Reference was also made to my substantial personal collection of original early postwar sex magazines obtained on the second-hand market as well as originals held by the Hentai Shiryōkan museum in Kagurazaka, Tokyo.

Japanese names are notoriously difficult to transliterate accurately. I have, where possible, checked pronunciations against records held at the National Diet Library but sometimes have had to make an educated guess at obscure authors' given names. I have followed Japanese tradition in listing names with surname first except when referring to Japanese authors published in English where I follow the Western order. Japanese terms and place names now common in English have been rendered without macrons in the text, however, when they appear as part of a citation in Japanese, they have been transliterated with the appropriate macrons.

Acknowledgments

This book was partly funded by a 2008 Discovery grant from the Australian Research Council and I am grateful to the Council for their continued support of my work. The idea for the book came about during my time as the 2007/08 Toyota Visiting Professor at the Center for Japanese Studies at the University of Michigan where I was able to access the microfiche of the Gordon W. Prange Collection housed in the graduate library. I would like to express my gratitude for the support and encouragement of Kenji Nikki, the Japanese librarian at the time, for his encouragement and support. I would also like to thank members of the CJS, in particular Mark West, Jane Ozanich, Jennifer Robertson, and Micah Auerback for their hospitality. I was fortunate to be able to do further work on the manuscript while a Visiting Fellow in Japan, at Sophia University's Institute for Comparative Culture in 2010 and Oita University's Center for International Education and Research in 2011. I would like to thank James Farrer (Sophia) and Kazumi Nagaike (Oita) for their kind hospitality during these visits. Material in Chapter 4 was first presented in the paper "Kissing Is a Symbol of Democracy," that appeared in volume 19, issue 3 of *The Journal of the History of Sexuality* in 2010. I would like to thank Matt Kuefler the journal's editor and the two anonymous referees for their comments.

A large number of colleagues have offered links to sources, encouragement, criticism, and advice at various stages of this book's journey. These include Matt Allen, Jeffrey Angles, Tomoko Aoyama, Jan Bardsley, Julia Bullock, Christine de Matos, Alissa Freedman, Sabine Fruhstuck, Todd Henry, Vera Mackie, Fran Martin, and James Welker. I would also like to thank Yumiko Ozawa, Katsuhiko Suganuma, and Masafumi Monden for their help in sourcing and cataloguing the many Japanese-language materials on which this volume is based.

Introduction

The idea for this book came about while seated reviewing some early postwar publications in the unfortunately named "Perverts Museum" in Kagurazaka, Tokyo, in 2004.[1] I was at that time collecting documents about early postwar sexual minority subcultures for my book *Queer Japan from the Pacific War to the Internet Age*. Although I was mainly interested in nonheterosexual expressions of sex and romance at the time, one illustration in a very dog-eared copy of *Modan Nippon* (Modern Japan), a kind of general-interest pulp magazine common in the years following the end of the war, caught my eye. The illustration accompanied an article on the newly introduced practice of coeducation. Here is what I wrote in my research diary at the time:

> Magazines such as *Modan Nippon* were instrumental in disseminating information that helped generate new modes of heterosexual interaction. The July 1949 edition, for instance, carried an article on "co-education" in which film actor Gary Cooper was held up as a model of masculine chivalry. It was suggested that many men were nervous about how to conduct a date—whether it was necessary to take a bath before hand, for example. The illustration shows a classroom full of mixed-sex couples wearing surgical masks as the instructor writes "kiss" on the blackboard.[2]

I wrote a memo to myself to "check this out further" before getting back to my search for articles about early postwar male prostitution. The chance to check out this kind of pulp publication finally came about in 2007 when I was invited to take up the post of Toyota Visiting Professor of Japanese in the Center for Japanese Studies at the University of Michigan. I knew that the Michigan Graduate Library owned one of very few copies of the microfiche collection of magazines and newspapers from the Gordon W. Prange Collection housed at the University of Maryland.[3] The Prange collection comprises the galley proofs of all publications submitted for precensorship to the Occupation authorities from 1945 through 1949 and contains practically everything published in Japanese during that time. I was thus not only able to revisit the *Modan Nippon* article I had discovered earlier, but to collect hundreds more on the topic of new dating practices that had entered Japan as a consequence of the country's defeat and occupation by the Allied forces.

The sheer volume of discussion about supposedly "new" and "modern" practices of courtship and romance, as well as an entire genre instructing young Japanese people in sexual technique was astounding. It is estimated that between 1946 and 1949 there were between 700 and 1,000 editions of magazines and newspapers published that included reports, articles, editorials, and stories that in various ways celebrated postwar "sexual liberation."[4]

As a sociologist I struggled with how to make sense of this sudden outburst of discussion about sex and romance and the many detailed instructions that Japanese people were supposed to follow in order to fully "liberate" their sexuality, a prerequisite it seemed for full participation in modern, democratic society. It just so happened that at that time I was developing an undergraduate course titled "Body and Society" that used the idea of the "habitus," as elaborated in the work of Marcel Mauss and Pierre Bourdieu, to explain to students how people's experience of embodiment differs between genders, cultures, and time periods. For Mauss, the habitus was a conglomeration of "techniques of the body"—socially engendered ways of using the body that differ markedly between "societies, education, proprieties and fashions, [and] prestiges."[5]

Bourdieu extended the idea of the habitus beyond bodily practices to include beliefs and prejudices, arguing that seemingly objective social structures are incorporated into the subjective, mental experience of social agents. Bourdieu's idea of the habitus is much more inclusive than that of Mauss; he refers to the habitus as a set of "dispositions" that he defines as enduring sets of *beliefs* and corresponding actions.[6] In his discussion of the habitus, Bourdieu points to a range of preferences for material goods and services such as clothes, furniture, food, music, and leisure activities. For Bourdieu these objects and lifestyle choices have significant symbolic power and are imbued with both social and cultural capital.

Back in the 1920s Mauss had already observed that "Hollywood cinema" was a major conduit via which American bodily actions and lifestyles were being globalized on account of the "prestige" that accrued to these representations.[7] During the Occupation, this process of acculturation, as Japanese people were introduced to a dazzling array of American consumer goods and lifestyles, gathered pace. One aspect of Japanese life that was to be radically impacted in only a short span of time by newly imported American models was courtship behavior. In particular, demonstrating one's ability to engage in new, modern, "democratic" styles of courtship became an important way of acquiring social capital in postwar Japan.

The habitus is a set of learned behaviors. Different individuals develop different kinds of habitus depending on the social situations or "fields" they encounter. Bourdieu uses the example of sport in which athletes develop a "feel for the game," which becomes second nature and automatic. As Bourdieu also points out, the rules of the game are arbitrary, as are the rules for all human interactions, and yet they come to seem "natural" to the participants through "a long, slow process of autonomization."[8] Social "fields" are highly dependent upon factors such as class, gender, ethnic grouping, and educational background. Individuals who have been socialized into the appropriate habitus for a given situation seem to fit into that situation seamlessly whereas others, for whom that situation is unfamiliar, feel conspicuous and out of place.

If we consider American-style courtship routines to be a new kind of "field" introduced into Japan after the war, not only through imported Hollywood movies but also through the very visible presence of the many GIs and their Japanese girlfriends on the streets and in the parks of Japan's major cities, then we can begin to understand why the press was so full of advice on how to navigate this new set of relations. Unlike Americans, who had been socialized to interact in a flirtatious and friendly way with the opposite sex since childhood,[9] the practice of dating prior to marriage, in which a young man or woman might "go steady" with several partners before finally committing to marriage was unknown among the Japanese.[10] In Japan most marriages were still arranged by parents, and "women from good families," at least, had very little opportunity to interact with their betrothed prior to the wedding day itself. Men, although free to consort with "professional women" of the pleasure districts, were likewise unable to court respectable women. Opportunities to learn the rituals of dating through participating in mixed social gatherings were basically nonexistent prior to the war's end. Hence, it is no wonder that increased "*danjo kōsai*" (male-female social interaction) struck many early postwar commentators as one of the most notable changes that the Occupation had brought about.

The realization that dating as a "field" of behavior was largely unknown in Japan helped me understand why such a massive advice industry sprang up in the popular press offering to instruct young men and women how to conduct themselves on a date. However this advice went much further than walking arm in arm, hand-holding, and kissing, and also extended to detailed instruction in sexual techniques. Why might this have been necessary? When thinking through this issue I found the notion of "sexual scripting" developed by sociologists William Simon and John Gagnon to be particularly useful. In the 1960s, Simon and Gagnon, influenced by emerging theories of social interactionism, developed a theory of sexual behavior that stressed the importance of environmental and historical factors over purely physiological or personal elements. They argued that "there is no sexual wisdom that derives from the relatively constant physical body. It is the historical situation of the body that gives the body its sexual (as well as all other) meanings."[11]

Their research showed that sexuality was constructed in terms of what they term "cultural scenarios" that "not only specify appropriate objects, aims and desirable qualities of self-other relations but also instruct in times, places, sequences of gesture and utterance."[12] It is these "qualities of instruction" that ensure that individuals are "far more committed and rehearsed at the time of our initial sexual encounters than most of us realize."[13] They posited that sexual behavior was "essentially symbolic" and that "virtually all the cues that initiate sexual behavior are embedded in the external environment."[14]

Simon and Gagnon's argument is an early iteration of the "social constructionist" approach to sexuality whose most famous proponent is Michel Foucault. Foucault argued that sexuality is not an inherent property of bodies, some kind of transcultural biological reality, but rather "the set of effects produced in bodies, behaviors, and social relations by a certain deployment deriving from a complex political technology."[15] This insight has important implications for sexuality studies since it helps us understand how seemingly "personal" experiences such as sexual responsiveness are in fact highly structured in relation to the transnational movement of power, people, ideas, and imaginaries. As Fran Martin reminds us, sexualities are not "inert, autochthonous forces planted in the soil of a given location" but rather "densely overwritten and hyper-dynamic texts caught in a continual process of transformation."[16] To build on Martin's metaphor, Japan's Occupation period was characterized by a voluble sexual discourse in which previous attitudes toward sex and the body were quite literally being rewritten in line with new orthodoxies and ideas encouraged by the Occupation authorities and disseminated through media such as radio, film, literature, and the press and through the very visible presence of American men and women on the streets.

Japan's catastrophic defeat at the end of the Pacific War and its occupation by mainly US forces from 1945 to 1952 ushered in a period of great social and cultural change in the realms of individual subjectivity and personal relationships as much as in the spheres of government, education, and the economy. Simon and Gagnon note that such periods of dramatic social change "have the capacity to call into question the very organization of the self"[17] and it is possible to understand the collapse of Japan's imperialist regime—and its supporting ideologies—at the end of the Pacific War as just such a moment, during which "the very ecology of the self

[was] disturbed."[18] Simon and Gagnon go on to argue that such moments require that "all aspects of the self that previously required a negotiated outcome must be re-established."[19] Hence, given the sudden collapse of Japan's imperialist regime and its attendant symbolic representations of appropriate gendered and sexual behavior, which occurred alongside the introduction of new and very visible representations of sex and gender embedded in American culture, it is not surprising that there should have been so much discussion in the early postwar press about the need to renegotiate and redefine male-female relationships.

Insights gained from Mauss, Bourdieu, and Simon and Gagnon have framed the overall argument of this book, although in the interests of readability I have avoided burdening the discussion with too much academic terminology. The essence of my argument is that far from being a "natural" outcome of attraction between the sexes, dating practices are learned behaviors that have symbolic value. The actions that we perform on a date, the "techniques of the body" such as walking arm in arm, smooth talking, and kissing are brought into play in the context of broad "cultural scenarios," that is, ways of understanding one's body and desires in relation to wider systems of thought that explain, contextualize, and naturalize ways of acting and thinking that are, in fact, highly artificial and contrived. Dating practices, like other "fields" of action, usually change quite gradually over time but in early postwar Japan we are able to discern a rapid transformation in male-female interactions that was widely remarked on by commentators at the time and that can be reconstructed to some extent through an analysis of contemporary media reports.

In this book I argue that despite the continuity of a masculinist bias in the construction of female sexuality, a series of disjunctures did take place between prewar and postwar attitudes toward male-female relations. Of particular importance was the clear connection made in the Japanese press of the Occupation period between the loosening of "feudal" strictures restraining individuals' bodily behavior, particularly between the sexes, and the process of "democratization." In the chapters that follow I try to unravel the manner in which the presence and actions of American *bodies*, fashions, and cultural products on the streets of Japan were as important as any political directive in bringing about a reassessment of Japanese male-female relations and of sexuality more generally. I suggest that this "bottom up" account, which pays attention to "sexual scripts" in the popular media, offers a different perspective from other accounts of the period that have stressed the influence of top-down policy on sexual behavior and attitudes.

Despite its focus on the new kinds of sexual discourse that exploded onto the cultural scene only six months after the arrival of the Americans, this book is not about American-Japanese relations. The multiple relationships that were established between American male Occupation personnel and Japanese women have been the subject of intensive scrutiny by other scholars.[20] Instead, this book focuses on the varied conversations and conflicts that took place *between Japanese themselves* concerning the "liberation of sexuality" that had supposedly been brought about by such factors as the collapse of the old militarist ideology, the lifting of the prewar censorship regime, the widespread reform of legislation relating to women's domestic and public roles, and the introduction of Hollywood lifestyles and romance. Indeed, because of the new censorship regime imposed by the Occupation authorities that prohibited, among other things, reference to fraternization, little mention is made of Americans in the bulk of texts on which this study is based. The focus, then, is very much upon the new scripts and paradigms for sexual interaction between Japanese men and women (and between men and between women) that were elaborated during the Occupation period that lasted from August 1945 to April 1952. Also, since even after the abolition of the prepublication censorship system in October 1949, a limited postcensorship system was maintained, some reference is made to texts published from 1952 to 1955 that look back on the Occupation period and offer reflections that it may have proven difficult to publish while American authorities still held sway in Tokyo.

The sources for this study are derived from the popular Japanese press of the period. By "popular"[21] I mean publications that addressed a broad readership, and that were cheap and easily accessible across Japan and not just in the major cities. The largest number of texts is taken from a genre that was known at the time as *kasutori* ("the dregs"). The history and typology of this genre are outlined in Chapter 3 but basically it comprised hundreds of short-lived newspaper and magazine titles published over a three-year period from 1946 to 1949 that took as one of their main themes the supposed "liberation" of sexuality. These texts were well circulated throughout Japan, contained articles by established as well as amateur writers, and many of the issues they addressed were taken up by other media such as literature, film, and the popular dailies. Although sometimes described as the "sex press," *kasutori* publications were characterized more by the great detail their authors lavished on sexual topics rather than by their coverage of sexual topics per se. The publication in America in 1948 of the Kinsey report into the sexual behavior of American men, in particular, provided an enabling context for the widespread and detailed discussion of sexuality that also took place across the Japanese mainstream and high-brow press.

Specific behaviors, such as the newly discovered (or reinvented, depending on who you believe) practice of kissing were widely discussed in both *kasutori* and mainstream outlets, including in the newly revitalized genre of movie magazines. The upsurge in male prostitution, which might seem a niche interest, was also taken up by the popular dailies, as were reports of female cross-dressers. Throughout the book I have done my best to search out a range of different sources including popular journalism, middle-brow commentary, and "expert" sexology in order to give a sense of the variety of opinions available on any one topic as well as the relative appeal that these issues held for the Japanese reading public.

Writing at a remove of over 60 years from the period described, our access to the lived realities of everyday life under the Occupation necessarily comes from accounts published at the time. Quite how these accounts relate to actual lived experience, especially in the personal realm of sexuality, is difficult to know. With this in mind, in this book I am mainly concerned with shifts in "discourse," that is, the ideas, "scripts," and "cultural scenarios" that were on offer in the media to help guide, structure, and make sense of sexual relations in the new "democratic" environment ushered in after Japan's defeat. However, where appropriate I have also pointed to some contemporary and later surveys that directly address the issue of behavior. Surveys of people's sex lives, as the controversy following on from the publication of the first Kinsey report attests, cannot of course be offered up as conclusive proof of actual behaviors. I offer this data here as yet another example of a discursive shift in postwar rhetoric about sexuality. This survey data is important not so much because it "proves" that a change in behavior had taken place, but rather for the way it was used in the popular press to establish "norms" to gauge individual practice. I have also made use of contemporary and more recent Japanese scholarship on the sexual customs of the Occupation period to give a sense of how this material has been discussed in the Japanese literature.

Outline of the Book

Chapter 1, "Love, Sex, and Marriage on the Road to War," offers an overview of the changing ways in which the newly founded Japanese state intervened to control and organize the population's sex lives following on from the reestablishment of imperial rule during the Meiji Restoration. Many aspects of previous Edo-period attitudes to sexuality such as the endorsement of concubines and male same-sex relations now came to seem feudal. Differing regional ways of organizing marriage, childbirth, and inheritance were done away with and a new nationwide regime instituting monogamy and marriage registration was set up. However these new patterns of relationship were not simply copied from the West. Indeed, as groups of young Japanese were sent overseas to study and an increasing number of foreign experts took up residence in Japan, the stark difference between Western and Japanese attitudes toward male-female relationships emerged as a contentious topic for debate. Many Japanese struggled to understand the Western concept of "romantic love" that as an ideal, at least, posited equality between the sexes and required that marriage be founded on mutual regard and sentiment. This companionate model of marriage was quite different from the Japanese tradition of arranged marriage and many Japanese felt that "love" was a somewhat egotistic and unstable basis on which to found a lifelong alliance. Although love matches were championed by some among the literati, some feminists and Christian-educated women, they were almost impossible to negotiate in practice since there were few circumstances in which young men and women could associate in public. Until defeat and Occupation in 1945, "male-female social interaction" was highly regulated in Japan.

Relations between the sexes were particularly constrained during the long war years (which for the Japanese began in 1931 with large-scale military incursions into China). As militarism tightened its grip on all aspects of society and censorship took hold of culture, Japan witnessed a "death of romance" as men were imagined as citizen-soldiers and women as mothers to the nation. It is no surprise then, after the long years of privation occasioned by the war, that Japan's eventual defeat was welcomed by many with a sense of relief and liberation from a regime that soon came to be seen as "backward" and "feudal" in its moral scope.

Chapter 2, "Sex and Censorship during the Occupation," looks at the impact that American policies on gender relations, fraternization between US troops and local women, and censorship of the Japanese press had upon the kinds of sexual culture that developed in the early postwar years. Although Japan's defeat and Occupation by the former enemy was experienced as an emasculating humiliation by some men, reforms instigated by the Occupation authorities actually improved the social standing of Japanese women. The constitution was rewritten to establish the equal rights of women, and family and labor laws were restructured so as to give women increased agency both in marriage and at the workplace.

However, the presence of large numbers of American military personnel also put vulnerable women at risk of sexual predation and exploitation. Concerns over the rapid spread of venereal diseases among the US troops led to humiliating crackdowns on the sex workers who catered to them in a range of state-sponsored "leisure facilities." Yet, despite the very obvious presence of sex workers on the streets, little mention was made of them in the press due to a stringent precensorship regime that forbade any reference to fraternization between local women and foreign troops. One unforeseen side effect of the censorship regime was that mention of sexual relations between Japanese themselves went largely unregulated by the US authorities, it being considered the role of the Japanese police to pursue publishers guilty of obscenity. The result was an enormous outpouring of sexual discourse previously unprecedented in Japan.

The first three postwar years have been characterized as a time of "sexual anarchy" during which previous paradigms regulating female sexuality, such as "good wife, wise mother," were in abeyance. Hence, Chapter 3, "Sexual Liberation," looks at the outpouring of sexual discourse in the popular press and considers the claim that Japan's defeat and Occupation had brought about the "liberation of sexuality." After reviewing early postwar rhetoric that attempted to position women as sexual and desiring agents in their own right, the chapter considers the rhetorical linkage made in Japan's early postwar press between new US-inspired heterosexual dating practices and the broader program of democratic reform. It is argued that this linkage facilitated the swift transmission and uptake of more "liberal" American modes of bodily comportment and male-female interaction. It was also during the Occupation that Alfred Kinsey's first pathbreaking study into the sexual behavior and attitudes of American men was translated into Japanese, and there was much discussion in the Japanese press about the role that "science" had to play in overcoming the moralism surrounding people's sexual lifestyles and choices. Kinsey's "American" and "scientific" pedigrees were used by sex reformers to establish the open discussion of sexuality as a fundamental necessity for the development of a modern, democratic, and open society.

Chapter 4, "The Kiss Debate," examines the impact that the physical presence of American bodies on the streets of Japan as well as Hollywood visions of American actors on screen had upon local understandings of physical deportment and gender relations. In particular, the controversies about kissing on the screen and in daily life are examined so as to point out the symbolic linkages made both by Japanese commentators and the Occupation authorities between sexual and political "openness." It is argued that shifts in the scripting of sexual behavior are most clearly visible in the "kissing debate" that was generated by the early postwar screening of Hollywood love scenes and, increasingly, love scenes in locally produced movies. It was openly acknowledged at the time that Hollywood movies, in particular, were the "scripts" being used by young people to negotiate the unfamiliar terrain of dating. The role that popular sexology played in promoting the "new idea" that sex was a recreational activity for men *and women*, a means of sharing *mutual* pleasure, in the context of courtship, is outlined.

Chapter 5, "The New Couple," looks at the new role that "sexual satisfaction" was now considered to play in the marital relationship through a discussion of the influential "couple magazine" *Fūfu seikatsu* (Conjugal couple lifestyle). In the prewar period the representation of marital sexuality had been out of bounds but a new genre of marriage magazines placed a "proper sex life" at the very heart of the "new" or "modern" marriage. These magazines traced a "course" of sexual discovery that dating couples should take from walking side by side, to hand-holding, to kissing and finally to the sexual acts performed on the wedding night. Both male and female partners were encouraged to educate themselves in an "*ars amatoria*" that would help them understand not only their own sexual responsiveness but how to attend to the newly discovered needs of their partners. In these texts American dating practices and American lifestyles in general (complete with all the necessary time-saving home accessories) were held up as an ideal for Japanese couples to follow. The publication in 1953 of Alfred Kinsey's volume on the sex lives of American women further reinforced the perceived need for Japanese women to "catch up" with their more liberated peers.

Although the bulk of sexual discussion in the print media of the early postwar years was heterosexual, it was not particularly oriented toward discussions of procreation. Indeed the previous militarists' reduction of a wife's main role to that of mother was frequently criticized as a "feudal" remnant and the need for mutual pleasure reinforced. Chapter 6, "Curiosity Hunting," investigates the Japanese term *ryōki* that translates as "curiosity hunting"—that was used as a descriptor for a genre of fictional and documentary reports about "strange" sexual activities and people. The *ryōki* paradigm embraced and even celebrated the strange and unusual in sexual practice, and was important in disseminating new ideas about female sexual agency through its discussions of sadism, cross-dressing, and female-female sexuality. Also important in this discourse was a discussion of *danshō*, male cross-dressing prostitutes, who were a visible feature of Tokyo's cityscape in the immediate postwar period. Although the sex lives of the "new couple" were very much oriented toward supposed American ideals, the *ryōki* paradigm was indigenous and functioned with little reference to the increasingly paranoid American distinction between hetero- and homosexuality that intensified with the onset of the Cold War. The evidence offered in this chapter is an important balance to some accounts of postwar sex and gender mores that stress the conservative and restrictive nature of sex reform during the Occupation.

The Afterword considers the extent to which the sudden upsurge in discourse about the "liberation of sexuality" was representative of changes in people's lived experience. As much other research into the Occupation period has shown, celebrating the new at the expense of the old was something of a postwar obsession. In many ways, as later Japanese feminist critique was to make clear, ideas about female sexuality that had been embedded in the "family state" ideology of the prewar period were carried through into recent times. However, there are too many contemporary accounts pointing to a shift in perspective among the "*apure*" generation (that is, *après guerre*, or postwar) to support the idea that relationships between the sexes remained fundamentally unchanged. That courtship was taken up *en mass* by young Japanese people was testified by endless accounts of "young couples on the streets" that appeared in the press. That the courting couple emerged as one of the most conspicuous symbols of the postwar period is evidence that the "cultural scenarios" governing male-female relations had indeed shifted. A more generous approach to minority sexual interests, too, which was first fostered in the "curiosity hunting" genre of the pulp press, lived on throughout the postwar period supported by a new generation of sexologists. Although theirs were not the voices influencing public policy, they did help establish a field of "queer studies" in Japan that is only now being reclaimed by contemporary sexuality scholars.

1

Love, Sex, and Marriage on the Road to War

Although love and marriage may well go together like the proverbial horse and carriage, neither love marriages nor horse-driven transport were part of Japan's social landscape prior to the "opening" of Japan to the West by Commander Perry of the US East India fleet in 1853. At that time Japanese people had hardly had any contact with the wider world for over 200 years due to the policy of national seclusion (*sakoku*) that had been enforced by the Tokugawa shoguns, the country's military leaders. During that period Japanese people were banned from leaving the country and only minimal foreign trade was permitted with Dutch and Chinese emissaries, mediated exclusively through a small offshore island in the southern port of Nagasaki. The circulation of foreign ideas, particularly information about Christianity, was heavily censored and even in-country trade and the movement of people were closely scrutinized and regulated by the authorities.

Given this long period of relatively peaceful seclusion during which Japanese people had not had cause to trouble themselves about foreign ways, the sudden irruption of American gunships into their world was massively disorientating and within 15 years had brought about the downfall of the powerful Tokugawa regime that had ruled Japan since 1600. The sudden realization that while Japan's rulers had been preoccupied with internal concerns, the United States, a vast and powerful new force, had arisen and was now challenging both China and the European powers for hegemony in the Pacific region certainly proved disorientating. However, the more astute among Japan's rulers and intellectuals realized that the United States and other Western powers had developed technology that so far exceeded that of Japan and China, that Japan must engage with Western science or otherwise fall prey to the same process of colonization that saw Japan's immediate neighbors unable to resist the incursion of Western influence in the region.

From the early 1860s Japan embarked on an enormous learning curve, sending young scholars overseas to the capitals of culture in Europe and the United States to learn everything possible about the running of a successful modern nation. Large numbers of foreign experts were invited into Japan, too, to teach about their respective languages, cultures, and technologies. Eager to respond to this widespread hunger for new knowledge, the Japanese publishing industry became a huge translating machine, making available not just medical and scientific tracts, but translations of Western literary classics, philosophy, religion, and, increasingly, popular reading. Japanese people's encounter with foreign ways and ideas, both in the flesh and via translated texts, proved shocking to many.

One of the most disorientating issues for many Japanese was the relatively free and easy association that existed between the sexes in Western nations, especially in high society. In a culture that was still strongly Confucian in orientation, elite women in Japan were extremely constrained in their movements and activities and had very little influence outside the home. Hence, the apparent freedom and agency that Western women exerted in running their own lives, participating in social events, and even organizing their own marriages, seemed peculiar if not downright immoral. Also odd was the extreme deference that Western men paid to their "ladies," at least in public. Although in the Confucian system men of lower status were able to show respect to high-status women without compromising their masculinity, the Western practice of "ladies first" in which men deferred to women in general seemed a peculiar idea, one that was still able to amaze Japanese people even in the early days of the American Occupation that was to take place almost a century later.

This chapter lays the groundwork for understanding this clash of ideas about the role and nature of women through looking at how Western ideas about marriage, sexuality, and romantic love were variously negotiated and challenged in Japan during the decades leading up to the Second World War. We first consider the ways in which the new Meiji state sought to redefine and integrate marriage into the nation-building project, partly through reimagining the imperial couple as ideals of marital harmony and civic duty. We also look at how the new emphasis on monogamous marriage as the foundation of the modern state led to a domestication of sexuality and a narrowing of acceptable sexual practice and gender roles for both men and women. Not only was the conjugal couple given a central role to play through structural changes to Japan's legal code, but the marriage bond was also made discursively central through the incorporation of Western romantic love ideology. Yet not everyone in Japan was comfortable with the new stress on the importance of sentiment within marriage and we look at some social commentators who criticized the "egotism" that they felt underlay love marriages.

Official ideology that stressed the importance of chastity and monogamy in the conjugal marriage was emerging at precisely the same time that Japanese society was being restructured from an agrarian to an industrial economy. In the early decades of the twentieth century the population of the cities grew at an alarming rate and many people from relatively conservative country areas were suddenly exposed to all the distractions and temptations of big city living. We look at reformers' concerns about the "harmful" effects of city life, and of modernity in general, particularly as they surfaced around the media's growing interest in stories featuring "erotic, grotesque nonsense." One of the main anxieties voiced in the 1920s surrounded the sudden appearance of "modern girls" out and about on the streets, tramways, and trains of Japan's big cities. With their hair cut short and wearing trendy Western clothes, the "*moga*" as they were termed, problematized the cultural connection made between the female gender and domesticity. However, the onset of war with China in 1937 saw the modern girl disappear from the pages of Japan's press as women, alongside men, were coopted into the war effort. Wartime saw a narrowing of gender roles and a greater surveillance of individuals' sex lives. Women, in particular, were encouraged to "bear children and increase the population," whereas men were offered a range of options for the "hygienic" management of sexual desire. During that time signs of "decadent" Western influence were expunged from popular culture—jazz, dancing, permanent waves, even blue-eyed dolls all faced official ire. It is little surprise then that by the war's end the population was thoroughly exhausted by both physical and emotional privation.

Changing Views of Sex and Marriage

Attitudes toward appropriate sexual relations between men and women changed rapidly in the decades following on from the Meiji Restoration. In feudal Japan, appropriate sexual behavior had depended to a large extent upon class and gender. With regard to marriage, men had much more freedom in choice of partner than did women but lower-class women faced fewer constraints than did women of the merchant class. Women of the samurai class, who had important roles to play in the management of the patrilineal family line, were particularly constrained. Poor rural women had more agency in choice of sexual partner than did women in the cities since folk religion, which remained strong in rural areas, was primarily interested in promoting fertility, not chastity, and it was usual for women to have had sexual experience with several men before getting married.[1] The traditional practice of *yobai*, or "night crawling" where young men would visit unmarried women at their parents' homes at night is well recorded in the Japanese ethnographic record and is documented as occurring as late as the 1920s.[2] Yet, although fertility was a prized attribute in a woman, among the rural poor in particular, it was not unusual to practice abortion and even selective infanticide (particularly of female children) as a means of population control. No religious or social opprobrium seems to have been attached to these practices.[3]

Marriage in feudal Japan had been a fairly loose institution. Since the propagation of the male line was paramount, a wife's infertility was grounds for divorce or reason to take a concubine. As well as one official wife, men of means were able to keep one or several concubines, often under the same roof, and the children resulting from these liaisons would be reared as part of the one family with the official wife being publicly acknowledged as the children's mother. Marriage was considered a purely secular affair, there were no wedding "ceremonies" to speak of, and marriages were frequently not registered with the authorities. Divorce was easily obtained and both men and women had the freedom to terminate unsuccessful unions.[4] Little stigma was attached to divorce and it was not unusual for divorced women to remarry since there was "no sacred or secular barrier to their doing so."[5]

"Sexuality," too, such that this Western term relates to the Edo-period notion of *iro*, probably best translated as "eroticism," was also less restricted than in the Western Christian context. In Japan no stigma was attached to masturbation and sex manuals happily offered instruction in the practice. Masturbating figures, particularly women, could be seen in the sexually explicit *shunga* or "spring pictures" produced by some of the most popular woodblock print artists of the time. Devices such as dildos to help with self-pleasuring were openly advertised and sold.[6] Both male-male and female-female sex acts were also depicted in *shunga* and stories featuring love between males, spoken of as *shudō*, or the "way of boys" and *nanshoku*, or "male eroticism," were standard fare both in literature and on the stage.[7]

Despite being heir to a certain Confucian prudery that regarded sexual excess with disdain, Japan was also heir to a long tradition of Chinese Daoist ideas about sexuality expressed in medical treatises that suggested exercises for the optimum exchange of yin and yang energies during sexual intercourse. Japan's own native Shinto tradition was also much concerned with fertility, and the union of male and female principles in coitus was seen as an act pioneered by the gods themselves. Although some sex manuals of the time referred to the role that the male deity Izanagi had taken in instigating sex with his female partner Izanami as establishing the male as the "leader" in sexual encounters, others stressed the mutuality of the sex act.[8]

That women could and should experience sexual pleasure was not disputed and, indeed, the number of texts offering advice on female self-pleasure underline the importance that was given to female sexual satisfaction at the time. However, as Anne Walthall has pointed out, Edo-period perspectives on female sexual response represent a "historical dead end" in that this knowledge was largely forgotten and this erotic tradition eclipsed as Japan attempted to refashion itself in line with modern European societies where "self pleasure" was seen as "self pollution" and homosexuality as a crime.[9] It was not until the early postwar period that sexologists such as Takahashi Tetsu would encourage Japanese people to reclaim these early-modern texts in the search for culturally appropriate expressions of a "liberated" Japanese sexuality.[10]

Following on from the Meiji Restoration, a range of state-sanctioned programs undertaken in the name of "civilization and enlightenment" sought to distance Japan from its feudal past and establish the nation on a competitive level with the modern nation-states of the West. Diverse feudal customs and behaviors were done away with in the attempt to build a unified modern nation—and attempts were made to discipline and rationalize marriage and sexual reproduction. A law enacted in 1873 required all marriages to be registered with local authorities by having the bride's name entered in her husband's family register. Since any changes to the register needed the assent of the family head, men under 30 and women under 25 were required to obtain the consent of family elders before contracting a marriage.[11]

Reforms to the Civil Code in 1898 established the "household system" (*ie seidō*) as the basis for Japanese society and introduced measures that sought to organize, rationalize, and control all aspects of the population from early education through to marriage and child-rearing. Within this system the basic unit of the State was not the individual but the male-led household (*ie*), a symbol of the nation in microcosm, in which the male head wielded considerable power and each member had to abide in his/her proper place.[12] The Code "fused in the public mind filial piety and loyalty to the Emperor—so much so that legal scholars of the time spoke of Japan as a 'family state' (*kazoku kokka*)."[13]

The new Civil Code did away with regional and class-based ways of ordering choice of marriage partner, child-rearing arrangements, and property succession. In rural areas marriage had been a loose affair and could be easily ended by the bride returning to her parents.[14] However, the Code made it compulsory to report all marriages and divorces in a nationwide register of family ties known as the *koseki* (family register). The principle of "one husband, one wife" was promulgated, divorce was made more difficult to obtain, and concubines lost all legal recognition. The impacts of the reforms on women were particularly far-reaching:

> Women suddenly found themselves unable to inherit property, assume the headship of households, or divorce husbands according to established custom. They became legal minors and were cut off completely from political activities.[15]

The Civil Code gave male household heads considerable control over all women and younger men in the family, including the right to intervene in the choice of marriage partners. Marriage was not considered to be a purely individual affair but "took on the character of duty toward the house."[16] Whereas in feudal times "personal choice in marriage . . . had been quite customary among people of lower social strata," from then on "only an arranged marriage came to be considered proper."[17] Since upon marriage a new wife was removed from the household register of her natal family and entered into the register of her husband's family, all prospective brides required the approval of the household head. This was important because in the absence of any kind of social welfare, household heads were required to make provision for all members of their family and could be compelled to do so. In most cases potential partners were organized by the head of the family using a go-between who sought out appropriate matches in the community and it was difficult for either prospective brides or grooms to refuse a match once both sets of parents had agreed. The paternalistic nature of the household system was but one part of an overarching patriarchy[18] embedded in the Civil Code that required obedience to senior male authorities—the most senior male figure of all being the Emperor. Within this system objection to patriarchal authority in the home could be construed as objection to the national polity and both community and official sanctions served to render family members acquiescent.

The Emperor, who had been a shadowy figure under the Tokugawa shoguns who effectively ruled Japan from 1600 to 1857, thus took on important symbolic functions within this new system, as did his family. Imperial consorts had previously received little public attention but from the 1890s onward the Emperor's wife and other female members of the royal family began to be portrayed as "paragons of womanly virtue" and as "ideal mothers and wives."[19] Celebrations for the Meiji Emperor's twenty-fifth wedding anniversary were an important turning point and from then on the media began to present the imperial family as "a national model" for all Japanese families.[20] The populace, too, were encouraged to start celebrating their own weddings with elaborate ceremonies and to observe their anniversaries. The marriage of the crown prince (later the Taisho Emperor) was another opportunity to celebrate the new ideal of the monogamous conjugal couple. This took some ingenuity on the part of the press however, since it would not have been fitting to mention that "the reigning emperor was not monogamous and that the crown prince was not the biological son of Empress Haruko."[21] Despite the obvious discrepancies in the actual behavior of the imperial family, the press "praised the younger imperial couple for providing 'the most beautiful and finest model for social customs.'"[22]

In essence, the Meiji Civil Code was an important tool in the broader project of civilization and enlightenment that sought to apply to the population as a whole a fusion of Confucian-inspired samurai values that stressed the superiority of men over women and newly imported Victorian ideas about the importance of monogamy and female chastity. The Confucian-inspired values that underpinned the Code had originally been common only among social elites in Japan but through the new compulsory education system they were gradually rolled out to the population as a whole. As rates of literacy increased among the rural poor, these new ways of thinking about women (and to a lesser extent men) were also promulgated through popular literature and journalism. The previously rather loose attitudes toward premarital sexuality that had been characteristic of rural dwellers began to be brought into line with official ideology. By the 1930s, ethnographer Emma Wiswell noted a gap between conservative village youth and the more liberal attitudes of their parents. She noted that "[f]ar from denouncing the youth of the time for their loose sexual morals, their elders found them positively conservative when compared with themselves when young."[23] The Civil Code was, then, an attempt to standardize and normalize family structures and the roles within them so as to provide a firm basis for national development. By the turn of the century, the dominant discourse was that of the family writ-large, "a 'nation state family' (*kazoku kokka*), in which the imperial household and the people were mystically bound together as a family."[24]

However in many ways the Japanese attitude toward sexuality was only superficially realigned to approximate Western standards. Japan's male legislators were not prudish about the sex act itself but were more concerned with the context and social status of the participants. As Iga Mamoru points out, in Japan it had long been the case that "strict restraint is not [placed] on sex but on [the] improper social context in which sex is expressed."[25] At the same time that women's sexual options were increasingly foreclosed, the authorities maintained a "tacit approval of male sexual freedom." The government imposed "a strict localization of the opportunities for sexual stimulation and enjoyment to brothel or semi-brothel districts whose existence was justified as an essential means of preserving the purity of the home."[26] Despite growing opposition, mainly from a small but vocal class of Christian-educated middle-class women, prostitution was to remain legal in Japan until 1958.

Despite societal tolerance of regulated prostitution, the new principle of "one husband, one wife" did place greater emphasis on marital sexuality, which came to be seen as the only truly moral expression of the sex drive. It was at that time, too, that the monogamous family relationship was established as the ideal and proper environment for the nurture of children. The optimum role for women within this system was that of "good wife, wise mother" (*ryōsai kenbo*), which, by the end of the Meiji period, "came to constitute the official discourse of women in Japan."[27] Women's ideological place at the center of domesticity was further underlined in legislation passed in 1890 that forbade women's participation in public affairs, including political meetings and organizations.

Alongside the new idolization of marital sexuality came debates over the need to preserve chastity (*teisō*), especially for women. The Western notion of "virginity" with its associations of chastity and purity had previously had no clear analogue in Japanese tradition; the closest term was *shōjo*, meaning simply an unmarried woman. Yet, by the end of the nineteenth century, *otome*, a variant reading of the characters for *shōjo*, had emerged to describe the "ideal" young woman—one entirely lacking sexual experience (and in the minds of many, sexual desire).[28] From that time on the new ideas that virginity was a woman's most prized possession and that she must protect it at all costs so that she could "sacrifice" (*sasageru*) it as a gift to her future husband became widespread.[29]

The Taisho period (1912–25) was a time when the "new bourgeoisie" began to set the cultural agenda. Educational reforms that mandated all children complete at least elementary education plus expanded opportunity for women's education at higher levels had resulted in a new literate and upwardly mobile class. However, education in imperial Japan did not necessarily open up new horizons for students, since the education system was not simply about teaching literacy but also ideology. Girls, in particular, were inducted into new ways of thinking about their lives, roles and destinies that did little to encourage freedom of thought or rebellion. A mixture of eugenic ideas from Europe and Christian and Confucian ideals of piety, chastity, and valorization of motherhood were taught to girls and young women, laying particular stress on the importance of maintaining virginity until marriage. Women's role as mothers in the perpetuation and management of the household system was stressed as was the need to preserve the purity of a household's "blood" through appropriate choice of marriage partner. To the extent that women were considered to experience sexual desire at all, it "was inseparably pervaded and guided by their desire to have children."[30]

Yet the ideal of chastity before marriage did not apply equally to all women. There was a conspicuous double standard applied to "daughters of good families" who had to guard their chastity and women from poor backgrounds and from Japan's colonies who were sold or otherwise recruited into the brothel world.[31] Women who were forced for a variety of reasons to work in the "pleasure quarters" were certainly not considered respectable (although it remained a possibility for some women to be bought out of their contracts and to achieve a measure of respectability as wives). However, they were not held in disdain to the same extent as "fallen" women in the Victorian Christian context because most women had not chosen this life but had been sold, tricked, or coerced into it by family members. Their acquiescence to family demands was to an extent understood as a sacrifice and therefore a virtue under the Confucian system. A curious effect of this idea was that even women of the pleasure quarters were not necessarily viewed as libidinous. Sex work was viewed as a "profession," entered into in a spirit of sacrifice, in a manner not dissimilar to the indentured factory work also commonly undertaken by women from poor backgrounds.

So far we have stressed the extent to which marriage for a woman was bound up with her role as wife and particularly mother. Given that before the war marriages, for the social elites at least, were largely arranged by parents in discussion with other family members, the quality of the emotional relationship between the couple was not given much attention. Contrary to the European tradition of romantic love, especially as expressed in literature, there was barely any courtship period to speak of when the prospective couple was able to develop a sense of shared intimacy, respect, and understanding.[32] However this does not mean that "romantic love ideology" (*ren'ai shugi*) was necessarily rejected by the Japanese, nor that this initially foreign idea exerted little influence on popular culture. As we shall see in the next section, the practice of romantic love was widely debated and although "love marriages" were not to become the norm until the postwar period, awareness of romantic love as an ideal did exert considerable influence on Japanese culture.

Romantic Love Ideology

In a compelling study of romantic love in Japanese and European literature, Takayuki Yokota-Murakami[33] advances the provocative notion that romantic love as it was elaborated in European novels at the end of the nineteenth century was a concept unknown in Japan prior to its opening to the West. He notes that "the 'equality' between male and female lovers or spouses described in Western literary discourse was often quite incomprehensible to Meiji intellectuals."[34] There were no terms in Japanese at the time that could adequately express the fusion of spiritual and physical love that underlay Western notions of romantic love. Tokugawa-period literature had certainly much to say about *iro* (eroticism) and *koi* (physical love) but these concepts were elaborated in relation to women of the "floating world" of brothels and never used in relation to wives. Confucian morality, which became increasingly influential in the latter half of the period, saw women as inferior[35] and sometimes evil and certainly not as suitable objects of admiration. To the extent that the Western concept of "romantic love" existed at the time, it was elaborated in the context of tales of "devoted male love" between older and younger samurai.[36]

As Yokota-Murakami points out, prior to the Meiji period Japanese terms dealing with heterosexual attraction were "devoid of the sense of spiritual comradeship that seemed to permeate Western counterparts."[37] Indeed, many of the male Western traders and foreign experts who made their home in Japan after the opening of the country in the 1860s were said to bemoan the "lack of emotional resonance" experienced in their relationships with their local Japanese mistresses.[38] The "submission and docility" of their Japanese lovers, although attractive to some men, left others nostalgic for the more companionate model of heterosexual relations that was part of the European ideal of romantic love.

The absence of a term approximating the English word "love" is conspicuous in early Japanese translations of Western novels where it was sometimes simply transliterated as "*rabu*." One particular problem for translators was the expression of female agency in a romantic love affair. Women in the Confucian system were generally regarded as subordinate in their relationships to men and hence the statement "I love you" spoken by a woman to a male lover would have seemed presumptuous and highly inappropriate. Yokota-Murakami reports how Futabatei Shimei got around this problem in his translation of one of Russian author Ivan Turgenev's novels by rendering "I love you" when uttered by a female character as "I could die for you."[39] To make this rendition intelligible, we need to consider the long history of *shinjū* or "love suicides" in Japanese romantic fiction where the heroine (or sometimes both partners) kill themselves for the sake of a love that is unacceptable to society. In these fictions the tension was between *giri*, that is, obligations due to family and society, and *ninjō* or the human feelings felt by the couple. In Tokugawa-period tales of "love," social obligations usually trump human feelings and many of these stories end with the death of one or both partners. The Western romance genre in which thwarted lovers persevere in the face of social difficulties and finally win respect because of their essentially *spiritual* connection was not part of Japan's literary repertoire.

It was not just Western literary descriptions of romantic love that shocked Meiji intellectuals. Early Japanese visitors to the West, even in chaste Victorian times, had been astonished by the intimacy expressed between mixed-sex couples in public settings such as theaters and at balls and dinner parties. Members of the first embassies sent from Japan to Europe in the 1860s recorded in their diaries that they found the kissing that took place before them "unbearable to look at."[40] Even after 70 years of interaction with Western peoples, the Japanese had not come to accept Western models of heterosocial (that is, mixed-sex) interaction that characterized "polite society" in places such as Paris, London, or New York. In Japan "traditionally, entertainment was designed for men only and supplied by professional women while wives stayed home."[41] In the Western context, women from good families, particularly those of the upper-middle classes and the aristocracy, were *expected to* attend society functions and to entertain at home. Elite Western women were often highly educated, well travelled, cosmopolitan in outlook, and quite capable of debating with their male peers on topics ranging from politics to art. It was commonplace for women renowned for their wit to hold salons in their homes and to be seen about town at society functions. Japanese patriarchal family heads however, evinced "strong resistance" to their daughters attending such public gatherings.[42] Japanese women from "good" families were not to be seen socializing with nonrelatives at mixed-company events and would not have been socialized to mix in such company. When women were required for entertainment purposes, "professional" women from the geisha class were employed. Even at "foreigners' parties" staged by overseas ambassadors or other dignitaries where wives were invited, "women gathered at one end of the room and men at the other."[43] The suggestion by some Christian-educated women that Japan should do more to encourage social interaction between the sexes met with sharp rebuke from male commentators who argued that "social intercourse between the sexes can never be pure; emphasizing platonic love is evil."[44] Japanese people of the Meiji period were simply not used to encountering expressions of affection and respect between male and female couples in the context of public gatherings.

Yet, as Leith Morton notes, "There is no doubt that by mid-Meiji a revolution was underway in regard to notions of love, marriage and the status of women."[45] By that time the notion of "romantic love," connoting elements of spiritual attraction between men and women, was being expressed in the newly coined compound *ren'ai.* This "shocking new perspective"[46] became an important talking point in the Japanese media and was popularized via women's literature and magazines and via Christian educators at private girls' schools. The spread of "Western learning" was blamed for producing the "new woman" who "always insists on equal rights in everything" and even "feels at liberty to propose."[47] Japan's first generation of feminists, including Hiratsuka Raichō, founder of the influential women's journal *Seitō* (Blue stocking), also debated the role of romantic love in the journal's pages. Raichō herself believed that equality for women could be advanced by "the union of spirit and flesh" (*rei niku ichi*) in a love marriage.[48]

Women's magazines featured discussions about romantic love in the context of articles on "the home" that "espoused spiritual love as the basis for the husband-wife relationship."[49] To an extent, the Christianized notion of "the home" (*katei*) based upon equality was in conflict with the hierarchical idea of the family as "household" (*ie*) enshrined in the Civil Code. Indeed, the perceived Christian origins of the notion of romantic love based on respect between the sexes led some thinkers to question its relevance to Meiji Japan. As one Japanese commentator noted, "Every member of the family is either the superior or the inferior of another; therefore the element of comradeship is lacking in the Japanese home."[50] Confucian ideas were still strong at the time and as we have seen the Meiji Civil Code recognized the family unit and not the atomistic individual as the foundation of society. In this worldview romantic love was seen as a radical, dangerous, and self-indulgent emotion that could lead to familial and thereby social disharmony. Hence there was much debate in the press about "whether or not romantic love was moral" and "whether or not it was compatible with the ideology of the Meiji state."[51]

Despite the misgivings of many social commentators, the discourse of romantic love had an enormous impact upon culture generally, especially upon literature. As Jim Reichert has pointed out, lacking indigenous examples, Japanese novelists had to find convincing ways to develop "new literary languages [and] new approaches toward characterization and plot"[52] in order to realistically depict romantic heterosexual relationships. One casualty of this process was that male homosexuality or, rather, *nanshoku* (male-male eroticism) and *shudō* or the "love of youths" that had been well represented in the literature of the previous period[53] was excluded from the new category. Despite this long literary tradition, *nanshoku* was now reduced to "sodomy" (*keikan*).[54] Since it was only through romantic love that lust could be transmuted into spiritual communion, male homosexuality came to be seen as increasingly base and "carnal." Its association with the then discredited "uncivilized" and "feudal" practices of the Tokugawa period further placed male-male eroticism outside the bounds of civilized morality.

Yet, Reichert demonstrates how the characteristically modern notion that "the most profound expression of human emotion is revealed through male-female love"[55] was at first fiercely resisted by some "hard line" (*kōha*) intellectuals, often ex-samurai, who resented the newly imported Western ideas that they saw as challenging traditional modes of Japanese masculinity.[56] For these men, Western notions of dress and deportment characteristic of "high collar" society were seen as self-indulgent and effeminate. The aping of all things Western by some of the nation's leaders was regarded as symptomatic of "a colonized manhood."[57] In particular these critics riled against the European notion of romantic love that placed women on a pedestal, declaring it "an effeminate emotion" that "offended against the canons of masculine superiority."[58] However, despite this early opposition, the spread of Western sexology that pathologized homosexuality, alongside the developing hegemony of romantic love, led to a narrowing of sexual identification and practice. Male homoeroticism did continue as a minor theme in Japanese literature, but as Jeffrey Angles points out, those authors who specialized in this type of fiction had to resort to a range of strategies to disguise their interests.[59] No longer could the "love of youths" be valorized as an ennobling experience or a cultural ideal.

The Meiji state endorsed the "modern family," which came to be viewed as the core unit of social stability and progress and the training ground for an individual's entire moral education. A new discourse of familial love (despite the lived realities of the family system) held love and fidelity between husband and wife to be the "pinnacle of reason and emotion," and, indeed, the greatest pleasure in human life.[60] The ideology of romantic love also came to be conjoined with new sexological perspectives that regarded romantic love as having an alchemical effect upon sexual desire sublimating it from mere "lust" into an almost spiritual communion between husband and wife. Love then came to be codified as an explicitly heterosexual sentiment, the experience of which was seen as an important aspect of self-realization for both men and women. Hence, throughout the first three decades of the twentieth century a range of writers pursued the notion of romantic love "as central to their own lives as well as to their literary creations."[61] Yet, although male-male romantic liaisons fell victim to this new system, female-female relations were treated somewhat differently.

Prior to Japan's defeat and occupation, education had been strictly sex-segregated and there were very few circumstances in which male and female young people could mix socially. During the early decades of the twentieth century, the number of high schools and junior colleges for girls increased dramatically and large numbers of girls and young women were brought together from around Japan and put into close proximity in boarding houses. These close living conditions and the lack of opportunity to mix with members of the other sex facilitated the development of close relationships among girls.[62] Media reports referred to these special "S"[63] relationships as expressions of "*dōseiai*," which had emerged as the most common Japanese term used to translate the European concept "homosexuality."[64] The term *dōseiai* was used for both male and female homosexuality but "came to be associated especially with female-female relationships."[65] This was partly due to an accident of translation since *dōseiai* literally means "same-sex *love*." Hence, the term "*ai*" (love) emphasizes *sentiment* as opposed to the English term that emphasizes *sexuality*. On the part of most girls, so long as there were no physical (*nikutai*) manifestations of these feelings, these relationships were acknowledged as "innocent" and "more or less accepted as part of the normal female growth process."[66] "S" relationships even came to be seen as a training ground for later heterosexual romance. A 1913 article on "same-sex love" in the highbrow journal *Chūō kōron* (Central review), for instance, went so far as to describe these schoolgirl romances as "toys," a safe way for girls to play at love before their bodies and feelings matured sufficiently for them to enter marriage.[67] The female author of this article seems to have assumed that sexual desire was something extrinsic to girlhood, an experience that it was necessary for contact with a man to ignite.[68]

Women who expressed their same-sex love in physical terms, or who extended these relationships beyond adolescence, however, were suspected of "bodily degeneracy" and characterized as abnormal. The pathologization of female-female relations was especially noticeable in a series of reports concerning several high-profile "love suicides" that took place between female couples in the early 1930s. These reports criticized female-female couples in which one partner took on a more masculine, active role, usurping male privileges and leading the younger, feminine partner astray.[69]

Despite the fact that by the 1930s, discussion of romantic love as the ideal foundation for a heterosexual relationship was commonplace throughout Japanese media, "marrying for love was rare in practice and considered a bold departure from tradition."[70] It was primarily among intellectuals, particularly well-educated women such as feminist Hiratsuka Raichō, for whom "marriage by free choice" was a pressing concern.[71] For most people, the restrictions on free choice of marriage partner embedded in the family system made a love match impossible and to insist on the primacy of one's own feelings seemed "improper, indecent, [and] 'egoistic.'"[72] Other commentators, despite recognizing some benefits to "free love," criticized its practicality since, when compared with arranged marriage, it was "time consuming and laborious."[73] There was widespread skepticism that romantic love could be the foundation for a stable marriage in practice as seen in the common observation that "arranged marriages start out cold and get hot, whereas love marriages start out hot and get cold."[74] Since "high status boys and girls were prevented from falling in love with each other by lack of contact," many love affairs crossed class lines and involved "nonsegregated inferiors," thus reinforcing the idea that impetuous love matches were destabilizing of the family.[75]

As Ōtsuka Meiko points out, romantic love remained a rather "vague and abstract notion" for the majority of the population. Most Japanese couples of the time would not have thought it appropriate to vocalize their feelings by stating "I love you." Although it was technically possible to translate the phrase into Japanese, situations in which it would have been considered appropriate to make this emotive declaration remained few. Indeed the casual and open manner in which Americans and Europeans were supposed to express intimacy between the sexes was often interpreted as a sign of Western decadence. In 1930, as relations between Japan and the United States began to sour, nationalist critic Ikezaki Tadataka published a book entitled *Sekai o kyōi suru Amerikanizumu* (Americanism that threatens the world) in which he compared Americans to "pleasure seeking barbarians" prone to "momentary, sensual excitements."[76] The contrast between American hedonism and sensualism and Japanese spirituality and discipline was to remain an important theme in war-time propaganda. Hence, unlike the "direct manner" in which couples in Europe and the United States were supposed to demonstrate their affection, Japanese wives were encouraged to demonstrate their love reservedly, through selfless dedication to the needs of husband and family. Through anticipating a husband's needs, and importantly, through subjugating her own desires, a wife was able to ensure "smoothness" (*enman*) in the marital relationship.[77]

In her analysis of articles in the popular magazine *Shufu no tomo* (Housewife's friend) published during the Taisho and early Showa periods, Ōtsuka notes that "love" was downplayed in favor of "harmony" (*wago*) as the basis for a stable marriage. Such harmony was usually to be obtained by the wife "assimilating" (*dōka*) to the husband's feelings, even to the extent of forbearance in the face of his infidelity. As Ōtsuka states, "Above all, the first test of 'harmony' between a couple was whether or not *the husband* was satisfied *with his wife*."[78] A curious result of this imperative was that husbands tended to be represented in rather infantilized terms in these narratives. Wives were exhorted to become "mothers" to their impetuous and selfish husbands and to manage their bad behavior. In one article published in 1927 entitled "The secret of husband love," wives were even told to regard their husbands as "despots" and "big babies" and that the wise mother should avoid crying fits by anticipating the needs of her "baby" in advance.[79] The fact that wives needed to be offered instruction in how to love their husbands itself suggests that for some wives at least love was not a spontaneous or preexisting emotion.

Hence the *mutuality* of the marital relationship that in principle at least was fundamental to the Western romantic love ideology was not a part of the Japanese iteration of "love" in the context of marriage. This extended to the bedroom where the needs of men and women were seen as asymmetrical. While a husband's "sexual satisfaction" (*sei manzoku*) was considered key to a stable marriage, and a necessary precondition to stop his philandering, this was not so for wives. Although it was acknowledged that wives did have sexual needs, it was assumed that these would be fulfilled in the context of the marital relationship. Men, however, due to their "fickle" (*uwaki*) nature, were harder to please. This asymmetry in sexual desire was also registered in the criminal code of the time where adultery on the part of wives was always a criminal offense whereas it was only criminal for husbands in specific circumstances (for instance adultery with another man's wife).[80] In this context the affront was to the honor of the cuckolded husband and not to the philandering man's wife. Adultery on the side of the husband, committed with an unmarried woman, was not only free of any legal sanction but any offspring could legally be forced upon the wife if the husband chose to recognize these extramarital children and "a 'good wife' was expected to resign herself willingly to this arrangement."[81] It is in this context that we can understand how the postwar "discovery" of women's sexual needs proved so startling to many.

So despite the range of discussions about romantic love as the ideal basis of marriage and family that took place in a variety of Japanese print media across the early twentieth century, there was little alteration in the way marriages were arranged. As Michiko Suzuki points out, "love marriage did not suddenly become a common phenomenon or eclipse the normative arranged marriage."[82] Indeed, even by the early 1930s there were still many who argued that "realizing the self through love marriage was an undesirable, nonconformist notion."[83] Resistance to what was still seen in some quarters as a foreign sentiment strengthened as Japan descended further into militarism in the 1930s. Mariam Silverberg notes how through popular culture of the 20s "modern culture was reformulating gesticulations" but there was also resistance from more conservative commentators who wished to draw distinctions between the behavior of Japanese and people from the West. Articles in the media, along with advertisements "prohibiting any male expression of affect" were common and, as the wartime emergency progressed, there was further critique of "the new expressiveness of the era."[84]

A sense of the difference between Japanese and contemporary European understandings of the connection between love and sex can be gleaned through considering the treatment of Dutch gynecologist Theodore Van de Velde's *Ideal Marriage*.[85] This was essentially a marital sex guide that was a best seller throughout Europe and the United States in the 1930s and although it was translated into Japanese in 1930, it was banned shortly thereafter.[86] The prohibition of *Ideal Marriage* might seem a strange decision given that Van de Velde's text was entirely conservative in its treatment of sexuality. Most notably, he insisted on the marital relationship as the only proper context for sexual expression, making it clear that procreation was the ultimate goal and rationale for sexual activity and accordingly avoiding reference to contraceptive practices. He also endorsed commonsense understandings of the "opposite" but complimentary natures of men and women. He writes the following:

> What both man and woman, driven by obscure primitive urges, wish to feel in the sexual act, is the essential force of *maleness*, which expresses itself in a sort of violent and absolute *possession* of the woman. And so both of them can and do exult in a certain degree of male aggression and dominance—whether actual or apparent—which proclaims this essential force.[87]

He goes on to emphasize male activity and female passivity in a passage describing sex in the "astride" (woman on top) position:

> The main disadvantage in complete and frequent practice of the astride attitude lies in the complete passivity of the man and the exclusive activity of his partner. This is directly contrary to the natural relationship of the sexes, and must bring unfavorable consequences if it becomes habitual.[88]

As Van de Velde goes on to point out, not only is this posture contrary to the "natural" predisposition of the sexes, but given the angle of intercourse, it is least advantageous to conception and therefore to be avoided.

Van de Velde's emphasis on the differences between the sexes, on the sanctity of marriage, and on the procreative function of sexuality would all have been in accord with prewar Japanese understandings of the marital relationship. Ironically what excited the attention of the censors was that Van de Velde discussed sexuality *explicitly in the context of marriage*. As Mark Driscoll has noted, the prewar censors were particularly concerned about depictions that brought the patriarchal home into disrepute and hence discussions of marital sexuality were off bounds.[89]

Van de Velde's detailed discussion of the sex organs and techniques for their arousal, his emphasis on the need for foreplay to arouse the female partner and his insistence that sex should result in simultaneous orgasm by both partners also flew in the face of highly functional Japanese ideas about the role of sex within marriage as "human resource management." Given that kissing was at the time considered a public obscenity, Van de Velde's recommendation that the husband deploy the "genital kiss" (cunnilingus) as part of foreplay, would have seemed indecent. In fact, a sex research survey published in 1947 reported that a full half of couples who responded engaged in sexual intercourse without any foreplay.[90] Hence, Van de Velde's insistence on the need for female arousal, too, assaulted common-sense notions of female sexuality at the time, women being considered to have little or no sexual desire. The suggestion that in an "ideal" marriage, both partners should strive for simultaneous orgasm, an idea that was to be widely promulgated in Japan in the immediate postwar period, appeared indecent to many.

Hence, although Japanese society was quite accommodating of men's sexual "needs" and had a long tradition of erotic art and literature, the traditional culture of eroticism had been elaborated entirely in the context of the pleasure quarters.[91] To the extent that female sexual agency and technique had been recognized, it was the provenance of "professional" women—geisha, courtesans, and such like. That wives, particularly those from "good families," should be instructed in the erotic arts struck men of the time as prurient and improper. Indeed, such was the state of ignorance of "good" Japanese girls brought up during wartime that many were under the impression that kissing could lead to pregnancy.[92]

Erotic, Grotesque Nonsense

Despite attempts by the authorities to impose a unified and sanctified model of marital sexuality on the majority of the population via education and reforms to the familial and legal systems, growing literacy rates alongside widespread migration to the cities actually led toward increasing heterogeneity in representations of sexuality if not in actual practice. As more and more young people received an education and moved away from their rural family networks and into the cities, all the distractions of modern city life awaited them, sparking widespread concern in the press about the breakdown of values.

It was during the Taisho period that a range of specialized and general interest media focused upon the newly elaborated concept of "sexual desire" (*seiyoku*)[93] and laid out regimes for its proper management and control.[94]

However, sexologists did not all speak with one voice. Mark Driscoll has drawn attention to two strands within early Japanese sexology. First, he notes a Euro-centric and "erotophobic" discourse that was obsessed with the delineation of "normal" and "abnormal" expressions of sexual desire.[95] Referred to by Japanese researchers as the "Ebing school" after German sexologist Krafft-Ebing, these intellectuals were inspired by Krafft-Ebing's *Psychopathia Sexualis*, an encyclopedic treatment of "perverse" sexual desires and activities first published in German in 1886. From about 1915 onwards, a series of reports in the popular press began to critique all expressions of nonmarital sexuality as "harmful" (*yūgai*). Masturbation was seen as particularly dangerous and debilitating as was homosexuality, which from this time on was designated a form of "perverse sexual desire" (*hentai seiyoku*). In this system, prostitution, although not exactly an ideal sexual outlet, was sometimes represented as a necessary evil as it helped prevent men from experimenting with masturbation and homosexuality, which were considered far more harmful.[96] The valorization of marital sexuality was not simply on "hygienic" grounds (given that monogamy protected from the transmission of sexual diseases) but was also due to the manner in which sex with one's spouse was seen as uniting sexual desire with sentiment. In this companionate model of marriage sex was seen as an expression of love and to engage in sex without love came to be seen as immoral if not downright unhealthy. Yet, as Greg Pflugfelder points out, despite the fact that high-brow sexology was concerned with obsessively delineating "normal" from "perverse" forms of sexuality, popular writers were often much more interested in the strange and the perverse, "thus giving the impression not only that 'perversion' was ubiquitous but that the connotations of the term were not entirely negative."[97]

The moralizing tendencies of the Ebing School and its supporters were opposed by what Driscoll terms a "nativist" strand within Japanese sexology that critiqued European ideals of chastity and virtue as puritanical and contrary to nature. The journal *Modern Sexuality*, first published in 1922, was one venue in which Japanese readers were "introduced to the new kinds of pleasures, passions, anxieties, and exhaustions elicited by modern capitalism in Japan's metropolitan sites."[98] Rather than seeing perversion as a state of disorder rooted in the psychology of individual sufferers, other writers posited that perversity was an effect of rapidly accelerating commodity capitalism and even a symptom of modernity itself. Both strands of sexology theory gained popular exposure, the former exerting an influence on public policy, which became increasingly eugenic in its approach to sexual management, and the latter exerting an influence on the popular press, which from around 1920 onwards became increasingly interested in reporting on "strange" and "unusual" sexual behavior as part of the popular cultural movement known as *ero-guro-nansensu* or "erotic, grotesque nonsense."

The fad for seeking out erotic or grotesque stories or, indeed, experiences, was closely aligned with the rapid development of metropolitan life with its convenient public transport systems and the seemingly limitless opportunities they offered for diversion.[99] Indeed some commentators pointed to the emergence of a characteristically modern psychological state that they termed "*ryōki*" or "curiosity hunting"—a compulsion to seek out strange and unusual experiences. This curiosity hunting was a product of the rapid pace of modernity that stimulated in city dwellers an insatiable appetite for the new and exciting. As Angles points out,

> The form of curiosity that manifested itself in *ryōki* was an ailment caused by the advance of modern capitalism, which, since the Meiji Restoration, had funnelled people into cities, brought them into contact with ever-increasing numbers of people, intensified the pace of life, and unleashed a flood of new commercial products and recreational activities.[100]

A vibrant print culture sprang up that fed these desires and catered to these interests. Silverberg estimates that between 1918 and 1932 the number of periodicals grew from just over 3,000 to over 11,000.[101] These included magazines with titles such as *Gurotesuku* (Grotesque) and *Ryōki* (Curiosity hunting) that featured a wide range of articles and illustrations about strange and often erotic practices that were taking place at home and abroad.[102] During the Taisho period there was also a limited and largely underground film culture catering to erotic, grotesque tastes. Roland Domenig has pointed to the circulation among members' clubs of "stag films" mostly imported from Europe. Some of these films seem to have been produced with the aim of educating medical professionals about sexual matters, particularly sexual dysfunction.[103] Domenig mentions one such film that was shown to an "adult only" audience that was, apparently, so confronting that several ladies in the audience fainted and had to retire to an adjoining room. However, the "thought police" were increasingly on the lookout for this kind of material and by the 1930s the distribution of these "secret films" had been largely suppressed.

Critics have noted that the public interest in the erotic and the grotesque grew up alongside the increasingly repressive political situation of the late 1920s and early 30s and represented a return of the repressed. Angles points out how, "the fad for *ero, guro, nansensu* represented a fascination with those primal, idian, irrational, erotic, and thanatotic urges ordinarily suppressed by the logical, civilizing superego of social ethics."[104] These magazines facilitated certain escapism from the constrictions of everyday life since through engaging with these narratives people were able to fantasize about lifestyles and activities that rejected incorporation into the nation-building program.[105] The *ryōki* paradigm was thus important for a whole range of individuals whose sexual interests fell outside the state-sanctioned marital model. One type of "perversion" in particular was an *ero-guro* favorite: the underground world of male cross-dressed prostitutes. These men were referred to in press reports as "new *kagema*" (*kagema* being an Edo-period term for cross-dressing male prostitutes, closely aligned with the Kabuki theater). Pflugfelder points out that "popular writings construed the male-male erotic subculture of the contemporary cityscape as a shadowy and secret world,"[106] and hence it was ideal *ryōki* territory. Articles about this subculture, albeit stressing the criminal and pathological nature of its demimonde, also directed readers where to find it.

Unlike the dire legal situation that faced those engaging in homosexual acts in many Western countries, even in supposedly enlightened regimes such as the UK and the United States where statutes prohibiting "sodomy" were the norm, the Japanese authorities showed relatively little interest in investigating or prohibiting either male or female homosexuality.[107] Throughout the wartime period homosexual relations remained unregulated by the country's criminal code and the military displayed none of the genocidal tendencies toward sexual minorities that typified the Nazi regime.[108] Likewise, there is no evidence that the military enacted policies to purge homosexual men (there were no women) from its ranks, or to prohibit their recruitment in the first place, as was common in the United States at that time.[109] On the contrary, early postwar accounts suggest that male homosexual relations were a not uncommon "sexual release valve" among officers and young recruits, and that these relationships were afforded a certain amount of visibility.[110] One startling report from a cross-dressing male prostitute published in the *Monthly Yomiuri* in 1950 describes his time in the army thus:

> Upon arrival, all of my superiors started to like me and I would go to their rooms, give them massages, and wash their clothes. That was the reason they liked me. When it was time to do exercises . . . I always made up a clever reason to just observe . . . telling them I had some sickness . . . [so] they offered to let me to stay in the hospital. While I was in hospital, I played (*asobimashita*) with the doctor, the captain, and the commander.[111]

Whatever value we afford these postwar accounts as accurate testimony, it is reasonable to conclude, as Pflugfelder does, that the Japanese authorities maintained a "relatively benign stance" toward expressions of male-male sexuality throughout the war.[112] This stance, which might best be described as benign neglect, was carried over into the postwar period and remained a significant difference between Japanese and Occupation authority attitudes toward homosexuality. The legacy of *ero-guro* interest in homoeroticism alongside the authorities' largely hands-off approach toward private homosexual practice were both factors that enabled a sudden resurgence in talk about "perverse" sexualities in the immediate postwar period, as will be explored in Chapter 6.

The Dangers of Modernism

From the late 1920s, numerous books and articles introduced the wider reading public to some of the more interesting or scandalous developments taking place in cities such as Tokyo. These included Sakai Kiyoshi's 1931 *Nihon kanrakukyō annai* (Guide to Japan's pleasure districts),[113] which introduced a new type of girl, the "stick girl," also known as "Ginza's Miss Strollers" (*Ginza no o-aruki-san*). These young ladies rented themselves out by the hour to walk alongside and "stick to" white-collar gentlemen and join them for refreshments in the many cafes lining up-market shopping streets such as Tokyo's Ginza. At that time it would not have been considered appropriate for "daughters of good families" to spend time with young men without a chaperone, no matter how innocent the pastime. In fact, young men had very little opportunity to enjoy female company outside the pleasure quarters and articles in the popular press "bemoaned the lack of opportunity for young men to meet young women, thus leading them to associate with café waitresses and geisha."[114] A typical "nonsense" incident reported in Sakai's book involves a "stick girl" who, upon attempting to claim her fee after strolling with a young man for an hour or so, is surprised to discover that her date is in fact a "stick boy," in other texts described as a "handbag boy"—a walking companion for rich widows. This kind of lighthearted and frivolous incident is typical of the "nonsense" genre of the late 1920s, as indeed are these descriptions of the city's flanneurs—characters who would have seemed very "modern" and exotic to the bulk of Japan's rural population.

One particular object of fascination was Tokyo's new class of "modern boys" (*mobo*) and "modern girls" (*moga*). In small but ever increasing numbers, women could be seen on the streets, in the department stores, in offices, and commuting to and from their jobs on buses and trains. Sporting new short hairstyles and wearing Western clothing, these women became conspicuously gendered signs of Japan's modernity. Young women's increased ability to travel about town unsupervised and to mingle with young men in the lively entertainment districts that sprung up around major train interchanges "confirmed many critics' belief that modern urban life was decadent and immoral."[115]

The 1920s in Japan, as in other parts of the globe, was a decade during which changing gender roles and attitudes were much debated in the popular press, highbrow journalism, and the arts. At that time, a small but vocal middle-class culture was developing in Japan that comprised both male and female salaried workers who had the funds and the leisure to enjoy a range of entertainments, especially movies.[116] Since there had been no tradition of female actresses, Japan's first Western-style plays and home-produced movies featured *onnagata*, that is, female-role players trained in the Kabuki theater.[117] However, by the 1920s Japan's first generation of actresses was appearing on stage, on screen, and on the covers of popular magazines. American movies in particular were blamed for popularizing new styles of mixed-sex intimacy and providing the scripts for "every single movement" of the *mobo* and *moga*.[118]

Concern was expressed over increasingly "modern" attitudes and ways of doing things, one of the most problematic aspects of which was women's employment outside the home. The *moga* was the most conspicuous of a range of "girls" who could be seen out and about town. These included the "hello girl" (telephone operators), "bus girl" (female conductors), "gasoline girl" (serving at the gas station), and the "it girl" (equivalent of the "flapper" who was to be seen about town at Western-style cafes and cabarets). By the end of the 1920s, a whole range of "girls" had become a conspicuous part of Japan's cityscapes and they did much to pioneer the wearing of Western women's dress and "bobbed" hairstyles on the streets. Bus girls in particular with their black dresses, white collars, black hats, and black shoes with white cotton socks "looked the height of Paris fashion" and helped establish the image of the bus as a mode of "stylish transport."[119]

Although these jobs were not well paying, they did offer some women an alternative to traditional options such as factory work, nursing, and teaching. The *moga* complicated the previously clear distinction between women of good families who were confined to the private sphere of the home both before and after marriage and the so-called public sex workers of the pleasure quarters by working in very visible public occupations—on view on the buses, on the streets, and in the offices. There were even female journalists who strode about town clad in Western attire and travelled on business trips. The *moga* and *mobo* also confused what had been clearly defined styles of gender performance. Men were worried that the *moga*, being financially independent, were likely to be promiscuous and to jilt their lovers when they spotted a better marriage prospect.[120] So-called *moga* wives were reportedly dressing in their husbands' clothes and strolling about town swinging walking sticks and spending money. The *mobo*, on the other hand, keen to preserve their youthful looks, had taken to wearing light makeup and riding around on the trains with an "effeminate" bearing and tone of voice.[121]

These modern girls and modern boys who consorted together in up-market areas of Tokyo and Osaka were a new, and for many, exotic, phenomenon. Although the number of modern girls was relatively low and their movements confined to the most fashionable and Westernized areas of Japan's major cities, a large number of women were able to participate vicariously in their world through the many women's magazines discussing the phenomenon.[122] Increased education opportunities for women as well as women's increasing economic power had given rise to a vibrant intellectual culture in which foreign socialist and feminist ideas were circulated and debated. However, women's new roles and heightened visibility outside the confines of the family were not welcomed by all and the "woman problem" (*fujin mondai*)—actually a series of issues including job opportunities and working conditions, love and marriage, birth control and premarital chastity—were openly discussed in women's journals and the popular press.

Although certain sectors of Japanese society embraced modernism across a range of cultural enterprises, by the early 1930s more conservative elements in the Japanese hierarchy had identified modernism as an alien threat to a specifically Japanese way of life and values. The "special higher police," charged with rooting out seditious thought, were empowered to survey all aspects of culture and bring to account anyone who was considered to be undermining the national interest. The erotic-grotesque subculture was under particular surveillance because of its perceived frivolity. From 1938 on, for instance, theaters that offered Western-style dance reviews such as Asakusa's Casino Follies were required to provide "special surveillance seats" for members of the police force who would drop by to check that none of the dancers' skirts were cut above the knee and no navels were showing.[123] These and other erotic entertainments were closed down completely when war broke out with the United States in 1941.

Tachibana Takahiro, a former Home Ministry censor, outlined the need for censorship in his 1932 memoirs thus:

> The raison d'être of the censor is to protect against the publication of seditious propaganda, which is rooted in Sovietism, and the products of eroticism (the so-called *ero* publications), which are influenced by Americanism.[124]

Tachibana goes on to identify "the demand for freedom in actions and morality and a desire for the moment's pleasure and physical enjoyment" as characteristic of modernism, concluding that "the censor's work confronts modernism directly."[125] Here the censor conjoins anxieties about sedition with obscenity and ties them both to modernity. Understanding this connection between what might be described as loose thought and loose morals is important for understanding the way in which frivolous pleasures, such as those exemplified in the *ero-guro* culture, could come to seem unpatriotic, especially at a time of spiritual mobilization in which the nation as a whole was being encouraged to throw itself behind Japan's militarist project. Jonathan Abel notes that "the political and the sexual were explicitly and openly connected by some of the key players" on both sides of the censorship debate.[126] Hence, as we shall see in subsequent chapters, the connection between the political and the sexual was not a postwar innovation but was already explicitly articulated in prewar and wartime discourses, albeit with opposite intent.

Sex and the Military

Following the Meiji Restoration, the transformation of the numerous provincial samurai militia into a unified national modern army was a central concern and "rich country, strong army" became a popular rallying call promulgated by the new regime. From the very beginning, the authorities were keen to regulate and supervise the potentially unruly libidos of the large numbers of young male recruits who were being drafted into the ever expanding armed forces.

In the course of just a few decades, Japan was transformed from an isolated and secluded country with a population of only 35 million, to a world power with a population of 75 million that controlled an expanding regional empire. The importance of the military to Japan's new sense of self-identity as a player on the world stage is easy to understand, given the role that the superior military power of the United States had played in the forcible "opening" of the country. The new Japanese polity was modeled on the constitutional monarchies of Europe—Germany, France, Holland, and Great Britain—themselves all imperial powers with vast holdings of land and "spheres of influence" spanning Asia, Africa, and the Middle East. In the political climate of the late nineteenth century, the ideals of "civilization and enlightenment" went hand in hand with colonial expansionism. The role that the military played in establishing Japan's sense of self as a modern nation and constructing its male citizens as "citizen soldiers"[127] was crucial to later social developments.

Unlike the clan-based militia of the Tokugawa period where eligibility to fight was determined by family background, the modern Japanese armed forces were founded on conscription. At age 20 all Japanese males had to undergo a medical assessment that classified them in terms of fitness for service. In peacetime, only those from category "A" (the fittest and strongest) were chosen for active service via a lottery system. Whereas recruits from the countryside, where life was harsh and the labor intense, often looked forward to selection, a two-year stint in the military was not looked on favorably by all, especially by better-educated youths from the cities. However, draft dodging was a criminal offense and nationwide campaigns aimed to expose those young men who failed to register, proclaiming that "[o]ne's life is not a privilege: draft dodgers shame the region."[128]

The patriarchal structure and familial ideology of the Meiji state was apparent in the military recruitment procedure. First the new recruits were seen off from their homes or local train stations by family and friends in an *omi-okuri* (send-off). Most recruits were sent to join regiments associated with their place of origin, which meant that they served alongside their peers from back home, thus reinforcing their "responsibility to meet expectations of family village or town."[129] Upon arrival at the barracks, recruits were placed in small 30-man companies and were instructed to regard the senior officers as father and mother and their second-year seniors as older brothers, thus, as Edward Drea points out, "the Imperial army was the natural extension of the prewar Japanese family writ large with all the trappings of respect for hierarchy and group versus individual identification implied in that notion."[130] Recruits would have been familiar with the ideology positing the Emperor as the father of the nation from their schooldays. This notion was further underlined by the organizational structure of the army—the Meiji constitution had established the Emperor himself, not an elected government official, as the chief commanding officer of the armed forces, and all soldiers and sailors were taught that they fought on the Emperor's behalf. This idea was constantly reinforced through the daily study and recitation of the Imperial Rescript to Soldiers and Sailors as well as other ceremonies paying homage to and offering thanks to the Emperor for his beneficence. As Sonia Ryang points out, an important example of the beneficence provided by the Emperor was the female sex workers who were transported alongside horses, ammunition, and other necessary "goods" for the soldiers' use.[131]

Like Japan's ally, Nazi Germany, which also "came to treat prostitution as a necessary outlet for productive male citizens,"[132] in wartime Japan, men's sexuality was understood via a hydraulic model that assumed that any blockage in the natural flow of men's sexual energies would cause physical and mental debilitation.[133] Accordingly, regular sex was necessary in order to properly regulate male desire and ensure optimum productivity. Japanese soldiers, in particular, were socialized to take a functional view of the female body. The worst example of this sexual double standard was evidenced in what was euphemistically known as the "comfort women" system in which poor Japanese women and women from Japan's colonies were forcibly recruited to sexually serve the Japanese armed forces both at home and abroad. There was no acknowledgment in public culture that women might have autonomous sexual feelings or desires; women's bodies were objects to be used by men as "sexual release valves" (*sei no hakeguchi*).[134] Discussion of pleasure was conspicuously absent in these narratives that treated comfort women as "hygienic public bathrooms"[135] and even as "semen toilets."[136]

Chastity was not entertained as an option for the hordes of young conscripted men. Rather, the "hygienic" provision of military controlled prostitution services via indentured "comfort women" in so-called comfort stations was seen as the most efficient way to manage their sexual desires. During wartime, the management of the civilian male workforce's sex lives was also seen as important and "male workers in war industries were often given reduced rates to licensed quarters by the Government."[137] Ono Jiyōtoku reports that condoms (*sukin*) were handed out to soldiers and sailors before their "sorties" to the comfort stations.[138] However, both the army and the navy offered their own brand of protection. The army provided a single condom in a paper envelope stamped with the official army seal and the phrase *totsugeki ichiban* (attack number one).[139] The navy apparently gave out its condoms along with a tube of "sea cream" or antibacterial lotion to be used in conjunction. Despite these measures, rates of sexually transmitted disease remained high. Young inexperienced soldiers were thought to have put on the condoms too tight resulting in breakage whereas others preferred to wear the condoms "*bōzu* style,"[140] making a deliberate tear in the top of the condom to leave the glans exposed so as to heighten sensation. Hence, many young men were introduced to commercial sex as a matter of course long before they were in a position to unite sentiment and desire as was recommended by some intellectual idealists. Having become accustomed to quick and efficient commercial sex, it might be supposed that many of these men carried over these habits and attitudes into their marital relationships.

Sonia Ryang notes how "odd" it was that "hand in hand with the state's institutionalization of the monogamous conjugal system as the norm, the same state instituted the military prostitution system as an important component of disciplinary life in the imperial army."[141] The state's endorsement of prostitution, even for married men serving in the military, therefore worked against the romantic love ideology that posited love as a necessary precursor and justification for sexual interaction. Ryang argues that the Japanese state, through institutionalizing the monogamous conjugal couple as reproductive unit while at the same time endorsing a wide range of extramarital commercial sexual options for men, produced a bifurcation of love and sex—and by extension types of women. Marriage and reproduction were the exclusive provenance of "girls from good families" whereas poor women or women from the colonies were available for recreational sex with men for a fee.

Engagement with the world of commercial sex became a core aspect of male homosocial bonding in Japan. Fruhstuck refers to a survey of over 1,000 male students' sex lives published in 1923.[142] Over half of the respondents stated that they had had their first experience of intercourse prior to turning 18 and among the men who had entered the workforce after graduating from middle school, almost half had had their first experience with a prostitute. Some of the men revealed that they had been enticed to visit the red-light districts by older colleagues. Significantly only 1 percent of these respondents reported that their first experience of intercourse was with their wives.

The results of a 1982 survey into the timing and nature of respondents' first sexual intercourse involving an opposite-sex partner note that the pleasure quarters were still an integral part of male socialization for the generations that came of age before the end of the Pacific War.[143] The survey authors note that respondents who came of age in the prewar and wartime periods commonly reported sexual initiation with prostitutes in their mid-to-late teens (today's middle- and high-school age). They note that "loss of virginity" (*dōtei hōki*) was a rite of passage for adolescent boys that often took place in the context of the pleasure quarters at the instigation of older male peers (sometimes family members). The survey findings suggest that for men of these generations, recreational sex was viewed as a commercial transaction and that the majority of men were inducted into sexual activity by professional prostitutes. Most respondents recall that the sex was extremely perfunctory, and was performed in a quick and business-like manner. One man recalling his first visit at age 16 to the pleasure quarters in a Manchurian city, remembers being pushed down on the bed and straddled by a prostitute with no preparation. As this was taking place, he remembers thinking "masturbation is better than this."[144] The world of commercial sex, then, was hardly the place to receive an induction into the experience of romantic love and men's easy access to sex in the licensed quarters was another factor that tended to work against romantic-love ideology that posited sex as only proper in the context of a monogamous love marriage.

Sex and Gender on the Road to War

Imperial Japan's gradual descent into militarism as conflict with China escalated in the early 30s saw an intensified polarity in gender roles resulting in women being cast as mothers whose purpose was to breed sons for the empire, and men being regarded as fighting machines, part of the "national body."[145] Even schoolboys were not exempt, as "military gymnastics" was made a compulsory subject for boys from elementary school onward. The aim of physical education was to train each boy "to be a soldier with patriotic conformity, martial spirit, obedience, and toughness of mind and body."[146] As Yoshikuni Igarashi points out, "the wartime regime subjected Japanese bodies to rigid regulations, attempting to create obedient, patriotic bodies by forging ties between nationalist ideology and bodily functions."[147] Sex, to the extent that it was discussed at all during wartime, was represented as a means of managing "human resources" (*ningen shigen*) and not as a source of pleasure or relationship building.[148] Japanese bodies, as "the basis of national production and reproduction," were caught up in an intensifying system of surveillance and management that sought to improve their productivity.[149] In 1940 a National Eugenic Law was promulgated, the main purpose of which was "building up a larger and stronger nation"[150] and severe restrictions on abortion were introduced and discussion of birth control suppressed. Condoms remained available and were freely advertised, but it was their disease prevention function that was emphasized. Yamamoto Akira notes that sexual acts of course continued to take place, but that there were few resources encouraging the population to enjoy sex and few sex-positive images publicly available, leading to an impoverishment of the "sexual imagination."[151] The range of sexual practices people engaged in also seems to have been impoverished. Research published soon after the war by the Ministry of Welfare noted that less than 30 percent of couples engaged in foreplay, men preferring to proceed straight to "attack number one" (*totsugeki ichiban*),[152] a slang term for coitus that was also the name of a popular brand of condom handed out to Japanese soldiers.[153]

Whereas in recent times in most Western nations, a couple's sex life, particularly decisions such as when and if to have children, have been considered purely personal issues, this was not the case in prewar Japan where the state actively sought to manage, increase, and "improve" the Japanese population.[154] Even today Japanese male politicians have been criticized for making public statements about the need for Japanese women to have more children in order to address the nation's falling birth rate.[155] As noted, in the run up to the Pacific War, women, who had little political agency to express their own views, were particularly constrained by an ideology positioning them as "good wives, wise mothers." As Silverberg points out, by 1937, the modern girl had largely disappeared from the pages of Japan's popular press to be replaced by more patriotic representations of mythical Japanese female figures and contemporary mothers. She notes that "[t]he modern girl did not age into womanhood. She merely disappeared and the wartime mother appeared."[156] During wartime, marriage and child-rearing were actively promoted as women's patriotic duty by a mixture of government policies, media reports, and social pressure.[157]

This ideological shift was registered at the level of popular culture in women's magazines: during wartime, the readers of *Shufu no tomo* (Housewife's friend) "were faced with the immaculate static mother without husband, who was married, as it were, to the nation."[158] To an extent this new vision of woman as mother was a challenge to the rather marginal role that women had been accorded as wives in the Civil Code. As Sheldon Garon points out, "Because the household existed as a hierarchical entity and did not form around the conjugal relationship, the legal status of 'wife' was not particularly important."[159] Wartime ideology however clearly figured women in their roles as mothers and household managers as central to family life and to the future success of the war effort.

Although contraceptives and information about contraceptive practices were never prohibited by statute, precise information about contraceptive techniques was often deleted from publications by the censors. As Ike Nobutaka points out, "opposition to birth control was not based on religious or ethical grounds, but rested ultimately on the issue of national power."[160] As militarist ideology increasingly took hold throughout Japanese society in the 1930s, there was the widespread assumption that the practice of birth control could lead to "race suicide," and by 1937 those who publicly advocated birth control risked arrest for promulgating "dangerous thought."[161] This was possible because a Special Higher Police Force (also known as the "thought police") had been set up to administer an "ideological prosecution system" targeting ideas considered contrary to the national good. By 1940, government directives were established "in order to secure large reserves of man power for the armed forces and for the exploitation of the occupied areas."[162] The National Eugenics Law aimed at "race improvement" through the compulsory sterilization of persons suffering from hereditary diseases and the National Physical Fitness Law introduced a range of hygienic measures aimed at promoting healthy young bodies. Here health was promoted not as a good in its own right, but with the aim of creating young people who could better serve the nation.[163] Women were particular targets of these "social education" campaigns since, as wives and mothers they were the guardians of the home that needed to be properly regulated and its members "hygienically" managed.[164] By the 1930s rising militarism and the demand for soldiers saw "a new emphasis on women as the bearers rather than the socializers of children."[165] As the war with China escalated, various initiatives "defined reproduction as a national project" and women were encouraged to *umeyo fuyaseyo* or "produce more children and increase the population."[166]

The regulation of sexuality, particularly women's sexuality, had much in common with similar eugenic practices undertaken by Japan's ally, Germany's National Socialist regime. Annette Timm points out that "[t]he totalitarian impulse to make even the most private of human activities serve national goals meant that Nazi leaders sought not only to define acceptable sexual behavior but to redefine sexual acts with public—not simply private—significance."[167]

In Japan, too, sex and reproduction were coopted into a national policy aimed at creating more healthy citizens essential for the building of an expanding empire. The "emphasis on motherhood from the mid-1930s made the Japanese state hesitate to fully mobilize women for factory work until the war was virtually over."[168] Unlike the situation in the United States and the UK where the absence of men during the war saw increased opportunity for female agency at home, at work, and in social life, given what Havens refers to as Japanese "static psychocultural views about the place of women in society,"[169] women in Japan were not coopted into a national labor policy to the same extent as women of Allied nations. Instead, women's organizations were coopted by the state to guide and monitor the behavior of other women. Rather than resisting this appropriation, many women, having previously been denied scant role in public life, actively embraced the opportunity to command a greater role in the public sphere and eagerly campaigned against "anti-patriotic behavior" such as smoking, drinking, attending dance halls, perming the hair, or wearing "gaudy clothes."[170] Dour-faced matrons could be found standing outside railway stations berating women they considered overdressed to adopt a more sober appearance in support of the war effort and, in an attempt to enforce more thrifty attitudes, "embarrassing photographs of conspicuous consumers on shopping sprees were published in the newspapers."[171]

Hence, although for the citizens of Allied nations, the Second World War is sometimes described as "the best war ever,"[172] and is often remembered as an exciting period of sexual experimentation and transformation, especially by women and sexual minorities,[173] wartime was an unremittingly bleak experience for most Japanese people. The situation in Japan was very different from that described in the United States and the UK where "[m]any young women took advantage of the new opportunities and enjoyed the attentions of a number of men in the more fluid wartime atmosphere."[174] A young British woman scientist noted the following:

> We all made dates that we could never possibly keep, and had the time of our lives, never expecting the war could be such fun. There was no question

> of settling down with anyone, just the sheer enjoyment of dancing with soldiers of different nationalities in different styles. We re-cut our mothers' dance clothes and wore as much make-up as we could, and loved every minute.[175]

Whereas in the UK, some young women experienced the opening up of a "new sexual aspect" during the war, many wives whose husbands were overseas engaging in part-time "swap loves" with the foreign troops stationed in the country,[176] in Japan it would have been unthinkable for "daughters of good families" to behave in this manner, especially at a time of "spiritual mobilization" that explicitly disavowed Western entertainments or ways of behaving.

The Death of Romance

By the early 1940s, the purview of Japanese popular culture had narrowed considerably and it had become hard to publish, perform, or otherwise disseminate material that was considered contrary to the war effort. Indeed, "[f]rom 1941, nothing could be published, broadcast or screened without prior approval."[177] Even traditional Japanese comedy routines known as *rakugo*, once characterized by their sexual ribaldry, came under scrutiny and in 1941 "routines that dealt with sexually transmitted diseases, prostitutes, drinking, and similar topics were buried during a ceremony at the Honpō Temple in Asakusa, Tokyo"[178]—albeit happily they were dug up again and reinstated in performances during the Occupation. Unlike in Nazi Germany where many intellectuals, artists, and performers fled the regime, most of the workers in Japan's culture industries supported the war effort. Indeed, "by the time of the China Incident, the Japanese entertainment world eagerly backed the imperial Japanese military."[179]

In particular, attempts to expunge "decadent" Western influence gained pace as Japan's position in the war deteriorated. The sporting of women's Western-style clothes, makeup, and permed hairstyles was now out of bounds since "to appear well dressed on the streets was to be branded as unpatriotic."[180] Men, too, took to wearing "somber-hued clothes of the cheapest material" since "it was felt that to take an interest in one's personal appearance was not conducive to supporting the national war effort."[181] By 1944 jazz and other American music styles had been officially banned as was the playing of instruments such as banjos and ukuleles.[182] Jazz had been introduced into Japan in the early 1920s and by the end of the decade it had become very popular with a newly emerging generation of modern boys and modern girls who outraged propriety by daring to dance together in Tokyo's many dance halls. Indeed, jazz was regarded as an important symbol of modernism by some cultural critics who argued that Japan should also be ranked among the world's "cultured countries" because it, too, had jazz.[183] However, by 1937 the Home Ministry was railing against the dance halls because they "encouraged frivolity in youth" and "disturbed the standards of womanhood." Soon, new regulations were introduced that meant that "'professional female dancers' and 'adult male customers' were the only legally sanctioned couples that could engage in social dancing,"[184] thus removing one of the few social activities that unrelated male and female youth could enjoy together. The regulations also required that customers register their names, ages, and addresses when entering the dance halls so that police would have a record of patrons. Not surprisingly these restrictions inhibited many customers and by 1939 many of the halls had closed due to lack of business. A nationwide ban on dance halls was finally announced on November 1, 1940.[185]

By that time, even Western-style "blue-eyed dolls" were deemed subversive. In 1943 the Ministry of Education campaigned for the eradication of some 12,000 dolls that had been presented to Japanese schools by American schoolchildren. The public was exhorted to "never forgive the enemy dolls" and many were publicly burned, stabbed, and decapitated.[186] It is worth considering the value given to a different kind of doll, especially among soldiers in the imperial forces. The character "*i*" with the meanings comfort, console, or cheer, used in the term *ianfu* or "comfort women," was also used as part of another compound in reference to another feminine figure that offered consolation to the soldiers: the *imon ningyo*, or "comfort doll." Ellen Schattschneider has documented how hundreds of thousands of such dolls were made between 1936 and 1945 by the mothers, wives, and sisters of men at the front as well as by schoolgirls. Made from scraps of cloth and containing the name of the maker, these dolls were included among the *imonhin* or "comfort goods" sent by civilians in the homeland to men serving in the imperial forces. The dolls served not only to remind men fighting overseas of their female loved ones at home, but were also thought to have talismanic properties. At the war's close, many of these dolls were given to members of the *tokkōtai* or "special attack forces" who were being sent on suicide missions. The men would wear them on their clothing or hang them from their planes' control panels on their final missions. At the war's end similar dolls were dedicated to fallen soldiers at the Yasukuni shrine as *hanayome ningyō* or doll brides for lonely soldiers who died unmarried. Schattschneider notes that these figurines "evoked the many different relationships with women that a man might have, including those with mother, sister, daughter, wife, friend and lover."[187] Schattschneider points out how the doll figures mediated between the female domestic space of the home and the male space of the battlefield, allowing men to remember their connection with the homeland and the women who made the dolls to imagine themselves figuratively present on the battlefield to support the men. The talismanic properties of the dolls were similar to the *sennin-bari* or thousand-stitch bellybands also made by women and sent to soldiers at the front. These talismans clearly had a very different resonance than the erotic pin-ups collected and displayed by many US servicemen that were used as templates for the nose art painted onto planes and bulkheads.[188]

Unlike in the United States where images of Hollywood screen goddesses circulated as erotic and romantic symbols, Isolde Standish has pointed to "the death of romance"[189] in Japanese film culture of the period, since romantic love was seen as incompatible with the "heroic masculinity" demanded by the war effort.[190] Standish points to a "discourse of sexual repression"[191] in films of the early 40s in which men's romantic love for women was displaced by a "homosocial brotherhood." Film heroines, when they appeared at all, were depicted as sublimating their romantic feelings for men into a "love of country."[192] This was a tendency contrary to that in the United States where the "government and the film industry cooperated closely during the war in the production and distribution of millions of photographs of Hollywood's leading ladies" as "surrogate objects of sexual desire."[193]

The militarist censorship regime had a major effect on representations of women and girls more generally and "'[f]eminine' fashions and concerns were decried in magazines as frivolous and decadent."[194] As Barak Kushner points out, "by the onset of large-scale war between China and Japan in August 1937, print media policy turned away from overt censorship and more towards propping up social support for the war."[195] The editorial staffs of various magazines were invited to attend meetings at the Home Ministry where they were encouraged to prohibit any articles that "went against the times" or contained themes considered "low class."[196] Work by Hiromi Dollase has shown how the image of the *shōjo* (girl) was reformed according to new militarist guidelines. After 1940, popular girls' magazine *Shōjo no tomo* (Girls' friend) was required to radically alter its content and style, most notably by dropping popular artist Nakahara Jun'ichi whose manga-inspired, dreamy, idealized representations of young girls were considered inappropriate in a time of national emergency. New more realistic illustrations were commissioned that better depicted *gunkoku shōjo* (girls of a military nation). The stories, too, became less romantic and more didactic in tone, providing homilies "that taught frugality" and urged girls to "recognize the situation that they were in and their responsibility as Japanese citizens."[197] The result of these changes was that girls' magazines came to see their roles as providing "cheerleaders for the state."[198] During wartime discussion of romance was definitely off the cultural agenda.

In this chapter we have looked at the complex set of ideas relating to the proper behavior of men and women and ideal relations between the sexes that developed in Japan from the Meiji Restoration till the close of the Second World War. Many different figures contributed to this ongoing debate, both conservatives and progressives alike. While it is true that opinions that contradicted the official government line were largely silenced during the war years when censorship and paper shortages made it difficult to publicize "unpatriotic" views, the fact that the debate over men's and especially women's role in courtship and marriage was to resurface so vigorously in the immediate postwar period points to the fact that many of these ideas had not been forgotten.

In the next chapter we will look at some of the official policies of the Allied Occupation that helped shape the early postwar debate about love, sex, and marriage.

2

Sex and Censorship during the Occupation

Historian of sexuality Shimokawa Kōshi has described the first three years of the Occupation, from 1945 to 1948, as a time of "sexual anarchy,"[1] and it is true that many accounts describe the early postwar years as a period of "sexual liberation." Igarashi Yoshikuni, in particular, has stressed the very visceral sense of release that many Japanese people experienced at the war's end.[2] As we saw in the previous chapter, the militarist authorities had established pervasive surveillance and censorship mechanisms that seriously constrained the expression of sexuality by men and particularly by women. Prostitution was tightly controlled and limited to specific licensed areas, unmarried male and female couples had almost no opportunity to mingle socially, and sexual expression in the press was stymied by the threat of prosecution by the "thought police." All these restrictions were removed within the first few months of the Occupation.

However, anarchy is probably not quite the right term since it suggests a complete freedom from formal control, but, as we will see in this chapter, sexuality continued to be highly regulated and supervised, albeit in different ways and with different goals in mind. The Japanese authorities fully expected that the incoming Americans would behave in the same rapacious manner as had their own forces when they advanced across China and were thus determined to put in place measures to protect the purity of Japanese women. The US administration, on the other hand, rather than viewing their troops as sexual aggressors, tended to see these young men as "clean, innocent and vulnerable" and in danger of "having their morals corrupted and their health destroyed" by "shameless Japanese women."[3] The policies that the Allies enacted were intended to protect their own troops' physical well-being, with scant regard paid to their effects on Japanese women.

Both authorities, Japanese and Occupier, were overwhelmingly concerned to regulate "fraternization" between local women and foreign troops and many academic studies have examined in detail the lengths to which both sides went to monitor and restrict potential interracial sexual contacts.[4] However, far less attention has been paid to the effects that the collapse of the military regime and the arrival of the American forces had upon Japanese male and female interaction and the representation of sexual discourse in the Japanese media. This chapter outlines some of the major policy decisions taken by the Occupation administration, particularly regarding the regulation of obscenity in the press that helped shape local *Japanese* sexual cultures during the Occupation period.

Background to the Occupation

Japan's conflict with the United States and its Allies, which turned into open warfare after Japan's attack on Pearl Harbor on December 7, 1941, was but one episode in a much broader conflict instigated by Japan that began as far back as the "Manchurian Incident" in 1931. With a growing population and limited homeland resources, the Japanese militarists had long been eyeing the vast and, from their perspective, underexploited resources in the north-east Chinese territory of Manchuria. In 1931 the Japanese military staged an attack on the Japanese-owned South Manchuria railway that they blamed on Chinese dissidents as a pretext for sending in troops to occupy the region. The Japanese then set up a puppet state in Manchuria under the new name of Manchukuo. It was the failure of the League of Nations (precursor to the United Nations) to recognize Japan's sovereignty over this newly created state that led to Japan's walkout from the organization in 1933 resulting in deteriorating relations with the United States and Britain. The Manchurian Incident was the beginning of what in Japanese is referred to as the "fifteen years war," the entrance to the "dark valley" that was to lead to open warfare with China in 1937, war with the United States and the Allied nations in 1941, and the total physical and moral collapse of the Japanese nation in 1945.

After the success of Japan's surprise attack on Pearl Harbor, an initial series of stunning victories saw the British defeated in Singapore and Hong Kong and the Americans routed in the Philippines. However, despite these early successes the Japanese military soon overextended its capacity and was unable to sustain its advances on multiple fronts. The tide turned against the Japanese after they lost the key battle of the Midway Islands in 1942. From that point on the US forces gained the upper hand and after further victories in the islands of Guadalcanal, Tarawa, and

Saipan, by 1944 the Americans were readying themselves for an attack on Japan's home islands. The incendiary bombings that began in May 1944 saw Tokyo largely destroyed with the loss of 80,000 civilians in one night alone. By that time the situation for most civilians, especially in the cities, was dire. All basic necessities such as food, clothing, shelter, and medicine were in short supply and the continuing air raids made it seem as though there was no future to fight for. News of the instantaneous destruction of Hiroshima, and a few days later, Nagasaki, by the unimaginably powerful new atom bomb in August 1945 confirmed the hopelessness of the situation. By the war's end the Japanese people had entered a state described at the time as *kyodatsu* or total physical and mental collapse. It therefore came as something of a relief to many when the Emperor finally made his radio proclamation announcing Japan's surrender on August 15, 1945.

When the advance guard of the Occupation forces arrived in Japan in early September 1945, Tokyo lay in ruins. It is almost impossible to imagine the scenes of destruction that greeted the arrival of the American soldiers. It was not just the scale of physical destruction, especially in major cities such as Tokyo, Yokohama, and Kawasaki that was confronting, but the almost unimaginable scale of human desolation and misery. In Tokyo hundreds of thousands of people were starving, camped out among the ruins of burnt-out neighborhoods. In many areas there was no running water, no electricity, no shops, no transport, no food, and no shelter. There was, of course, no waste disposal, and the destroyed cities stank like a sewer.

British correspondent John Morris, who had lived in Japan prior to the outbreak of hostilities, wrote upon his return to Tokyo in 1946: "To understand what has happened it is useless to think in terms of destruction as we came to know it in Europe; you have to give a new meaning to the word."[5] Travelling around the city trying to visit old haunts and gain news of Japanese friends, he wrote: "[Y]ou just travel from one ash heap to another and although the names of the districts are, of course, unchanged, there is little else by which to recognize them."[6]

The situation in major cities like Tokyo actually deteriorated over the coming months as 5 million Japanese, both military from the battlefronts and civilians from the former colonies, began to be repatriated—many with no homes or families to return to.[7] Tokyo was full of "drifting human wreckage,"[8] both "burnt outs" and "repatriates," all with shocking stories of loss and privation to tell. Many had not simply lost their homes and possessions but sometimes their entire families had been killed in the incendiary raids during the closing months of the war. They had seen the bloated bodies of their neighbors, burned beyond recognition, stacked by the roadside waiting to be carted away to mass graves. Simply keeping their own bodies alive for one more day was all many survivors could hope for.

Those returning to Japan from the colonies, demobilized soldiers and civilians alike, had often suffered terrible journeys. The civilians had effectively been abandoned by the military at the close of the war and left to fend for themselves in hostile territory. Able only to bring what they could carry, farmers who had migrated to Manchuria in search of a new life, had had to leave the fruits of years of toil behind. Trying to get back to Japan, harried by the advancing Soviet army and Chinese bandits, some had abandoned their sick or elderly relatives and others had sold or sometimes given away their children to Chinese families, believing that that was the only way to ensure their children's survival.

Homelessness was just one problem among many; people were also sick, wounded, and malnourished. Children, many of whom had lost their parents and even their entire families in the air raids, were a particularly pathetic sight, left friendless and alone among the rubble. Children in their teens, both boys and girls, would soon start to sell their bodies—to Allied soldiers as well as Japanese with food or money to spare—in order to survive.[9] Some women, in a state of utter desperation, would shamelessly proposition men in full view of others, offering sex in exchange for money or just something to eat.[10] People were "forced to live 'bamboo sprout fashion,' selling off their possessions one after another as young bamboo shoots quickly shed their sheathing leaves."[11]

What food was available was rationed and distributed via the same neighborhood associations that had been set up to ensure community compliance with wartime restrictions. However, the amount and quality of food was pitiable and delivery unreliable, forcing most people to turn to the rapidly developing black market.[12] One of the most common meals available in the marketplaces was *zanpan shichū*, "leftovers stew." Made from edible items picked out from the refuse discarded by Occupation facilities and served out of huge oil drums, it was not unusual to find discarded condoms among the ingredients.[13]

As one eye-witness noted at the time, "Words like democracy and liberty can have little meaning for a people whose whole energies must at present inevitably be devoted to solving the difficulties of mere existence."[14] Yet it was the democratization of Japan that General Douglas MacArthur, the Supreme Commander for Allied Powers, saw as the ultimate goal of the American mission, a goal he pursued with determination.

The Supreme Commander for Allied Powers

Although more correctly referred to as the Allied Occupation of Japan, since representatives of all the Allied nations—the Soviet Union, China, and the British Commonwealth as well as the United States—had personnel in Tokyo,[15] Japan's postdefeat reconstruction was an American-dominated affair and is largely remembered by the Japanese as an "American Occupation." Plans to administer Japan had already been drawn up by the US State Department in the closing months of the war. Although each of the Allied powers had a voice in the Far Eastern Commission, a Washington-based body representing the interests of all Allied nations, in practice, General Douglas MacArthur, given the title Supreme Commander for the Allied Forces or SCAP (a title that was used interchangeably for the Occupation authorities in general) was given complete control over Occupation policy. MacArthur set up his general headquarters (GHQ) in Hibiya opposite the imperial palace and proceeded to rule indirectly over Japan via the organs of the existing Japanese government. Local military organizations were set up across Japan and these teams served to channel the thousands of memorandums, orders, and directives received from GHQ to local Japanese administrators who were responsible for enacting them. MacArthur, who was a devout Christian, introduced an almost messianic tone into Occupation attempts to reconstruct Japan according to democratic principles. During the six-and-a-half years of the Occupation, a range of initiatives attempted not only to dismantle the militarist infrastructure of the wartime regime but to proactively create new structures and new thought patterns reflective of democratic principles. This was no small task.

In the wake of defeat, the Japanese people were in transition as an "imagined community."[16] The militarist paradigm had posited the Japanese as a superior race descended from a divine Emperor who all shared a common spirit that set them apart both from the backward countries of Asia and the materially advanced yet spiritually corrupt societies of the West. The Japanese during wartime were a good example of what Mary Louise Pratt, drawing on Benedict Anderson, refers to as "citizen-soldiers," connected via a "deep horizontal comradeship" that allowed "millions of people not so much to kill as willingly to die."[17] This model of community Pratt terms *fraternal* but in the context of the Japanese "family state" headed by the Emperor, is better described as *filial*. However, Japan's catastrophic defeat resulting in the instantaneous loss of its colonies and the Occupation of the homeland by an enemy force seriously undermined the imperialist ideology that had underpinned the war effort. Under American guidance, the Japanese were now encouraged to reimagine themselves, this time in terms of Western paradigms of nationhood based on the "imagined" ideals of "equality, fraternity, [and] liberty."[18] The Japanese were encouraged to come together once again in a project of national construction, this time founded on democratic principles.

With this end in mind two different organizations were set up to help inculcate democratic thinking among the Japanese. The Civil Censorship Detachment (CCD) was entrusted with rooting out ideologies associated with the militarist regime through a strict policy of prepublication screening of all Japanese print media. Its remit also included the screening of some mail and telecommunications. The Civil Information and Education (CIE) section, on the other hand, had the task of encouraging democratic thought through intervening in the preproduction stages of all aspects of the Japanese media so as to ensure that democratic ideals were properly embedded. This had some unforeseen consequences as will be discussed later.

SCAP's program of reform began with the dismantling of Japan's empire and the repatriation of Japanese military and civilian administrators who were scattered about the region. A series of purges sought to identify and hold to account individuals who had held positions of responsibility in Japan's war effort and numerous officers were tried for war crimes, some given long sentences and others sent to the gallows. The *zaibatsu*, or massive industrial conglomerates, that had profited from Japan's overseas colonies and fuelled the militarist economy were dismantled so as to make room for more small and medium-size enterprises. Land reforms saw the huge holdings of the landlord class broken up and allocations made to tenant farmers. Japan's aristocracy was abolished and the Emperor, albeit allowed to keep his exalted position, was required to renounce his divinity and take on the role of a constitutional monarch. These structural reforms, which took place at a bewildering pace, were also accompanied by a range of educational and cultural initiatives aimed at reorienting Japanese people's attitudes toward basic democratic principles. One of the main areas considered in need of reform was the traditional status of women.

As previously noted, throughout the long war years the Japanese government had instigated paternalistic policies regulating gender roles, particularly where the behavior of women was concerned. Likewise, the US Occupation authorities were keen to involve themselves in gender policy in an attempt to "liberate" Japanese women from what were considered feudalistic customs, attitudes, and practices. As Mire Koikare points out, "American occupiers felt tremendous zeal and enthusiasm for their project of liberating Japanese women and intervened extensively in Japanese gender relations."[19]

Under close scrutiny from SCAP, the Japanese constitution and labor and family laws were extensively rewritten so as to enfranchise women and dismantle the "household system" that had given family patriarchs considerable influence over women's lives, including choice of marriage partner. Article 14 of the 1947 Constitution was progressive for the time, outlawing discrimination on the basis of "race, creed, sex, social status or family origin." Article 24 explicitly addressed the imbalance between the rights of women and men under the previous Civil Code, requiring that marriage "be based on the mutual consent of both sexes" and that it should be "maintained through mutual cooperation with equal rights of husband and wife as basis." Alongside choice of spouse, "other matters pertaining to marriage and the family," namely, property rights, choice of domicile, and inheritance, were also to be "enacted from the standpoint of . . . the essential equality of the sexes."[20]

These measures were enacted despite fierce opposition from the Japanese authorities who rightly recognized that they "threaten[ed] the basis of male domination and female subordination in the family."[21] Susan Pharr notes that "Japanese authorities made a persistent effort to dilute, omit, or change the intent of SCAP's women's rights provisions."[22] In particular, they attempted to insert clauses that acknowledged women's supposed "different" (that is, inferior) physical and moral capabilities and social functions. Of course, as Pharr points out, the Americans were not advocating a radical feminist agenda; rather "they accepted the idea that woman's primary role in adult life is to be wife and mother, but believed that married women simultaneously could and should play other roles as well, such as citizen, worker, and participant in civic and social groups."[23] However there was one aspect of social life during the Occupation in which Japanese women's participation was not welcomed, and that was in interactions with male military personnel.

The Politics of Fraternization

Despite SCAP's high ideals of liberating Japanese womanhood from centuries of feudal oppression, the lifting of one set of constraints only led to the imposition of a series of others. Japanese-American relations were fraught with anxieties concerning the deleterious effects of "fraternization," especially where Japanese women and American men were concerned. These anxieties were strong on both sides. In the few weeks between Japan's capitulation and the arrival of the first US soldiers, Japanese officials had warned the population to send young women away to relatives in the countryside, or if their young daughters and wives must remain in the cities then to keep them indoors.[24] Although the atrocities perpetrated by Japanese troops on the women of their former colonies, not least the military endorsed system of "comfort stations" had not been reported in the Japanese media, at the time of Japan's defeat it was estimated that there were some 84,000 "comfort" women across the territories controlled by Japan.[25] There would have been few men among the military or civil administrations in these areas who were unaware of the poor treatment these women had received. Furthermore, Japanese wartime propaganda had painted a similarly unattractive picture of US soldiers as had been typical of American propaganda concerning the Japanese themselves, and it was widely expected that the incoming troops would violate Japanese women. As Igarashi points out, "many Japanese anticipated their encounter with the arriving Americans in sexual terms."[26]

The scenes of mass rape and pillage envisioned by the authorities did not, however, eventuate, although there were sporadic reports of rape and abductions by the newly arrived American forces. On August 31, GIs in a jeep abducted two Japanese schoolgirls and subjected them to gang rape on the banks of the Tama River. The next day a separate group of GIs invaded a home near the air base in Atsugi and raped three sisters, one of whom died from the injuries she sustained. On September 3, GIs raped a mother and daughter, and the mother later killed herself. On September 10, before the new censorship regime that would prohibit negative reports about Allied personnel had been put in place, the *Mainichi* newspaper reported nine rapes as having taken place in the first week of the Occupation, although there were many other incidents that were not reported.[27] Shocking although these individual instances were, they did not point toward sexual abuse on a mass scale as had happened during the Japanese occupation of Chinese cities such as Nanking,[28] and the panic concerning the arrival of the foreign troops soon subsided.

Demonstrating the long-standing grouping of women into two opposing "professional" and "chaste" camps, Japanese officials went about recruiting an organization of sex workers who might act as a "female floodwall" to protect "daughters from good families" from the rapacious sexual appetite of the foreign occupiers. Registered sex workers as well as poor young women with no other options for survival were recruited to serve in the Recreation and Amusement Association (RAA), comprising a series of establishments designated as "restaurants," "dance halls," and "beer halls" but essentially serving as brothels for the incoming military personnel.[29] Licensed prostitution was legal in Japan and the authorities had had a great deal of experience in providing "comfort" facilities for the Japanese troops. The RAA was thus set up "with extraordinary speed and showed a remarkable ability to secure buildings and facilities in short supply."[30]

The recruitment procedure was anything but clandestine; indeed, advertisements for "special female workers" were placed in mainstream newspapers.[31] In most prefectures throughout Japan it was the police who were ordered to recruit both licensed and unlicensed prostitutes and encourage them to cooperate as well as supervise the establishments to make sure that things did not get out of hand. Although, unlike the comfort system set up for the Japanese troops, most of the women recruited by the RAA offered their services out of choice, this choice was made under duress. The offer of free food and housing came at a time when "the entire population of Japan was suffering from food shortages, and malnutrition and starvation were widespread."[32] For many young women, including some who were still high-school girls, there were no other options available.

The most notorious facility set up by the RAA was known as the International Palace, or "IP," described by an eye-witness as "probably the largest brothel in the world."[33] Its "assembly line" set-up that enabled a soldier to deposit his shoes at the entrance and "pick them up, cleaned and shined, at the other end" after he had finished his business was reminiscent of the barrack-like comfort stations set up for Japanese troops in the colonies. In an attempt to prevent the spread of venereal disease the Japanese authorities released a stockpile of 1,800,000 condoms for use in this and other similar facilities.[34] However, given the scale of women involved (some 10,000 in Tokyo alone)[35] it proved impossible to prevent venereal disease, which was soon spreading out of control among the sex workers as well as the troops. Alarmed by the sudden increase in infections among the Occupation forces, SCAP introduced a range of measures, including compulsory health checks among women working in the "service industry" and the release of its valuable supply of penicillin to treat infections. At the instigation of the Army and Navy Chaplains Association, which was worried about the "moral degradation" that mixing with prostitutes would engender among the troops, the authorities also began to place more emphasis on education programs.[36] A series of seminars and workshops was set up, aimed at promoting "continence, character, guidance, provision of religious education and physical education"[37] in an attempt to stem the VD epidemic through "building character."[38] From this point onwards the American authorities devoted ever increasing energy to attempts to educate their men about correct attitudes toward sexuality.[39]

SCAP was also embarrassed at how the long lines of young men queuing up outside these "leisure facilities" looked in reports in the American media and ordered the "licensed prostitution system" to be disbanded at the beginning of 1946.[40] The result was that sex workers were either driven onto the streets or into unlicensed and unmonitored premises and it became even harder to monitor their health or prevent the transmission of sexual diseases. SCAP responded by ordering the forcible roundup of women who were found out on the streets after a certain hour, detaining them over night, and requiring them to undergo medical examination at the Yoshiwara hospital, "sometimes with snickering MPs nearby."[41]

Many women on other business, including women working for GHQ, one female member of the Diet, and even a cross-dressed man[42] were caught up in these unpopular roundups. One young woman was so humiliated by the treatment she received that she later committed suicide. A report in the *Asahi* newspaper noted that the autopsy had revealed her to be a virgin.[43] SCAP responded to this negative publicity by transferring the responsibility for the roundups onto the Japanese police thus inadvertently reinstating their wartime duty as guardians of public morals.

The closing of the licensed brothels marked the beginning of greater clampdowns on "fraternization" between Japanese women and male Occupation personnel through limiting access to the places where interracial liaisons might be made. Japanese restaurants had always been off limits due to the local food shortages, but from March 1946, bars, cafes, theaters, cinemas, and even river banks and beaches were placed off limits.[44] Facilities set up for SCAP personnel were likewise made off limits to Japanese people and the military police spent a lot of time trying to prevent or interrupt liaisons between the Americans and the Japanese. Some MPs acted like bullies, not unlike the "Special Police" who had exercised a great deal of moral control over the civilian population during the war, and many Japanese who witnessed the imperious manner of the MPs must have been left wondering just how their behavior could be reconciled with American notions of freedom and democracy. Yet despite these efforts to discourage fraternization and the discovery of the great effectiveness of penicillin in curing venereal disease, anxieties about contamination—not just of bodies but also of minds—actually increased as the Cold War set in.

Mire Koikari notes that "sexual and moral issues were understood in political terms, as containment narratives made a clear connection among venereal disease infection, sexual and moral laxity, communist menace, and American national (in)security."[45] Hence it is not surprising that the regulation of American male sexuality intensified during that time and was to reach a peak during the Cold War years of the 1950s. As Koikari demonstrates, among the Occupation authorities "preexisting understandings of sexuality and morality were being reconfigured within the Cold War containment context" resulting in "hegemonic understandings that linked sexuality, body, religion, nation and anti-Communism."[46]

However, as I hope to demonstrate in the chapters that follow, there were movements within Japanese popular culture that were going in quite contrary directions. Rather than a closing down of sexual discourse during the Occupation years, there was a vast proliferation of discourses of sexuality that were by no means contained within a marital or even heterosexual framework. The "Cold War sexual containment of American servicemen"[47] thus stands in contrast to the opening up of sexual opportunities for Japanese men (and women) to explore not only heterosexual but a range of other sexual options, as demonstrated by discourses widely available in the popular press. To understand how discussion of sexuality was considered to have been "liberated" in the Japanese press in the immediate postwar environment, we need to look in detail at the censorship regime instigated by the Occupation authorities and the role given to the Japanese police in enforcing obscenity legislation.

Press Censorship under the Occupation

As we saw in the previous chapter, although such alarmingly "modern" trends as working women and love marriages had been discussed in Japan in the late 20s and early 30s as part of a popular cultural movement commonly referred to as *ero-guro-nansensu* (erotic, grotesque nonsense), from 1933 onwards Japan's descent into militarism severely curtailed the freedom with which such frivolous topics could be discussed in the press. From 1939 the government control of paper supplies made it all but impossible to print material disapproved of by the authorities and "even the word 'kiss' was banned."[48] Sex, to the extent that it was discussed at all in the wartime press, was represented as a means of managing "human resources" (*ningen shigen*) and not as a source of pleasure or relationship building.[49]

During the war, the strict censorship and shortage of paper had seen the number of publishing companies in Japan dwindle to only a few hundred. However, by 1948 the number of publishers had risen to an astonishing number of 4,581 before falling back to 1, 541 by 1953.[50] This was in large part due to one of the first acts of the Occupation authorities, announced on September 27, 1945 (known as SCAPIN 66), requiring the Japanese government "to render inoperative the procedures for enforcement of peace-time and war-time restrictions on freedom of the press and freedom of communications."[51] Another pronouncement on October 4 (known as SCAPIN 93) further prohibited the Japanese government from interfering in freedom of thought or expression and encouraged unqualified media discussion of the Japanese government and the Emperor.[52]

As Etō Jun[53] points out, SCAP's censorship policy is a compelling frame through which to view the nature of Japanese-American interaction during the Occupation. SCAP was concerned not simply to dismantle Japan's wartime government, institutions, and machinery but also to reengineer Japanese culture. A range of policy initiatives were "aimed at transforming not only Japanese thinking but even the deep-seated memories of the Japanese mind itself."[54] There was a certain irony in this process, for the "common sense" understanding among the victors was that the Japanese people had been deliberately misled and coerced into adopting a fascist mentality through a range of "top-down" government initiatives and institutions. In order to reverse this situation, not only was it necessary to dismantle the systems through which these thought practices had been engendered—the armed forces; the police; the political, economic, and education systems—but it was also necessary to retrain the Japanese in "democratic" ways of thinking and acting.

Paradoxically, one of the main ways in which democracy was promoted was via censorship of anything that reeked of the old, feudal order. Despite the fact that in a memorandum issued on September 10, 1945, SCAP "decreed that there shall be an absolute minimum of restrictions upon freedom of speech,"[55] from 1945 throughout 1949, the Civil Censorship Detachment[56] did in fact enforce a "very strict censorship operation over Japanese media: newspapers, radio scripts, motion pictures, dramatic productions, phonographic records, books, magazines and newspapers." So thorough was the censorship regime that "not even . . . *kamishibai* (paper picture-card shows for children) could escape the scrutiny of the Occupation censors."[57]

Media censorship was overseen by three Occupation organizations: the Civil Communications Section (CCS), the CCD, and the CIE. The CCS was given oversight of the more technical and administrative aspects of broadcasting. The CCD handled all forms of censorship pertaining to material broadcast, in print or on screen, with the specific purpose of rooting out antidemocratic thought. The CIE had more of a mentoring role aimed at educating media producers about their democratic responsibilities, based on American models. Hence Japanese commentators have argued that "[t]he reconstruction of Japan involved massive educational effort through books, periodicals, motion pictures and other cultural media. As an antidote to Japanese imperialism, the American and Western way of life functioned as a representation of democracy, and as such it was distributed, and favorably shared by the Japanese people."[58]

Hiromi Ochi goes so far as to argue that one result of this paternalistic guidance regime was "a self-colonizing hegemony" on the part of the Japanese people, many of whom accepted unquestioningly the superiority of the American way of life. However, as will be seen below, the lifting of the wartime censorship regime enabled a range of previously suppressed Japanese voices to speak, often with unforeseen consequences for both the Allied and Japanese authorities.

One factor that encouraged the outpouring of erotic material was that SCAP's policies concerning press censorship largely overlooked depictions of sex, eroticism, or "obscenity" in general.[59] *The Press Code for Japan* put forward on September 19, 1945, provided an extensive list of guidelines regarding prohibited material.[60] There were three general areas under surveillance: any criticism of the Allied authorities, any kind of "propaganda," and any reference to daily problems (such as food shortages), but absent from the policy was mention of morals or regulations concerning obscenity. In fact, the Occupation authorities made it clear that they were not responsible for policing material of a salacious or "immoral" nature, that being the job of the Japanese police who, under paragraph 175 of the legal code, were vested with powers to prohibit "obscenity" in print and other media.[61] For instance, the censorship records for the magazine *Momoiro raifu* (Pink life), dated August 22, 1949, contain the oft-recorded note that "the publishers have been advised that censorship approval does not mean exemption of publication [*sic,* prosecution] from Japanese laws involving penalties for publication of obscene material."[62]

The comparatively lax attitude taken by US authorities toward sexual expression in the Japanese press was a source of conflict with the Soviet Union (also nominally an occupying power) who would have preferred greater control in this area.[63] Like the presurrender Japanese regime, the Soviet state and its media "stressed sexuality in the service of the nation and shunned explicit and erotic representations of sex as bourgeois."[64] The US authorities, however, left sexual expression concerning the local Japanese population largely unregulated. Hence, the dismantling of the militarist censorship system led to a vast proliferation of salacious material and very little effort was made by Occupation authorities to restrain freedom of expression in this area.

Only six months after Japan's defeat, a vivacious print culture known as *kasutori*[65] or "the dregs," including newspapers and magazines specializing in "sex journalism" (*sei jānarizumu*), had emerged as a conspicuous forum for the discussion of sex and eroticism. The *kasutori* publishing industry was but one expression of the "chaotic, hybrid nature of Japanese popular culture in the late 1940s."[66] The *kasutori* press, in a series of reports that left little to the imagination, commonly portrayed the immediate postwar period as one of "sexual liberation" (*sei kaihō*).[67] Hence, in the immediate postwar period, it became possible to discuss sex publicly with unprecedented freedom in the public sphere. Indeed, even the graffiti in public toilets was said to have "been liberated."[68]

Christine Marran argues that in order to distract the population from the activities of the Occupation forces, the Japanese cabinet "cooperated with the new government to create the '3-S' strategy, that allowed, even promoted what were called the three S's of sports, screen and sex."[69] In fact, one magazine with the title *Esu* (S) expanded this list even further, advertising its contents as including "Screen, Stage, Show, Sports, Style, Sing, Song, Story, Sense, Smile, Summertime, Step, Studio," and last, but not least, "Sex."[70]

American Journalist Ralph Chapman, writing at the time, noted that "the U.S. Army censors . . . and General MacArthur's Civil Information and Education Section did nothing to stem the tide of obscene writing that at one time threatened to engulf the entire publishing field."[71] Chapman put the "lost standards" of Japan's publishing industry down to MacArthur's removal of the imperialist regime's censorship mechanisms alongside the continuing shortage of paper. With little oversight of material once considered injurious to public morals, and in a situation where paper was expensive and in short supply, publishers refused "to gamble paper on anything that was not sure-fire," the result being presses turning out what he described as "lurid tripe."[72] John Dower points to a survey of some 1,600 issues of *kasutori* magazines that found the predominant "symbolic images" included "kissing, strip shows, underpants, panpan and 'leisurely women,' chastity, incest, masturbation and lonely widows."[73]

The censorship regime set up by the Occupation authorities was rather different from that pertaining during the militarist period. In both pre- and wartime Japan the authorities had been open about their intent to censor speech and writing in the national interest and many publications went to press with offending words and passages simply deleted or represented by circular marks or exes.[74] When books in their entirety were banned, this was reported upon in the media, and lists of banned authors were circulated to publishers. Hence it was obvious to authors what topics were likely to be banned and it was relatively easy for authors and editors to gauge what kind of comments were considered problematic from the excised passages. SCAP, however, given its mission to introduce "democracy" to the Japanese, sought to hide the fact that the media were subject to censorship by repressing information about the censorship process itself. Publishers were not allowed to indicate censored passages in any way or acknowledge that material had been omitted. This meant that "Occupation censorship was even more exasperating than Japanese military censorship had been because it insisted that all traces of censorship be concealed."[75]

Between 1945 and 1949 all material to be published in Japan was required to be submitted in galley form for preapproval to the CCD. The hundreds of censors would check the material for complicity and if they found offending passages or illustrations, would require the material to be removed in its entirety or replaced. Since in the final publication there was no indication that any material had been censored, it was sometimes difficult for publishers to work out in advance what was and was not permissible. However, after reviewing surviving censorship documents in the University of Maryland's Gordon W. Prange Collection, it is clear that "obscenity," per se, was not an object of particular concern of SCAP's censorship policy.

Documents show that the CCD certainly had its eye on "obscene" publications but accounts show that in general the context in which "obscenity" was invoked as a reason to stop something going to press was in cases when reference was made to fraternization between US troops and local women or when reference was made to the supposedly loose morals of "Caucasian" women. The censorship reports themselves evidence how sensitive the issue of fraternization was. Take, for instance, a report outlining the reasons for the suppression of an article entitled "Temporary wife" that was to have appeared in the May 1946 edition of the magazine *Toppu* (Top), the censor notes that "[t]he general tone of this article is very detestable. The theme of it is that foreigners—obviously Americans, although it does not manifestly state so—can get Japanese girls as their concubines." The censor recommended that the article be suppressed on the grounds that it "disturbs public tranquility and [contains] destructive criticism of Allies."[76]

Even incidental passages suggesting a sexual connection between Allied personnel and Japanese women were excised, as can be seen in a report dated April 25, 1947, where an examiner by the name Groening recommended the excision of the following italicized passage from an article about the Tamanoi prostitute quarters: " . . . The women are examined once a week by the ambulance officers of the metropolis, *sometimes attended by the GHQ personnel.*"[77] Even a reference to a passing "American soldier clad in a swanking jacket" in a popular Japanese song entitled *Tokyo Flower Girl*, was sufficient to have it taken off air since it was considered "too provocative."[78]

It was not just material that hinted at Allied personnel's involvement in prostitution that drew attention but almost any reference to "Caucasians," especially white women, in a sexual context. Even serious literature by established authors was not immune to this kind of censorship. For example, a section from a short story by famous novelist Tanizaki Junichirō submitted to the literary magazine *Shinbungaku* (New literature) was suppressed in June 1947. In the story, Tanizaki reminisced about taking English classes in his youth and speculated whether a group of attractive Western women living on the second floor of the foreign manor housing the classes may have been high-class prostitutes.[79]

The reasons given for censoring such references bear detailing in full. For instance, in a memo from "RRZ" to "AMO" dated April 12, 1948, detailed instructions are given for the filing of an "obscene report."

> In your reports, please indicate whether the material is concerned with Japanese and is just erotic or whether it also concerns Allied nationals and could be construed as being criticism of Allied nations. This one,[80] for

> instance, has a caucasian [*sic*] on the cover. That should be pointed out as well as instances of other pictures and stories concerning caucasians [*sic*]. It might be well to compare the volume of references to Caucasians (and thus, potentially Allied) personnel with the volume of material referring only to Japanese. This might be part of a concerted effort on the part of the Japanese to discredit the Caucasian race.

Sensitivity about the representation of Caucasian women continued even after the replacement of the mandatory precensorship system with warnings issued about material already in print. Under this new more relaxed system, if material was found to be offensive to the Allies "authorities immediately reprimanded producers of the material and curtailed future publication . . . of their material."[81] For example, the April 1949 edition of *Momo iro raifu* (Pink life) was "postcensored" and a warning issued that material published violated the press code. In this instance the violation was identified as "[t]he photogravure on the reverse side of the front cover [that] deals with two naked Caucasian women," that constituted "Criticism of Allied Powers" in the opinion of the censor.[82]

The records cited above make a clear policy distinction between erotic material that concerns only Japanese and erotic material concerning Allied nationals, it being the latter category that was blacklisted. This supports earlier research that argues that the antifraternization policy was about maintaining racial barriers and shoring up national identities. Yet despite their sensitivity to mixed-race relations, erotic material "referring only to Japanese" was routinely passed by the censors, it being left to the Japanese police to pursue prosecution of material that they deemed obscene. However, due to purges and reorganization, the police were a "decentralized, inexperienced, and minimally armed force"[83] who had much else to do in the immediate postwar years—it was not pornographers but gangsters who were their main priority. The period between 1946 and 1947, in particular, was marked by gang warfare over black-market control of scarce provisions, and "the fights were frequently large in scale and bloody since the gangs were armed with military weapons and fired on each other indiscriminately."[84] It thus took some time before the police were able to start to rein in magazines and newspapers specializing in "sex journalism."

When the Japanese police did begin to relaunch obscenity prosecutions in early 1947, they tended to target material that infringed on ideological grounds, thus carrying over the sensitivities of the previous militarist regime. This suggests that Allied initiatives had little impact upon police ideas about what constituted obscenity in sexual mores. It is worthwhile attending closely to the first postwar case invoking Japan's obscenity legislation since the topic targeted goes against rather than supports suggestions of US influence in this area.

The Prosecution of the Magazine *Ryōki*

On January 9, 1947, for the first time in the postwar period, charges of obscenity were laid against Akane Shobō, the publishers of the magazine *Ryōki* (Curiosity hunting).[85] The charges were thought to have been prompted by two articles that appeared in the December 1946 edition of the magazine. One, a story entitled "Mrs. Captain H,"[86] dealt with an adulterous affair between a student and a soldier's wife, and the other "Humorous tales of dynastic lust,"[87] concerned the goings on among past Emperors' concubines. The decision to prosecute was the result of a discussion between the Public Security Department of the Ministry of Internal Affairs and the Internal Security Section of the Metropolitan Police Department. Although this decision was announced in the press with much fanfare, all the authorities could do was confiscate 873 copies of the magazine on January 12, 1947, since the issue had already passed CCD precensorship and more than 60,000 copies had been published and were in circulation.[88]

As we saw in the previous chapter, the Japanese term *ryōki*, or "curiosity hunting," refers to a well established prewar genre of writing obsessed with strange and bizarre events that was part of the 1920s preoccupation with "erotic, grotesque nonsense." That a magazine with the title *Ryōki* was the first postwar publication to be prosecuted by the Japanese police might suggest that they identified the entire *ryōki* genre, with its interest in, among other things, "sexual perversion," as injurious to public morals. Indeed, unlike some magazines that sought to disguise their prurient interests under a scientific or educational guise, the editors of *Ryōki* had always been unapologetic about the content of the magazine. They declared on the first issue's contents page that *Ryōki* had "no intention whatsoever to educate or enlighten" its readers (see fig. 2.1).

Instead, it was intended for those "exhausted by the task of reconstructing the nation" and after it had supplied a few moments of amusement and distraction, it should simply be thrown away. The magazine *Ryōki* is thus a particularly self-conscious example of *kasutori* culture, typifying "the banishment of authority, the absence of orthodox or transcendent values" that Dower suggests typified the genre.[89]

However, when the details of the specific stories that brought about the prosecution are taken into account there are barely any *ryōki* elements present. "Mrs. Captain H," was a tale of simple adultery, and the explicitness in the details was characteristic of a range of early postwar sex

獵奇

創刊に際し

敗戰といふ嚴めしい現實の下に、平和が蘇へると、種々な娯樂雑誌が一時に、花瓣を撒散らした様に出版された、だが現實が苦しく、衣、食、住の問題に惱み疲れてゐる私達に、その中の何册が官能の面に於て、うるほひを、あたへて與れたでせう。

「月刊雑誌『獵奇』は、讀者諸賢を啓蒙しやうとか、教育しやうとかいふ大それた氣持は、全然有りません。

讀者諸賢が、平和國家建設の爲に心身共に、疲れきつた、午睡の一刻に、興味本位に讀捨て下されば幸です。

味氣無い生活の中に一册位、こんな雑誌が有つてもよからうかと編輯した次第です。」

讀者諸賢の御鞭撻を乞ふ——

—目次—

Figure 2.1 Editorial from the inside cover of the October 1946 edition of the magazine *Ryōki* (Curiosity hunting)

Note: Original in the Gordon W. Prange Collection at the University of Maryland.

publications.[90] Similarly, the humorous tales of misadventure among the Emperor's consorts were not particularly graphic—more problematic was the fact that the article "touched on the topic of the imperial family."[91] The reason that the police acted against these particular stories, despite the fact that there were many hundreds of other stories in circulation that were as or more graphic or perverse in their details, lies in the role the police saw themselves as playing in protecting public morals.

During wartime, the Japanese police force, particularly the division referred to as the "Special Higher Police" (*tokkō keisatsu*) had played an important role in maintaining solidarity behind the war effort. The Special Police were also referred to as the "thought police" (*shisō keisatsu*) since part of their mandate was to investigate and prosecute "seditious" thought—this included not only antiwar rhetoric but a wide range of attitudes and behaviors that were construed as contrary to the national interest. As Barak Kushner points out, "various levels of police . . . felt it their duty to guide and persuade the home populations in correct behavior."[92] The police did not see their role as simply that of preserving public safety, but rather as the preservation of the country's honor—an ideology that continued to inform their ideas and practices in the immediate postwar environment. During wartime, "loose women," that is, women who sought out "illicit" love affairs had been regarded by the authorities "not only as antiwar, but as threatening the fabric of Japanese society."[93] "Mrs. Captain H" described such a woman. Indeed the very abbreviation of her name as Mrs. "H," is a pun on the homophonous term "*ecchi*" (possibly deriving from the English term "letch") meaning "sexual."[94]

The narrative concerns Takao, a spoiled high-school student who, due to his parents' influence, was able to obtain a fake medical certificate to avoid the draft. Toward the end of the war he was evacuated to the countryside where he took up residence in the annex of a house owned by Captain H, a friend of the family. Captain H was seldom at home but on one occasion after a long absence, Takao heard strange noises coming from the bathroom shared by the couple. After sidling up to the window, he peered in and witnessed the couple making love (the next four pages of the story detail what he witnessed!). After watching such an event for the very first time, Takao became obsessed with the captain's young wife and sought out opportunities to be alone with her during the captain's absences. On one occasion he used the pretext of borrowing a book to gain access to the house and was surprised when the wife behaved coquettishly toward him. She invited him to return later that evening and share her bath. The couple's bath time was, however, interrupted by an air raid siren and they fled to the shelter in the garden. It was there that they made love. The story ends with the announcement that after the surrender, Captain H was arrested and executed as a war criminal, thus allowing the adulterous pair to continue their relationship.

The police operation against *Ryōki* proceeded in a manner similar to cases handled under the militarist regime, avoiding public debate about the category of "obscenity" through handling matters out of court. Hence, when arrested and charged with obscenity, both the author and publisher of the story pleaded guilty and paid a fine of 250 yen and it was unnecessary to take the matter to trial. It therefore remains off record what aspects of the story in particular the police considered obscene. Contemporary press accounts of the case identify the adultery as a key factor that led to the prosecution.[95] Yet, since the act of adultery itself was in the process of being removed from the criminal code by Allied command, it is difficult to see why a description of the act would have been problematic. It is likely that the complicating factor here was that the adultery was instigated by a soldier's wife, took place with an "unpatriotic" student and that the reputation of the soldier himself was sullied by allegations of war crime. Ironically these very factors would probably have been viewed favorably by the CCD censors since the themes were suitably "antifeudalistic" and clearly opposed wartime rhetoric. Indeed, CCD censors had let the pulp story "Mrs. Captain H" pass whereas in August 1946 they had suppressed a literary piece entitled "A fujin no tegami" (Letters from Mrs. A) by famous author Tanizaki Junichirō simply because they considered the devotion expressed by Mrs. A toward an unnamed Japanese pilot to be supportive of militarism.[96]

Later Japanese scholars have argued that the motivation for the police to move against *Ryōki* was ideological. Hasegawa Takuya suggests that the story about "Mrs. H" caused concern since in 1947 those charged with dealing with obscenity in the Ministry of Internal Affairs and the Metropolitan Police Department were still under the sway of wartime ideologies mandating respect for imperial soldiers and decrying "moral decline." Furthermore, adultery (on the part of wives) was still a touchy subject since it had long been considered a criminal act and was not removed from the Criminal Code until October 1947.[97] Indeed three years after the *Ryōki* incident in 1950 when the translator and publisher of D. H. Lawrence's *Lady Chatterley's Lover* were also charged under paragraph 175, it was argued by the prosecution that the adulterous nature of the sex described was an aggravating factor in the book's "obscenity." Mark Driscoll's work on prewar censorship also suggests that adultery was likely to have been the trigger for this prosecution. He notes how the Confucian-inspired censorship code of the prewar years "led to an exclusive focus on the sacrosanct patriarchal home"[98] and that adultery, illegal on the part of women in real life, was a particular target for censorship.

Both Hasegawa[99] and Yamamoto Akira[100] note that most early postwar obscenity prosecutions involved stories "centering on war criminals and adultery" and accounts of "lust and wrongdoings in the imperial dynasty." Since neither of these topics was of ideological concern to the Allied censors, Yamamoto in particular uses the prosecution of these topics to argue for the independence of the Japanese police in respect to the censorship of sexual mores.[101] Ann Sherif concurs, noting that "[f]or the Japanese government officials and the police, SCAP's relatively loose policy on sexually explicit materials meant that the local authorities could stand as the 'authorizer of discourse' for at least one facet of society—the regulation of sexual expression."[102] Indeed in the *Lady Chatterley* trial that unfolded in 1951, an attempt by the prosecution to introduce as evidence a letter from an Occupation official supporting their case "backfired dramatically" as the judges "balked at this intrusion of a foreign authority in their courtroom."[103]

Hasegawa reports that the Civil Censorship Detachment did get involved in the *Ryōki* case, but only *after* the matter was brought to their attention by the Japanese police. The publisher was summoned to headquarters to explain himself and ordered to publish an acknowledgment of his wrongdoing in the next issue of the magazine.[104] However, Hasegawa speculates that it may not have simply been complaints by the Japanese police that urged the CCD to act since there was significant disagreement among the Allied powers themselves over the (lack of) censorship over sexual issues. He notes that the USSR often expressed dissatisfaction over America's lukewarm control of the rapid spread of pornography and the sex industry in postwar Japan, thus underlining the fact that there was hardly one coherent set of opinions even among the occupying powers.

Hence, a close look at Allied and Japanese policies concerning the regulation of sexuality in print media suggests that there was not a coherent and unified approach shared by both authorities. What both parties *did* share was a common interest in how "their" women were being represented. The Americans were touchy about any representation of "Caucasian" women in a sexual context, fearing that such depictions might constitute a criticism of the Occupation and its gender reforms. The Japanese authorities, too, were anxious about depictions of Japanese women, in particular military wives and imperial concubines, whose betrayal of their husbands was read metonymically as a betrayal of the Japanese nation.

The early years of the Occupation were clearly not a time of sexual anarchy given that interracial couplings were the site of such intensive anxiety, intervention, and control by the Allied authorities and ideological limits on sexual expression were still being enforced by the Japanese police. Although Japanese women were in some contexts seen as victims of a feudal

Japanese patriarchy in need of liberating through democratic reform, they were in other contexts seen as unruly bodies, liable to corrupt and contaminate the US troops. The indiscriminate roundups of Japanese women and their forced subjection to venereal disease examinations is a harsh reminder of the limited agency that all Japanese, women in particular, exercised under foreign occupation.

However, the emphasis that has been placed in previous scholarship on the restrictions on *inter*-racial sexual expression has perhaps obscured the way in which Japanese-Japanese sexual expression was opened up in the early postwar years, giving rise to an erotic publishing culture almost unparalleled anywhere prior to the "sexual revolution" of the 1960s. The next chapter will explore this erotic print culture in detail.

3

Sexual Liberation

Japanese and Western commentators alike have been unanimous in pointing to the radical shift in the discussion of sexual mores that took place soon after Japan's defeat. Ronald Dore comments that "the confusion which followed [Japan's] defeat was catastrophic to the old morality. In some cases it was catastrophic to moral restraint of any kind."[1] Jay Rubin notes that "the Japanese were sick to death of being preached at constantly to be good, frugal, hardworking, and self-sacrificing" and were consequently attracted to "a decadence that was simply the antithesis of prewar wholesomeness."[2] John Dower describes the rapid escalation of "a commercial world dominated by sexually oriented entertainments and a veritable cascade of pulp literature" that was known by the popular colloquial term *kasutori* or the "dregs."[3] Japanese intellectuals remarked on the rapid shift from a "spiritual" to a "carnal" culture, celebrating what Igarashi Yoshikuni refers to as the "raw, erotic energy of Japanese bodies."[4]

One of the most visible symbols of this new attitude toward sexuality was the very public display of brightly dressed female sex workers known as "pan pan" girls in the streets and parks of Japan's major cities. Dower notes that "their self-indulgent carnality was as sharp a repudiation as could be imagined of the stultifying austerity and discipline the militarists had demanded."[5] One eye witness recalls that the first pan pan girls to offer their services immediately after the defeat were "starved and filth covered girls [standing] . . . on bomb gutted, rubble-clotted street corners"[6] but they soon began to organize into gangs and stake out territory. These gangs offered some protection since "older, capable, experienced girls became leaders" who looked after the other mostly teen-age girls. These older women "formed a compact matriarchal body for the rest of the members and most efficiently helped them out of any difficulty—financial, social or physical."[7] Some of these "elder sisters" even became well-known figures in their communities and were respected for their business acumen.

Journalist Narumigi Ichirō, writing in 1953, noted that alongside the "four presents" bestowed by the Occupation authorities: respect for human rights, equality of men and women, freedom of speech, and women's political enfranchisement, there also came about "the liberation of sex." In particular, he emphasized the impact that the pan pan girls' fraternization with the Occupation troops had upon the public, remarking that their "demonstration of friendly relations outside the train stations with the young men of the Occupation was a sign of unabashed love that swept over us."[8] Prior to the war's end prostitution had been well regulated by the authorities, concealed in designated pleasure districts, and street prostitutes were few in number. However, compared with the women working in the licensed quarters, the unregulated pan pan girls were "obtrusive and conspicuous" and openly "hustled their trade in the city streets."[9]

Although the majority of Japanese people were disapproving of the open display of prostitution,[10] throughout the Occupation period as many as 70,000 women worked as pan pan girls targeting GIs and other foreigners as well as local Japanese men, and brought as much as 200 million dollars in foreign exchange into the economy.[11] In October 1946 a survey of female sex workers who had been brought to the Yoshiwara hospital to undergo compulsory health checks found that their average monthly income was 5,750 yen, over ten times the regular monthly salary of a male company employee.[12] Hence, although there was much criticism of the supposedly low morals of pan pan women in the press,[13] there was some support for them, too, since many children and families depended upon the high income that they brought in. One American-educated Japanese mother wrote in defense of her daughter who worked at a cabaret entertaining Allied personnel that "working from seven to eleven every evening, [she] is by far the biggest money earner in our family circle."[14] The fact that this woman's youngest daughter, who had not even graduated from highschool, earned more than her salaryman father, translator mother, or doctor sister is a good example of how established hierarchies were challenged by new postwar realities.

Whereas in the prewar environment the public display of intimacy would have resulted in police intervention, many pan pan girls could be seen with Allied soldiers in the streets, parks, and train stations of Japan's major cities resulting in erotic encounters being flaunted in public to an unprecedented degree.[15] Despite an official policy discouraging "fraternization," the streets surrounding GHQ adjacent to the Imperial palace in the very center of Tokyo attracted hundreds of Japanese women looking for a hookup with SCAP personnel. British correspondent John Morris wrote in 1946 that "when darkness fell the numerous little parks with which Tokyo is studded, and even the open space in front of the Emperor's palace, were crowded with Allied soldiers and their lovers."[16] Indeed, "[t]he moat around the Imperial Palace was so clogged with used condoms it had to be cleaned out once a week with a big wire scoop."[17] Whereas "for a man and a woman to walk abreast would have been considered immoral during the war,"[18] the very public fraternization between GIs and Japanese women did much to sweep aside such "feudal" attitudes.

These unprecedented displays of erotic encounters affected Japanese men, women, and children in different ways. Japanese men, many of whom as soldiers would have availed themselves of the services of so-called comfort women while serving overseas, could not but experience shock, dismay, and envy at the sight of their countrywomen being "toyed with by hairy foreigners in plain daylight."[19] Many Japanese women who, unless they had worked in the brothel districts, had previously had very little exposure to public displays of eroticism also looked on with interest and some envy because of the pan pan girls' access to scarce commodities and luxury items including foreign fashions and cosmetics.[20] Indeed, the access that some Japanese women had to foreign luxury items in the precarious postwar years was the cause of resentment for Japanese men, as can be seen in the censors' decision to suppress the August 1946 cover of popular magazine *Van*. The cover "portraying a skinny Japanese man starving to death, surrounded by some vigorous Japanese women attired in ultra-American style bathing suits" was considered liable to disturb public peace and tranquility.[21] Children, too, were intrigued by the sexual shenanigans going on around them and "pan pan play," in which boys impersonating American soldiers would stroll about with local girls on their arms was a common children's game in the city streets.[22] It was no longer Japanese tradition but American GIs who "set models for the exchange of gestures between boys and girls."[23]

This newly conspicuous culture of eroticism was part of a broader reaction against the "spiritual" values and austere lifestyles urged by the defeated military regime. The characteristically Japanese "philosophy" that had underpinned imperialist ideology was discredited not simply because it had led the nation to disaster but also because of the ease with which so-called intellectuals had repeatedly switched sides from opposition to, support for, and again to criticism of Japan's imperialist project. The intellectual idealism and spiritual sacrifice that underlay the notion of the *kokutai* or "national body" was rejected in favor of a renewed emphasis on the importance of the lived experience of each individual's *nikutai* or "physical body."[24] Indeed, as Igarashi points out, "for many survivors of the war, their bodies were the only material objects they managed to rescue from the air raids."[25] Popular writers such as Tamura Taijirō developed a new literary genre that came to be known as the "literature of the flesh" (*nikutai bungaku*) that dealt with the daily struggle for survival. As Rubin points out,

> the sexual themes in serious literature were simply one aspect of the generally *physical* thrust of a literature written by people whose recent experience of hunger and death had had few precedents in world history, and who had been shown beyond doubt that the "spiritual" values supporting their "sacred war effort" had been no match for material Western culture.[26]

Although the "serious literature" of the *nikutai bungaku* has been extensively translated and commented upon in English-language scholarship on Japan, less attention has been paid to the far larger body of "mass entertainment magazines"[27] dealing with similar themes that appeared from 1946 to 1949. Yet, as Dower points out, participants in *kasutori* culture "also exhibited an ardor and vitality that conveyed a strong impression of liberation from authority and dogma."[28] Hence, as Yamamoto Akira notes, a *fūzokushi*,[29] that is, a "history of (sexual) customs/morals" of the early postwar period, needs to take account of this important body of texts. In this chapter I provide an overview of the development of this genre and the new kinds of sexual knowledge that it pioneered. I also look at the fortuitous publication in 1948 of Alfred Kinsey's report into the sex lives of American men. The fact that an "American scientist" was able to delve into every corner of men's sexual experience, uncovering some embarrassing facts on the way, emboldened Japanese sex reformers. The Kinsey report became an important exemplar for those Japanese calling for greater transparency in the discussion of Japanese sexual mores.

Sexual Discourse in the *Kasutori* Press

The decision on the part of the Civil Censorship Detachment (CCD) not to impose censorship on Japanese "sexual customs" (*sei fūzoku*) did not mean that the administration was not interested in reform of the most intimate aspects of people's lives. On the contrary, various initiatives encouraged Japanese people to be more open about eroticism than had been permissible under the imperialist regime. Images of "romance," in particular, were supported through the notion that engendering chivalry on the part of Japanese men would help elevate the position of Japanese women from that of servant to partner. Thus, while authoritarian regimes commonly repress erotic, alongside political, expression[30] in the case of postwar Japan an unusually vibrant and explicit erotic culture developed and was freely represented in the press, on the stage, and to a more limited extent in literature and film. In fact, in a curious turn of events, it became much easier to talk about sex in the Japanese media in the late 1940s than it was in the United States or elsewhere in the Anglophone world. Indeed, "sexual liberation" (*sei kaihō*) and "free love" (*jiyū ren'ai*) were openly discussed in the *kasutori* press in the late 1940s in a manner not apparent in the American media until the 1960s.

However it is important to note that "sexual liberation" in late 1940s Japan was very different from the so-called sexual revolution that was to take place in the United States and across the Western world two decades later. After all, in the context of Japanese culture male sexuality had never been confined to the marital relationship—men who had the means had always been able to take advantage of the legally regulated "floating world" of commercial sex venues. In the postwar context, it was husbands and wives, and to a lesser extent courting couples, who were encouraged to "liberate" their sexuality and to explore pleasure as an important aspect of relationship building. It was the emphasis upon the centrality of sexual satisfaction (as opposed to procreation) in the context of the marital relationship that seemed so liberating. Furthermore, the "free love" that was called for in late-40s' Japan meant the freedom for men and women to choose their own marriage partner without parental or societal interference. As radical as the *kasutori* press's celebration of sexual desire might have seemed at the time, it was still very much centered on a model that saw courtship leading to monogamous marriage as the only legitimate expression of sensual desire *for women*.[31] Men, however, were still offered a variety of scenarios for the exploration of sexual possibilities as will be seen in Chapter 6.

It is also important to emphasize that the "liberation" of sexuality was highly asymmetrical. On the whole it was men, whether American or Japanese, who were offered greater access to highly sexualized images of women. Whereas in the prewar period there had been a sharp distinction made between the professional women of the licensed quarters who serviced men's sexual desires and the so-called daughters of good families who were destined to become good wives, wise mothers, in these early postwar years, men were encouraged to think of "women in general" (*ippan no josei*) as potential erotic objects. As Igarashi notes, "the body that received attention in occupied Japan was gendered: female bodies and sexuality became the focus of celebration and commodification."[32] It is certainly true that *kasutori* culture was full of images of sexually active women, but these women were not necessarily free agents, instead they were "caught up in market forces that offered them to male desire at a price."[33]

Despite a range of reforms aimed at increasing female agency at home and in the workplace, in the early postwar years women were still at a distinct disadvantage.[34] Lower-class women with little social or cultural capital were particularly vulnerable to sexual predation by both Allied personnel and Japanese men alike.[35] Many hundreds of thousands of married women had lost their soldier husbands during the war and eligible bachelors were in short supply. It was estimated in 1952 that among men and women in the desirable age range (between 20 and 29 for women and between 24 and 34 for men), women outnumbered men 7 to 5. In Tokyo alone there were estimated to be 23,000 women looking for husbands.[36] Some women were forced into undesirable part-time associations with Japanese men who were already married, known as "Saturday wives" or "business-trip wives," they were understood to be modern-day concubines. Occupation officers, too, had their "only-san," women with whom they contracted relationships during their tour of duty, often to abandon at the train station upon their return home.[37] Despite the enthusiasm of the press, in this environment women were not always able to negotiate with their partners "democratically."

The circulation and reach of the *kasutori* press is difficult to ascertain but it is estimated that between 1946 and 1949 there were between 700 and 1,000 sex-related magazines and newspapers printed.[38] It is difficult to come up with an exact figure since publications rapidly went out of print, but new publications—sometimes with the same or similar titles—sprang up to feed the demand. Significantly, not all titles were published in Tokyo. Other regional centers including Osaka, Nagoya, and even rural areas such as Gifu were also involved in the *kasutori*-publishing business. To a large extent, place of publication depended upon the availability of local paper supplies, which were still hard to come by in the immediate postwar years.[39] The picture is further complicated by the fact that some publications were amateurish fly-by-night operations that, taking advantage of local paper supplies, were hurriedly got together, printed secretly, and sent off to market and sold before the authorities became aware of their existence.[40] Often in the chaotic postwar years, the real writers and publishers of this material proved difficult to track down.

An editor of some of the earliest postwar sex publications mentions print runs of 70,000[41] noting that these early publications "sold in an instant as if they flew off the shelves."[42] Such was the demand that buyers are mentioned as coming to Tokyo and Osaka in order to purchase copies to sell on at a profit in rural areas.[43] CCD records note more conservative circulation estimates—*Abekku* (Couple) was noted as 35,000 and *Ryōki* (Curiosity hunting) as 20,000[44]—but Yamamoto mentions that the magazines were on sale all over the country and that a single issue would pass through many hands.[45] Looking back on this period in 1953, Narumigi states that "anyone could easily buy [obscene books and erotic materials] on the black market or at public gathering places."[46]

Hence, given their widespread availability, the *kasutori* magazines and newspapers published during the early postwar years are a key resource for studying the changes taking place in popular ideas about male/female relations and about sexuality more generally. As Yamamoto points out, these publications are valuable for gauging attitudes among the general population since they were not entirely authored by intellectuals or professional writers, but relied upon reader submissions for much of their copy.[47] Although the editors had one eye on the police and the other on quick profits[48] and the writing, much of it contributed by university students, may seem "astonishingly bad,"[49] the contents do give an insight into themes and ideas that struck people of the time as interesting, significant, or simply entertaining. These magazines also had an impact far beyond their readership to the extent that their contents influenced other popular media such as cinema and literature. Yamamoto, for instance, cites a movie director who was working at the Matsutake studios in the late 1940s who acknowledged the impact of the *kasutori* press on his filmmaking. He says, "The *kasutori* magazines were an important resource for me when creating movie hero/heroines for those living at the very bottom of society."[50]

According to Yamamoto,[51] there were three different phases of *kasutori* publications. The first, from January to October of 1946 saw the emergence of magazines such as *Riberaru* (Liberal) that were influential in disseminating the new vocabulary of "free choice" and "romantic love" in intimate relations. However, it was the massively popular reissue of Van de Velde's marital sex guide in two different editions, an entire translation issued as *Kanzen naru kekkon* (Perfect marriage) in June 1946 and a shorter edited version entitled *Kanzen naru fūfu* (Perfect couple) issued shortly after, that heralded a new more sex-oriented genre of publications such as *Ryōki* (Curiosity hunting), first issued in October 1946. From January of 1947, the magazines became even more explicit in their discussions of sexual issues and more graphic, including photos and illustrations of seminaked women which, from mid-year, increasingly included the use of color, thus increasing their "visual impact."[52]

The explicitness of magazine content increased throughout the next 18 months. It became common to include color inserts of erotic illustrations that had far more impact than regular photographs due to the skillful manner in which they visualized the sexy scenarios suggested by the text.[53] From August 1948, new magazines such as *Ōru ryōki* (All curiosity hunting) began to publish female nudes for the first time and the number of such magazines in circulation reached the hundreds. The final phase of the *kasutori* press, which Yamamoto dates from June 1949 to May 1950, saw publications such as *Fūfu seikatsu* (Conjugal lifestyle) moving away from "sexual anarchy" and more toward "sexual management" of the married couple.[54] In an attempt to establish legitimacy, several editions of *Fūfu seikatsu* featured a preface by a notable expert such as the director of the National Diet Library, and the magazine often featured lifestyle-oriented advertisements for luxury items such as American-style bedroom furnishings and domestic appliances.

Although the upsurge in sexual discourse in the *kasutori* press had mostly run its course by the end of 1949, what was known at the time as "sex journalism" carried on into the early 1950s. This included the development of journals that adopted a more serious and instructional tone and included more articles geared toward sex education by accredited experts such as doctors, thus courting a "middle brow" readership. Two examples, both founded in 1950, which were aimed at a readership of "intellectuals" and "cultured persons," were *Ningen tankyū* (Human investigation) and *Amatoria*, edited by prominent sex researcher Takahashi Tetsu.[55] These magazines offered more sober analytic discussions of sexuality and were remarkable in the early postwar period for their supportive approach to a variety of "sexual perversions," especially male homosexuality.[56]

Given the almost complete absence of sex education and erotic materials during the war years and the state of "spiritual mobilization" that looked down on sensual indulgence or displays of any kind, the sudden emergence of public discourse about sex and romance was startling. In terms of readership, a key market was male students who would read and discuss these articles communally in their dorm rooms.[57] Yamamoto, who was a middle-school student in 1948, recalls his sense of shock at the time when he first came across an article discussing female masturbation.[58] He remembers feeling extremely disappointed that women, particularly the girls he idolized from afar, could engage in such a practice. In accounting for his naiveté, Yamamoto points out that during the war years, male and female students had virtually no contact with each other, leading to an idealization of the opposite sex. He also mentions the extremely limited sex education available that left most young people unclear as to the actual mechanics of reproduction. It was a commonsense assumption among men that women experienced little sexual desire and were very keen to preserve their chastity. So strong was this commonsense reasoning, Yamamoto recalls, that men were reluctant to entertain the idea of female sexual agency.[59]

Much sexual discussion was of course prurient and directed by male editors and writers, and women in these accounts often featured only as passive objects for male exploration and education. However, women readers were also addressed in a number of general publications as well as in a variety of "romance" magazines that appealed primarily to a female audience. For instance, in 1948 the *Shinsō shimbun* (True-tales newspaper) featured a regular "world of love" feature that it advertised was "edited solely by women"[60]—indicating an awareness of a female readership and the need for "female perspectives."

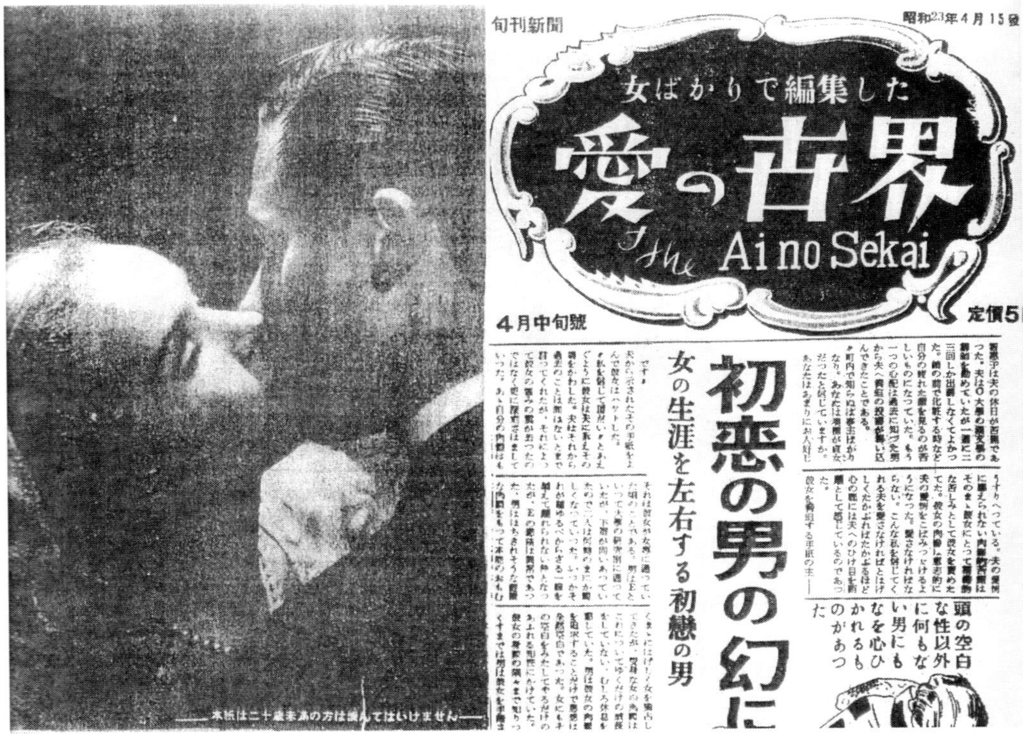

旬刊新聞

昭和23年4月15日發

女ばかりで編集した

愛の世界

Ai no Sekai

4月中旬號

定價5

初恋の男の幻に

女の生涯を左右する初戀の男

頭の空白な性以外に何もない男にも心ひかれるものがあった

本紙は二十歳未満の方は讀んではいけません

Figure 3.1 A section on the "world of love" advertising itself as edited solely by women in the April 15, 1948, edition of *Shinsō shimbun* (True tales newspaper)

Note: Original in the Gordon W. Prange Collection at the University of Maryland.

Women were also featured as authors and as participants in roundtable discussions that were transcribed and published in the press. These included the voices of respectable women who discussed the implications of recent social reforms in terms of courtship and married life, as well as women who had been forced into a life of prostitution due to poverty and lack of other options in the immediate postwar chaos.[61] Women writers also contributed fictional narratives, including well-known author Koito Shinobu, several of whose serialized novellas dealing with "the problem of sex" were later made into films.[62] In fact the need for "female perspectives" on a wide variety of topics, from "first experiences" of courtship and lovemaking[63] to prostitution and the practice of bedroom arts, was widely recognized. [64]

The emphasis on "women's rights" and "women's perspectives" resulted from "a particular ideological pairing between democracy and feminism that occurred during the Occupation."[65] As discussed, SCAP believed that the treatment of women under the previous regime, where their freedoms had been extremely constrained in both the public and private spheres, was a clear and demonstrable example of the kind of feudalism that needed to be rooted out if the new Japan was to take its place at the world table. The reform of women's roles in courtship and lovemaking thus also emerged as an important topic in discussions of democratization.

A range of different women was given the chance to speak in the sex press. In April 1948, for instance, the magazine *Ai* (Love) ran a "roundtable" group interview with self-identified pan pan women, ostensibly to discover their reasons for entering that profession.[66] Despite the manner in which prostitution was looked down upon, the tone of the interview was rather upbeat with the male interviewer expressing admiration for the women's commitment to self-responsibility and survival. He opens the interview by commenting, "You have been living your lives with strength despite others' misperceptions. In today's meeting, I would like to hear your true feelings of pleasure as well as distress in order to better understand you."[67]

Throughout the discussion, the interviewer is keen to hear more about the social situation facing the women and there is little attempt to sensationalize their lives or delve into more sexualized aspects of their experience. All the interviewees were unanimous that it was economic privation that brought them into the sex trade, commenting that in the circumstances it was all but impossible for a woman to live without support from a male breadwinner. To this extent they saw some equivalence between their own situation and other women who also relied upon male support in order to survive. However, despite earning comparatively large incomes for the time (at least twice that of the male interviewer), all the women expressed a desire to leave the trade at the earliest opportunity and to enter into a love marriage. The women in that interview, despite the necessity of adopting a mercantile attitude to sex, were still hoping to find "someone who will love [them] regardless of [their] past." In their desire for a "loving and supportive husband," even these sex workers were drawn into the romantic love ideology being promulgated in the *kasutori* publications.

Of interest, too, is the manner in which the *kasutori* press also gave voice to individuals who we would describe today as members of sexual minorities. One example is a roundtable discussion between *danshō* or cross-dressing male prostitutes that was published in the magazine *OK* in August 1949.[68] We will look at the contents of the conversation in detail in Chapter 6. However, it is sufficient to note here that such an article would hardly have been possible in the United States at the time given that "sodomy" was still a crime and the very mention of homosexuality could be considered obscene. Despite the fact that similar communities of cross-dressing male prostitutes had also existed in New York since the end of the nineteenth century,[69] censorship laws in the United States were such that it would have been extremely difficult to publish a nonpathologizing account of their lives.[70]

Hence, the *kasutori* press was crucial in disseminating sexual knowledge more widely. The experiences explored were not always heterosexual or procreative in nature, as recognized in the title of one of the most notorious of the *kasutori* magazines, *Ryōki*, whose title is a term popularized during the "*ero-guro*" boom of the 1920s[71] and meaning something like "hunting for the (erotically) bizarre." Articles in this and similar magazines were interested in exploring the impact of the war and Japan's defeat upon the sexual sensibilities of both men and women. One theme frequently explored was the notion that Japan's defeat had created a nation of masochist men and sadist women.[72] The freedom with which the Japanese press under the Occupation was able to explore (and thereby disseminate information about) a wide range of heterosexual and nonheterosexual "perversions" (*hentai seiyoku*) thus qualifies previous accounts of this period that have stressed the conservative and restrictive effects of US sex and gender policies in Japan.[73]

In terms of discussion of male-female sexual interactions, Van de Velde's marital sex guide proved to be a ubiquitous influence on early postwar sexual discourse (indeed the Japanese translation remained in print until 1982). The book itself was widely read—*Kanzen naru kekkon* sold 3,500 copies in just two weeks in one Osaka bookstore alone.[74] However, text and diagrams from the book were also widely excerpted and published in the press, thus extending its readership and influence.

Van de Velde had placed a great deal of emphasis on the need for simultaneous orgasm in the context of a "perfect" marriage and his text exhaustively explores every conceivable sexual position to bring this about.

He also went into great detail explicating (with charts and diagrams) the differences between the onset, peak, and duration of male and female climaxes. Van de Velde's influence was reflected in the many articles in the *kasutori* press on the theme of "sexual technique," by which was meant techniques that men should practice in order to bring about orgasms for their female partners. Indeed, the need for the "sexual satisfaction" of both partners became a key symbol of the new equality between the sexes and the term was used accordingly to differentiate "modern" from "feudal" forms of coupledom.

The concept of sexual technique and the elaboration of different positions were not, of course, new in Japanese culture. As we saw in Chapter 1, Japan was heir to a long tradition of erotic art and literature but the transmission of this knowledge had been seriously interrupted from the Meiji period onward through the precensorship of published materials. What was new about Van de Velde's treatment of sexuality was his presentation of sex as a "process" based upon an academic, if not exactly scientific, analysis.[75] Hence, whereas Japan's traditional exposition of eroticism seemed somewhat backward-looking, if not outright "feudal," Van de Velde's text was very much situated as part of a new, forward-looking, "modern" discourse of sexual equality.

The widespread influence of this "new approach" can be seen in the title of Fukuoka Takeo's 1949 book *Sei no atarashii ninshiki to rinri* (New consciousness and morals of sex) that made liberal use of Van de Velde's and other Western sexologists' ideas. Fukuoka was head of the Japan Society for Sex Education's communications office and sometimes participated in NHK radio broadcasts on sexual problems as well as offering sex counseling in publications such as *Ningen tankyū* (Human investigation) and *Fūfu seikatsu* (Conjugal couple lifestyle).[76] In the book he was keen to stress how in the new Japan, "custom" must give way to "sexual science" when regulating male-female interaction. No longer could male and female relations be properly managed through "the separation of male and female from age seven," as had been the Confucian custom.[77] Pointing out that although humankind was the highest of all the animals, people were animals none the less, he argued that the workings of the body were best left to scientists to explain.[78] A "proper sex life" could only be founded on correct knowledge, not ignorance, and the inculcation of this proper understanding needed to begin in childhood.

The tone of the many discussions about sexual technique was matter of fact and instructional, women being regarded almost as machines in need of fine-tuning by their technician husbands or lovers. In a typical article on "sexual love techniques" published in December 1947, for instance, it was noted that female frigidity was the result of a lack of skill on the part of a woman's male partner, particularly insufficient foreplay. The average length of intercourse, at three minutes, was judged insufficient for female pleasure and it was suggested that men's lack of interest in female response was ungentlemanly and reflected poor etiquette. Male readers were encouraged to study the charts depicting the onset and development of male and female orgasm and to regulate their own climaxes so as to better optimize ideal conditions for the climaxes of their partners.[79]

Articles directed at husbands, exhorting them to improve their sexual technique, were also paralleled by articles encouraging wives to ask for more sexual attention from their husbands.[80] The tone of these discussions was quite different from prewar women's magazines that tended to stress the need for women to acquiesce to male pleasure.[81] One unfortunate outcome from the repeated demand to enjoy mutual orgasms was an "orgasm obsession" as evidenced in an outpouring of letters from both men and women testifying to their "failure" to achieve this end and questioning their sexual health and normalcy.

The highly functional, hydraulic understanding of sexuality characteristic of the war years that had stressed the public value of this very personal act was soon challenged by this new discourse that sought to redefine the meaning of sex, particularly for women. As Christine Marran notes, the *kasutori* press was influential in disseminating "anecdotes and interviews to prove not the perversity but rather the normalcy of female sexual desire,"[82] an idea that in the early postwar years "seemed startling."[83] The new discourse posited sex as a recreational activity to be enjoyed equally by both partners. "Sexual love" (*sei ai*) was inscribed as a central aspect of the new "romantic-love marriage system"[84] and was discussed with reference to a wide variety of classical erotic texts from around the globe, particularly India. An article in the August 1949 edition of *Shin fūfu* (new conjugal couple),[85] for instance, concluded that the Japanese were "weak in sexual love," the period of their lives in which they were sexually active being considered shorter than that of other races. Indeed, it was suggested that the Japanese needed to learn more from Indians, who were, sexually speaking, the "strongest race" (albeit the only evidence proffered for this claim was the erotic classic, the *Kāma Sutra*).[86]

Numerous other articles attempted not only to expand the range of sexual practices (as well as the duration of the sex act) but also to expand the definition of the sexual. A 1949 article subtitled "sex life from the perspective of the nose," for instance, discussed a range of scents that had traditionally been used as aphrodisiacs in an effort to encourage couples to experiment with and enjoy the smell of their partners.[87] Another article explored the "taste of kisses," suggesting that while men sought out sweet, sugary tastes in their partners' mouths, women preferred bitter tastes such as tobacco. Women were also said to enjoy the sensation of kissing men with beards.[88] Igarashi notes that under the militarist regime, "Japanese bodies had been forced to endure the deprivation of sensory stimuli"[89] and therefore through emphasizing sensory indulgence through sex, Japanese people were able to express their defiance of the regulatory regime that had demanded bodily sacrifice. He suggests that in the immediate postwar years popular culture "celebrated sexuality" because it "was a means of moving beyond the state's regulatory mandates."[90]

Whereas during wartime marital sexuality had been framed in reproductive terms, coopted as a means of producing and managing "human resources," postwar discussion of sexuality frequently made reference to contraception. Information about birth-control practices had been tightly restricted during the war but within a year of the defeat it was possible to read detailed descriptions of contraceptive techniques in the popular press,[91] and newspapers and magazines were full of advertisements for birth control and prophylactic products such as condoms and pessaries.[92] In a direct affront to wartime ideologues who had considered the use of contraception akin to "race suicide," left-leaning intellectuals such as birth-control campaigner Majima Kan[93] argued that unlike in the animal world, the true significance of sexuality among human beings was not reproduction but "recreation."[94]

The militarist regime had been against the provision of family planning advice. Their solution to the problems associated with a growing population and limited resources had been to pursue a policy of overseas expansion. As we saw in Chapter 1, Japanese people were encouraged to "give birth and multiply" so as to provide new citizens for the army and colonies. In that system every healthy man and woman had a patriotic duty to marry and produce children and the use of contraception aimed at limiting family size was seen as contrary to the war effort. In the immediate postwar years, however, Japan faced a population crisis. Over 5 million Japanese who had been residing overseas in the armed forces and in the colonies were repatriated at a time when Japan's economy and food production were in crisis. Housing, especially in the cities, was limited, and it was difficult for people to raise children in that environment. Hence, the new Japanese government, albeit anxious that too much information might fuel a decline in morals, generally supported birth-control measures. The Ministry of Health was involved in the development of a series of "birth-control movies" (*basukon eiga*) as well as pamphlets and brochures that detailed methods for family planning.[95]

In the face of this looming population crisis, newspaper polls conducted in 1949 indicated that a majority of respondents supported contraception in principle but although two-thirds supported the use of contraception only one-third to one-half of married couples reported practicing it on a regular basis. There was a large difference between rural and city dwellers, with only one-fifth of country dwellers using contraception. Reluctance to use contraception was not due to any moral misgivings; however, respondents suggested that it was "not reliable," "bothersome," or "expensive."[96] Many of the sex-advice magazines sought to counter these attitudes by discussing the pros and cons of different contraceptive devices, and one magazine went as far as to include coupons for contraceptive pessaries that could be redeemed at pharmacies.[97]

Fashioning Identities

Other ways in which Japanese people were encouraged to demonstrate a break with the past and their embrace of more democratic way of living was through fashion. Via discussions in the *kasutori* press, Japanese couples were not simply directed to act differently but to dress differently too. Fashion had been a conspicuous casualty during the later stages of the war as the Japanese homeland faced ever greater restrictions on common commodities, especially food and clothing. By the war's end, even those few with the resources necessary to maintain a comfortable lifestyle were required to show restraint and avoid ostentation. By 1944, the sporting of permanent waves, make-up, and colorful clothing had been banned (not that such things were available for purchase anyway). Yet, by that point in the war there were few occasions on which such frivolous accessories would have been appropriate, given that the dance halls had long been closed and even Western instruments such as banjos, ukuleles, and steel guitars had been silenced by official decree. Upon Japan's surrender in August 1945, the personal and emotional life of the Japanese people seemed as drab and lifeless as the burned out remains of Japan's major cities.

However, soon after the surrender, both sound and color began to return to the streets of Tokyo. Appreciation of jazz music had long been a part of Japan's café culture and musical theater until it was suppressed by the militarists after the commencement of the Sino-Japanese war in 1937 on the grounds that these foreign sounds were contrary to the state of "spiritual mobilization." Hence, "liberation of the American jazz sound was one of the American gifts most sought after" by fashionable city dwellers.[98] Jazz music almost became the soundtrack to the Occupation as a consequence of the adoption in November 1945 by NHK radio of a "blanket coverage" system that did not allow for dead air—and since there was at that time insufficient material to fill all the broadcast time, "American jazz music was played instead."[99] Colorful aloha shirts, available for barter on the black market, began to brighten up men's appearance, replacing the "somber-hued clothes of the cheapest material" that were common during the war years.[100] However, given that Western garb had already long supplanted men's kimono in Japan for all but ceremonial occasions, it was Japanese women's appearance that was transformed most radically.

It was the so-called pan pan girls and the "taxi-dancers"[101] working in dance halls frequented by Westerners who were among the first women to pioneer Western fashions "whereas ordinary women were still clad in wartime work trousers."[102] Women who specifically catered to men of the Occupation were referred to as "*yō* [Western] *pan*" and it was their appearance that was most radically transformed due to their access to much prized clothes, make-up, and other "breath-takingly marvelous things"[103] available from the "PX" (post exchange) stores via their foreign lovers. Though at first it was young people, particularly black market racketeers and pan pan girls, who pioneered these new fashions, "Japanese people were sick of all shades of khaki, which they had been made to call the 'national defense color,'"[104] and colorful, stylish new clothes were highly prized as symbols of the *après la guerre* spirit.

By 1946, the style of the many second-generation Japanese-speaking Nisei women from Hawaii who had come over to assist the Occupation forces was also having a strong impact on native Japanese women, many of whom were keen to set their hair in permanent waves at the many beauty shops that "cropped up like mushrooms after the rain"[105] among the ruins. The adoption of Western women's fashions, which had not been widespread in the previous period, spread throughout Tokyo as quickly as material and purchasing power would allow. At first, existing Japanese clothes were reworked to approximate Western fashions such as cardigans and sweaters. Entrepreneurs set up sewing shops amid the ruins and magazines featured how-to sew guides to cater to the sudden boom in demand for styles and colors not previously seen on Japan's streets.[106] Most of these new businesses were run by women and the recycling of old clothes became an important way for women to earn extra income. These fashion entrepreneurs were but one example of the kind of "war-impoverished, aggressive-mannered girls" who were beginning to take advantage of new opportunities amid the postwar chaos.[107]

As with other changes in Japanese behavior, fashion choice, too, was often rhetorically linked with talk of democracy. Writing in 1952 columnist Junsei Ijichi noted that

> [c]onsciously or unconsciously [Japanese women] have adopted American dress because they believe that is the hallmark of democratic culture.

> The family system of old Japan has been legally abolished; the relations between parents and children, brothers and sisters, now stand on a new basis; and the women have been freed from the conventions of feudal society. New freedom, new dress—such seems to be the motto of Japanese women.[108]

Dress, or the lack of it, was an important symbol of liberation on the stage, too. Beginning in early 1947 a number of small theatres in Tokyo began to advertise "picture frame shows" that featured scantily clad young women posing on stage within wooden frames in imitation of famous nudes in Western art.[109] The first such actress to pose in that way was Miwa Kai whose impression of Botticelli's *Birth of Venus* caused a sensation. It was not long before any pretence at artistic enlightenment was cast aside and the nude show turned into the *sutorippu* (strip) where women would tease the audience by gradually disrobing. Capitalizing on the demand for more graphic sexual entertainment, some theater owners began to offer mixed programs that interspersed short "birth-control films" with live striptease. Roland Domenig records an eyewitness report from one such show in Asakusa, Tokyo, in the following words:

> The tiny theatre that is already overcrowded at 100 people, was jam-packed with 150 people. When some people tried to move in the crowded space that did not allow any movement, the wainscoting and the pipes behind it broke and the sewage spilled over the feet of the audience. The audience, however, didn't care at all, but continued to watch the program.[110]

These shows were largely staged for a local audience and were looked down on by the Americans who found Japanese men's earnest fascination with women's exposed flesh to be amusing.[111] At first the strip shows were indeed clumsy and inelegant. Japanese who had witnessed more professional performances in Paris before the war complained that the exotic fans made of ostrich plumes had in Japan been replaced by tawdry imitations made of chicken feathers. However, it did not take long for the performances to become slicker as "the glitter and streamlined production of the American chorus line was introduced."[112] These popular shows, set to American jazz and jive music, reintroduced the Japanese public to an increasingly globalized kind of feminine glamour that could be seen on the stages of New York, London, or Paris.

Many people wished to appropriate the symbols of freedom and modernity associated with America. Dower points out how in Japan's war-ravaged cities, the US military exchange posts were the source of "voluptuously decadent" symbols of prosperity such as liquor, cigarettes, sweets and delicacies, lipstick, and nylon stockings. Given their access to these goods via fraternization with male Occupation personnel, Japanese women, and in particular the "pan pan" girls, with their "brightly rouged lips and colorful clothing" were "part of a mystique of American glamour and fashion that made a spectacular impact after the drab parsimony of the war years."[113] The pan pan girls became "harbingers of a hedonistic, materialistic, American-style consumer culture."[114] As Hiromi Ochi argues, "the political discourse of democracy [was] materialized as cultural and economic discourses" that stressed both the superiority as well as desirability of Western, particularly American, lifestyles.[115] Above all, it was the pan pan girls who influenced styles of dress and deportment that were later embraced by other Japanese women. In particular, it was the visible presence of the pan pan girls on the streets of Japan's major cities that opened up opportunities for more public displays of courtship and romance among Japanese "new couples" more generally.

Yet, despite the fact that women's agency in conducting their romantic affairs was clearly enhanced by Occupation reforms, it needs to be borne in mind that the early postwar "liberation" of sexuality was not particularly democratic in that the loosening of sexual mores benefited men over women. After all, what the removal of the militarist censorship regime enabled was men's increased access to sexualized representations of "women in general." Whereas during the war years, men's access had been primarily to "professional" women's bodies and was restricted to clearly defined pleasure quarters in Japan's cities and throughout its colonies, by 1947 sexualized representations of women were available for all to see in the press, on the stage, and even on the streets. Advertisements for the newly popular "nude shows" could be seen on billboards across Japan's cities and multiple entrepreneurs sought to profit from the public interest in the female nude. For instance in December 1947 the magazine *Asahi gurafu* (*Asahi* graphic) ran a double-page photospread of a Tokyo print shop whose entire front window was taken up with a display of female nude photographs.[116] As well as offering close-up photos of the artfully posed nudes themselves, the magazine featured 11 photographs taken at different times of day recording the different kinds of passersby who crowded the window to check out the wares. These included groups of suited salary men in hats, war veterans on crutches, and even a threesome of giggling schoolgirls dressed in sailor-suit uniforms. "Is this art or curiosity hunting?" demanded the headline—clearly for both the magazine readers and the casual bystanders it was more of the latter. Despite the fact that the article proclaimed the new visibility of the (female) nude an important "opening up of unexplored regions," in reality what was being opened up was not mutual sexual exploration by both sexes but men's access to women.

Reception of the First Kinsey Report in Japan

Another factor that emboldened Japanese reformers who sought to "liberate" sex from its wartime straitjacket was the first Kinsey report on *Sexual Behavior in the Human Male* released in the United States in 1948 and hurriedly published in Japanese translation in 1950. From 1948 onwards, the mainstream press made many references to Kinsey's controversial findings. What impressed Japanese commentators was not only the ability of a US academic to carry out such a large-scale and comprehensive survey of individuals' sex lives, but also the very great variety of sexual practices that he uncovered. Readers in Japan were particularly interested in Kinsey's discussion of the prevalence of masturbation and homosexuality among American men as well as the widespread occurrence of pre- and extramarital sexuality including premarital sexual practices such as "petting."[117]

Kinsey's *Sexual Behavior in the Human Male* was the first large-scale scientific survey of American men's sexual activities and the breadth of its findings challenged previous taken-for-granted assumptions about what constituted "normal" sexual interests and behaviors. Based on interviews with some 12,000 men, Kinsey and his collaborators discovered a wide variety of sexual experiences including high rates of premarital sex, marital infidelity, and homosexual contacts. So challenging were these findings to received opinions that in reviews and editorials the book was frequently compared to Charles Darwin's *On the Origin of Species.*

Despite the controversy that the survey's release generated in the US media, Japanese commentators who were keen to push forward an agenda of sexual reform were able to harness the book's scientific and American pedigrees to bolster their arguments for the further liberation of sexual mores.[118] Information about the Kinsey report was widely dispersed in Japan and included articles in regional as well as national newspapers. For instance, on March 29, 1948, an article in the *Kyūshu taimuzu* (Kyushu times) summarized some of Kinsey's most confronting findings. These included the facts that some 85 percent of American men surveyed had experienced sex before marriage, nearly 70 percent of men had at some stage paid for sex, and 37 percent had had at least one homosexual experience. This was followed by another report on April 17, pointing out how sales were strong and the book had become a publishing sensation. Given that at that time "negative criticism" of Allied nations was still subject to censorship, it is interesting that this and similar reports were allowed to circulate.

Such was the popular interest in the Kinsey reports that a Japanese translation was quickly prepared in a collaborative effort between scholars at Tokyo, Keio, Meiji, and Nippon universities and released by the Kosumoporitan company in 1950. Despite the fact that the book's reviewers were keen to stress the scientific nature of the text, emphasizing that it did not pander to "curiosity hunting tastes" (*ryōki shumi*), the translation did prove popular in Japan. Indeed, such was the interest in the book that on February 12, 1950, the evening edition of the *Yomiuri* newspaper reported that a high-school teacher had been held up in the street and his copy stolen "by a group of three student-like persons."

Although summaries of Kinsey's more eyebrow-raising findings were widely circulated in the Japanese press and detailed reviews had appeared in specialized scientific journals soon after the book's release, it was not until the 1950 publication of the Japanese translation that commentators were able to fully assess the book's implications for Japanese sexual mores. A front page editorial in the evening edition of the *Yomiuri* newspaper on March 17, 1950, for instance, was keen to distance Kinsey's report from the "carnal literature," "nude shows," and "pulp fiction" considered to be inflaming the public's interest in sexual issues. The author argued that the main impact of Kinsey's findings was that "desire for sex [alongside food] is a fundamental part of nature" and that sex education must start from this premise. Although many people still believed "sex is dirty" and insisted on outmoded ideas such as "boys and girls should not sit together from age seven," sexual desires "cannot be covered up by putting a lid on them." On the contrary, recognition of the reality of sexual desire was necessary for "proper sex education" and "proper sexual etiquette" to develop. The author of this review appealed to the *scientific* authority of Kinsey's report (comparing Kinsey to Darwin) in an attempt to wrest sexuality away from the "old moralists" who would have maintained the feudal customs of the past.

The Kinsey report was also important in providing support for similar sexological surveys of the Japanese population. As Fruhstuck points out, postwar sexologists "set out to 'free Japan of the militarist suppression' of sex in order to allow research and education on sexual matters."[119] Although limited sexological surveys had been carried out in Japan's imperialist period, the findings were only circulated among elite medical specialists or had been suppressed altogether. However, in the early postwar period there was a boom in such surveys and their findings were eagerly pored over in the popular press.

One of the first postwar surveys was conducted by Shinozaki Nobuo[120] who collected 1,500 responses from Japanese men and women in both rural and urban areas. In an article by Shinozaki reporting his findings published in the March 7, 1950, edition of the *Yomiuri* newspaper, he bemoaned the low level of sexual information among the Japanese population. Unlike the supposedly scientific-minded Americans who cooperated with Kinsey, Shinozaki reported being criticized by many of his Japanese interviewees who considered his questions about their sexual backgrounds to be rude. He was even "interfered with" by some respondents who "got the wrong idea!"

Another researcher, Yasuda Tokutarō, whose early attempts to survey the sexual behavior of male university students in the 1920s had been stymied by the authorities, greeted the release of the Japanese translation of the Kinsey report "with great emotion." In an article in the February 1, 1950, morning edition of the *Asahi* newspaper, he expressed admiration at the scale of the Kinsey report, the "noble character" of the authors, and the power of "American science." Yasuda was also impressed by the forthright nature of the interviewees whose supposed love of science was held responsible for their candid answers. On the other hand, he shared Shinozaki's skepticism about the ability of Japanese people to respond with similar candor.[121]

Yasuda's glowing review of the Kinsey report made no mention of the extreme controversy that both Kinsey's methodology and findings had caused among the American public, many authorities branding the methodology ill-conceived and the findings immoral. Instead, the readers of the morning edition of the newspaper were treated to a detailed outline of the kinds of sexual practices that Kinsey had found to be widespread throughout the American male population. These included masturbation, wet dreams, sexual experience before and outside of marriage, homosexual experience, and sexual contact with animals. Yasuda went on to argue that only empirical evidence gained from widespread surveys of this kind could "clarify the average norm (*noruma*) of sexual behavior of Japanese people." He argued that the important question of what constitutes normal sexual behavior "should not be left to the narrow clinical experience of medical doctors" who had little to offer other than "desk theories," nor should the populace be subject to uninformed "sermons from the authorities." Yasuda concludes his review with the statement that "Japanese who are judged by the opinions of the authorities are less fortunate than the Americans," his inference being that the greater freedom of expression of the Americans is due to their greater appreciation of science.

The fact that the Kinsey report was able to be presented to the Japanese people as an example of "American science" was clearly a useful strategy for reformists who were keen to discredit as outmoded and feudal the ideas of Japan's former leaders. However, the scientific basis of the report was useful, too, for those Japanese who wanted to launch a critique of the American occupiers themselves. The fact that the Japanese translation of the Kinsey report was published in 1950, after the precensorship of the Japanese press by the CCD had been discontinued, meant that the reviews of the book were able to fit other agendas, including criticism of the Americans.

For example, in an article published in the February 1, 1950, morning edition of the *Asahi* newspaper, Minami Hiroshi, a social psychology professor at Japan Women's University, began by welcoming the Japanese translation of the Kinsey report, mentioning that reviewers had likened it to classic works by Adam Smith, Karl Marx, and Charles Darwin. Minami pointed out that the report's strong point was that it was written not by a moralist or a specialist in "sexual science" but by a biologist and that this was an important point for the American reading public who had confidence in the "supremacy of science." Despite the fact that there were flaws in Kinsey's statistical methods that led him to make overbroad claims, Minami found the book to be of value. However, rather than using the report's findings to argue for greater freedom in Japanese sexual mores, as was a common script among reviewers, Minami went on to use the scientific status of the text to criticize the Americans for their "hypocrisy," specifically "the significant gap between what is said about sexual behavior and sex education by the authorities in America and Americans' sexual behavior in reality." Having made this observation Minami segued into a broader critique of the American character that would have almost certainly been expunged from his account had he tried to publish it earlier. He noted that "the contradiction and difference between American 'morals' [unclear in the original] and reality is not limited to the field of sexuality. It has penetrated into various aspects of society. The ideal of wealth and freedom hides the reality of poverty and less freedom." For Minami, the value of the Kinsey report is thus in the "spotlight" it shone on fundamental contradictions in the American character—the difference between American talk and action.

In sum, the publication of the first Kinsey report in 1948 and the rapid release of the 1950 Japanese translation were important events that fueled the already heated debates in the Japanese press about the "liberation" of sexuality. Those commentators who were keen to pursue an agenda of sexual reform were able to use the scientific and American pedigrees of the report to call for a similar "objective" approach to human sexual variety in Japan. The conservative statements of both Japanese and American authorities were argued to be based on now outmoded moral principles, unlike the progressive agenda of scientific researchers whose views were shaped not by ideology but by empirical evidence.

Kinsey's influence continued well into the 1950s, reaching new heights after the release in 1953 of his long-anticipated volume on the human female (the response to which will be discussed in Chapter 5). An example of this impact can be seen in a 1954 discussion printed in the journal *Amatoria* between popular sex journalist Kabiya Kazuhiko[122] and well-known sexologist Ōta Tenrei[123] who discussed the apparently new popularity of "petting" (a term popularized after the release of Kinsey's first volume) among young couples in postwar Japan.[124] Ōta disagreed with early sexologists such as Magnus Hirschfeld, who had, apparently, claimed that such acts as kissing were unknown in Japan. Rather, Ōta claimed that kissing and other activities associated with petting had been known and practiced but they had been done so only as a prelude to intercourse; what was supposedly new in the postwar context was the adoption of this practice by "*abekku*" (from the French *avec*, that is, "with") or dating couples as a recreational activity, one not intended as a prelude to coitus. The role that these expanded narratives of heterosexual interaction, and kissing in particular, played in reforming ideas about romance, dating, and marriage is the topic of Chapters 4 and 5.

4

The Kiss Debate

In 1943 American anthropologist Margaret Mead was in Britain on an important wartime mission: her task was to study the interactions between American servicemen and the local residents. In the monograph she published describing the experience Mead uncovered an important cultural difference between the two societies, a source of continual misunderstanding and conflict: English girls didn't know how to date. When it came to dating, a practice that Mead argued American boys and girls began "in the early teens, long before they are emotionally mature enough to be interested in each other for anything really connected with sex,"[1] young English people didn't have a clue. Why was this? Mead concluded that British society was more sex-segregated than the US society. In fact, she opined, British boys didn't really enjoy the company of girls and "if they just want to spend a pleasant evening, more often they spend it with other boys."[2] Apparently, British people couldn't see the point of a date unless it was a prelude to marriage. That young men and women might want to spend time dancing, going to the movies, or just hanging out struck many British people as odd and not a little suspicious. Surely the Yanks had other things on their minds than chit-chat?

However, Mead argued, for Americans "dating is quite different from being in love, or looking for a casual love partner,"[3] and resembles a popularity game rather than genuine courtship behavior. She pointed out that when an American took a girl's arm without so much as a by your leave, he wasn't about to drag her into the bushes, since "a casual hand on the arm does not mean anything; it is not a preface to greater and unacceptable familiarity."[4] However, to British eyes such a gesture signified a proprietary familiarity and would only have been undertaken in the context of courtship. In her monograph Mead lists a range of such gestures, what Marcel Mauss termed "techniques of the body."[5] These are ways of looking, gesturing, talking, and moving when trying to impress a member of the opposite sex—what can collectively be described as the "habitus"[6] of dating. She notes how these gestures were differently coded and understood in Britain and America and thus became a source of mutual incomprehension.[7]

That two societies with a common language, a shared history, and strong cultural links could differ so markedly concerning courtship raises the question how bizarre American dating practices must have seemed to the Japanese when introduced via Hollywood movies and American GIs during the first years of the Occupation. Even in the late 1950s, after more than a decade of exposure to American values, it was noted that "[t]he American system of casual dating without serious intentions strikes conservative Japanese as a shocking form of exploitation."[8] Although the American convention of dating was eagerly adopted by many couples in Japan in the early postwar period, it was a practice usually taken up *after,* not prior to, engagement since an air of "delinquency" still hung around young men and women who mingled indiscriminately in public.

Despite the large literature that has focused on the political, economic, social, and cultural reforms enacted during the Occupation,[9] little attention has been paid to the impact that the US presence had upon Japanese interpersonal relationships, especially those between men and women. Japanese ideas about courtship, in particular, were radically overhauled during the Occupation period due to the sudden influx of American people and culture into the country. Based on accounts preserved in the popular Japanese press of the period, this chapter investigates the impact that the US troops and US popular culture more generally had upon Japanese notions of courtship and romance in the immediate postwar years through an investigation of what has come to be known as the "kiss debate." The fierce arguments that erupted over the meaning, practice, and cultural appropriateness of kissing helped to spread the new discourses of sexuality that were emerging in the *kasutori* press across the Japanese media in general.[10] Commentaries in the daily newspapers, letters, and advice columns in women's magazines, and, given the furor over "kissing scenes" on screen, articles in movie magazines, all served to make kissing a popular topic for scrutiny and debate.

As we will see, in order for Japanese people to accept the act of kissing as a mark of mutual regard and affection between heterosexual couples, the meaning of the act needed to be renegotiated. In the postwar period kissing was taken out of the bedroom where it had previously only played a role in foreplay and was openly displayed on the screen and on the streets as an emblem of the new "democratic" relations between the sexes. Kissing was even described as a "symbol of democracy" itself.[11]

A Kiss Is Not Just a Kiss

What later Japanese commentators have termed the "kiss debate"[12] gathered pace during 1947. Representations of the "erotic kiss" had been visible in Japanese art of the pleasure quarters during the Tokugawa period, where it was referred to as *kuchi sū* or "mouth sucking,"[13] gesturing toward the extremely carnal nature of the act. However, what was termed the "common" (*kanshū*) kiss such as that exchanged in greeting between the sexes was not a Japanese custom.[14] Kissing, on the lips or on the cheek, whether between lovers, married couples, family members, parents and children, or close friends was not commonly practiced in Japan where etiquette required a cool distance to be observed in personal relations, at least in public. As one Japanese commentator observed in 1915, "Husbands and wives, parents and children, and young lovers have never known anything of the process of osculation."[15]

Indeed, from late Meiji through till the end of the war, the representation of kissing in art, on the stage, or in film had been prohibited, and in 1924 even the proposed exhibition of Auguste Rodin's famous sculpture *Le Baiser* (The kiss) was cancelled due to police objections.[16] From the early 1920s kissing in public had been deemed an obscenity and was cracked down on by the police who would patrol city parks at night on the lookout for potential offenders. Although some particularly daring 1920s' "it girls" were reputed to offer kisses to their paramours, the act was considered so personal (and also potentially unhygienic) that before lips could meet they would interpose a "kiss racket," a small device fitted with a fine mesh that prevented use of the tongue. "Kiss masks" made of gauze were also available.[17] For those girls less daring, kisses could be indirectly exchanged through the sharing of a cigarette, a popular attraction in trendy cafes.[18] However, sexologists warned against such practices, arguing that sharing cigarettes with women of dubious character was a surefire way to contract syphilis.[19]

Even in the more liberal postwar environment, kissing maintained a strongly sexual charge. In 1949 John Bennett, an anthropologist working for the Civil Information and Education Section (CIE), noted the "special significance" of the kiss, expressing his surprise that "even hardened prostitutes will often avoid kissing."[20] Kissing in the context of the "floating world" of brothels and geisha houses, too, seems to have been something of a novelty. In his survey of late-nineteenth-century Western representations of geisha, Hashimoto Yorimitsu notes that kissing was not understood to be part of their repertoire and that this was one erotic art in which Western men considered European women to be more adept.[21] Liza Dalby, too, suggests that kissing was considered "outrageously exotic," even for courtesans;[22] albeit some early postwar commentators argued that geisha did in fact practice a form of "tongue sucking" referred to as *o-sashimi*, a reference to tongue-like slices of raw fish that are inserted into the mouth.[23] Hence, unlike in Europe where the kiss had a range of significations, as a consequence of these legal and cultural prohibitions, in Japan "the kiss remained only, singularly, sexual."[24]

Initially, kissing struck Japanese as a foreign practice, contrary to Japanese tradition, unhygienic, and funny to look at, akin to Eskimo nose rubbing. Even the compound term used to express the idea of kissing was a relatively recent introduction into the Japanese language. The two Chinese characters used to express the noun "kiss" consist (in their separate Japanese readings) of *setsu*, with the meaning of touch or make contact, and *fun* referring to the sides of the mouth. When put together they are pronounced *seppun*. Even in Chinese it is not a particularly old compound, first appearing in 1777 in a book describing social customs in Russia.[25]

The compound was not introduced into Japan until the beginning of the nineteenth century where it was glossed as *kuchi sū* or "mouth suck" and *kuchi tsuke* or "fix one's mouth on."[26] Yet the term *seppun* maintained its shock value well into the twentieth century. For example, in 1925 well-known fiction writer and journalist Kikuchi Kan published a serialized story under the title *Dai ni no seppun* (The second kiss). This was "a sensational title that was meant to stand out" and the title was duly emphasized in large newspaper advertisements.[27] The provocative nature of the term *seppun* is evident from the fact that although reference to kissing was permissible in the title of a work of literature, the censors considered its inclusion in a movie title to be beyond the pale. Hence, when the story was made into a movie in 1926 the title was changed to *Kyōko to Wako* (Kyōko and Wako), the names of the two female protagonists. Yet, the movie studios were able to capitalize on the recent fame of the novel while at the same time avoiding the censors by also advertising the movie under the alternative title of *Dai ni no XX* (that is, The second XX), where the offending term "kiss" was simply omitted.[28] Given the notoriety of the original story, however, readers would have had no problem making the connection between the popular novel and the film.

It was about that time, during the "erotic grotesque" boom of the late 1920s, that Japanese readers were introduced to the full range of meanings that kissing had acquired across the world's cultures. An article published in 1927 in the *ero-guro* title *Hentai shiryō* (Perverse documents), for instance, by an author with the pen-name "Bonbon," went into the history and symbolism of kissing in exhaustive detail and even went so far as to offer advice on kissing etiquette. The most important step was, according to the author, to "make sure you get the permission of the woman first." Once this hurdle had been overcome, potential kissers were warned about serious faux pas that must on all accounts be avoided. Kissers were advised not to make chicken-like pecking noises while kissing, not to kiss all over a woman's face, not to mess up her hair or clothes, not to step on her toes, and certainly not to let her know if this was your first experience of kissing![29] However, advice on how to actually perform the act of kissing was more difficult to come by due to censorship. A 1929 article entitled "Kissing" that appeared in the high-brow journal *Chūō kōron* (Central review) attempted to explain how kissing techniques differed across cultures but was rendered largely unintelligible by the number of deleted passages.[30]

For many, the first ever kissing to be seen in public in Japan took place between GIs and the ever-present pan pan girls at the beginning of the Occupation, thus further reinforcing the sexual connotations of the act. However, as Yamamoto Akira points out,[31] from May 1946 wives of senior officers began to be brought over to Japan to accompany their husbands who were working for SCAP. It became common in Tokyo to see officers strolling hand-in-hand with their wives and kissing them hello and goodbye. According to Takahashi Tetsu, the new authorities had to instruct the police that kissing in public was not an offence against public decency.[32]

The impact that the presence of the Americans, with their casual behavior and communication, particularly between men and women, had on the Japanese population should not be underestimated. Despite the multiple individual acts of insensitivity, discourtesy, and worse perpetrated by Allied soldiers, many Japanese people were clearly fascinated by the Americans that they saw on the streets, in the market places, and riding around in their open-air jeeps. Wearing their caps at a jaunty angle, something that would have been inconceivable for Japanese in uniform, they seemed "as relaxed and unregimented as civilians."[33] As one eye-witness noted,

> The tilted caps of the Allied soldiers were a big curiosity to us. Peculiarly folded, always worn a bit tilted, they gave an easy, causal air, so different from the stiffness of Japanese soldiers who had had to wear their 'sacred military cap' perfectly straight, or be punished.[34]

There was a spontaneity about the Americans, a willingness to act and take initiative without thought for repercussions, that impressed Japanese observers.[35] "America" soon lost the negative connotations manufactured by wartime propaganda and came to represent a new, more open way of living and being in the world. Hollywood screen idols, important as they were in representing these new ways of behaving, were but part of the picture. Also of great importance were the American bodies encountered on the streets and in daily interactions with the Japanese. The various "techniques of the body," ways of walking, talking, dressing, communicating, or simply occupying space that make up a national habitus,[36] differed markedly between the Americans and the Japanese. Over the course of the Occupation there were between 60,000 and 100,000 Allied personnel stationed in Japan, and during that time most Japanese would have had at least one encounter with one of these foreign bodies. Many of these encounters were sexual in nature; it being estimated that in 1946 as many as 40 percent of GHQ male personnel "had regular Japanese girl friends."[37]

Hence, given the new visibility of kissing on Japan's streets, numerous newspaper and magazine articles debated whether this was a practice that had a place in Japanese tradition, many considering it to be unhygienic and others, unaesthetic. That kissing was a new practice in which Japanese youth required instruction can be seen in Figure 4.1, which humorously depicts a "kissing class" at a coed university.[38]

For traditionalists, the new visibility of kissing on the streets and in the parks was a sign of the degradation of Japanese society and a further emblem of American colonization.[39] For reformers, the kiss was an important symbol of liberation from feudal values. Hence, the stakes in the kiss debate were high. Takahashi, for instance, believed the kiss to have ramifications far beyond bedroom etiquette—he considered the public display of kissing to be an important aspect of sexual liberation and a cornerstone of democracy,[40] a position supported by other writers who recognized public displays of kissing as a stand against prewar feudalism and fascism. In a 1946 article entitled "An argument concerning the 'revival' of kissing in Japan's sexual customs' history," Takahashi was eager to point to Japan's long tradition of erotic art in order to counter the suggestion that kissing was not a Japanese custom. Takahashi used illustrations from Edo-period erotic texts to show that kissing had indeed been a part of lovemaking in Japan's past and went on to argue that the "revival of kissing" marked the end of "gloomy feudal customs" and the beginning of a "real democratic system."[41] As if to reinforce the importance of kissing as a practice central to the expression of a new liberated masculinity, Takahashi's article was followed by an almost full-page photo of Rudolph Valentino locked in a passionate kiss with Nita Naldi from the 1922 film *Blood and Sand*. The accompanying text praised the "beauty" of Valentino's face, body, and deportment, pointing out how they were sure to stimulate young women's "sexual sensitivity" (*seiteki shinkei*).[42]

For many kissing commentators, the ubiquity of the practice in Western society, art, and literature was an important sign of its importance as a form of human communication. Literary critic Yarita Ken'ichi claimed

Figure 4.1 A humorous depiction of a "kissing class" from the July 1946 edition of *Modan Nippon* (Modern Japan)

Note: Original held in the Gordon W. Prange Collection at the University of Maryland.

that it was impossible to make sense of Western literature since the Renaissance, especially poetry, without attending to the various symbolism of kissing.[43] He pointed to the role that Western literary texts could play in educating Japanese people about kissing. Other authors approached kissing from different perspectives. Medical doctor Wani Saburō, for instance, suggested that people who were anxious about the spread of disease via mouth-to-mouth contact should consider kissing other parts of the body, as detailed in the *Kāma Sutra*.[44] Given the previous lack of public display of kissing in Japan, authors were, of course, eager to proffer advice on how to kiss: what to do with the tongue, where to look while kissing and, importantly, how long each kiss should last.[45] As Yamamoto states, the most important contribution of this new discussion of sex and romance in the *kasutori* press was that it helped those who previously had only been able to conceive of "sex for pleasure" in the context of the brothel district to comprehend it as an important aspect of daily life.[46] Kissing thus attained a symbolic value that it had not previously had. Kissing between couples was no longer understood as a purely sexual act, instead becoming associated with the "democratic" expression of "free love."

Kissing on Stage and on Screen

Kissing was suddenly visible on stage[47] and at the movies, too. Apparently, kissing had been "entirely absent from the Japanese stage until 1946."[48] The first kiss scene to be seen in a mainstream performance was in a play entitled *The Love of Priest Takiguchi*, one of the first performances to be put on at the Tokyo Theater in 1946. "This controversial eroticism was deemed a demonstration of the kind of democratic behavior advocated by the Americans," and the Occupation authorities were said to be so impressed by this display of emotional honesty that they decided not to requisition the building for their own use.[49] Kissing scenes were on view, too, during a production of Gilbert and Sullivan's *The Mikado,* staged before an elite audience of invited Japanese guests in January 1948. Although the dancing, singing, and mischief-making on stage caused considerable mirth among the Japanese, it was noted by the journalist covering the event that during the kissing scenes, "the audience sat in intense silence." As he explained, kissing in Japan "is preliminary to more serious business."[50]

Less demure kissing scenes could be witnessed in smaller, less well-known theaters. John Bennett, for instance, mentions going into a small theater in the Shinjuku district of Tokyo in 1949 expecting to see a movie but instead finding himself witnessing a stage play, the climax of which was a two-minute long kissing scene. He notes that "the kiss was played up as even more intimate and daring" than a sex scene that occurred later. However, even in the context of this full-on drama that depicted the lives of street women living beneath the railway arches in Tokyo, the kiss itself was "masked from the audience by having the girl stand in front of the man."[51] Even so, Bennett noted that the audience was "shaken to its roots" at the sight.

It was however via love scenes on the silver screen that most Japanese people were introduced to the first public displays of kissing. Kissing at the movies was, of course, artistically handled and glamorous, intended to entice rather than shock the audience. Commentators noted that although American grannies had first seen kissing at the movies at the end of the nineteenth century, the screen kiss was a new experience in Japan.[52] Although foreign movies with romantic themes had been screened in Japan in the past, as soon as the camera honed in on two pairs of lips about to meet, the resulting kiss scene would be cut and the actors shown suddenly moving away from each other, causing confusion.[53] During the wartime years in particular, "the slightest amorous expression had been condemned as a symbol of Western decadence,"[54] a situation that led to the "death of romance" in Japanese filmmaking from 1941 through 1945.[55] Kissing scenes in particular had been "proscribed as the quintessential example of an excessive individualism and decadence that promoted personal desires and pleasure at the expense of self sacrifice and obedience to the imperial state."[56] From the outbreak of the Sino-Japanese War in 1937, the militarist government had intervened in a very direct way in order to use film as a mass propaganda device to shore up the war effort. Film policy encouraged the creation of films that glorified self-sacrifice, the "Japanese spirit," and Japan's "unique" family system that stressed respect for elders. These stories were meant to "re-educate Japanese people, especially to counteract the 'Westernization' of Japanese women and the erosion of Japanese values."[57]

Hence, the Occupation authorities were well aware of the powerful influence of film and were keen to use Hollywood and other foreign films to help spread images of the happy democratic lifestyles enjoyed in the West. Under orders from SCAP in 1946 a Central Motion Picture Exchange was established to import primarily Hollywood movies that supported Allied reforms.[58] Although many cinemas had burned alongside other buildings targeted by the Allied air raids in the closing year of the war, in Tokyo at least, several major cinemas in the heart of the city close to the imperial palace had survived. Other makeshift movie houses were hastily constructed to feed the demand for venues such as temporary halls and department store basements. Mostly American movies, subtitled in Japanese, were screened daily from noon and it was not unusual to see lines of Japanese queuing for tickets from early in the morning.[59] Popular movies would be booked out weeks in advance.[60]

Among the many films licensed for importation and screening in Japan were those deemed to have "reorientation value" because they depicted "admirable aspects of American life."[61] This included kissing scenes, since the Americans "thought that kissing in both American and Japanese films would show the Japanese how open societies with equality between the sexes operated."[62] Hence Hollywood films from which kissing scenes had been routinely excised[63] could now be screened in their uncut glory. The first film screened in Japan with uncut lip action was reportedly the 1943 *His Butler's Sister,* which debuted in Tokyo in February 1946. Romantically retitled in Japanese as "Prelude to Spring" (*Haru no jokyoku*), the film, starring Deanna Durbin, tells the story of a young woman who visits New York to stay with her half brother and also try to launch a singing career. The storyline was considered a "good textbook of American democracy" and it was hoped that the sympathetic female character played by Durbin would "teach the Japanese how lovely democratic society was."[64] Released at the same time was the 1944 *Madame Currie*, about the pioneering female scientist who discovered medical uses for radioactive isotopes. Both featured strong female characters in charge of their own lives and proved a hit with audiences in Tokyo and across 12 regional centers where they were "solidly booked" for the rest of the year.[65]

With the liberalization of Hollywood imports, new kinds of women, so-called vamps and sirens appeared on the Japanese screen, offering images of sensual, desiring, and sexually active women.[66] These women were visible on the streets, too, since many cinemas erected large billboards outside their premises on which close-ups of Hollywood stars, and particularly kissing scenes, were clearly depicted.[67] Movie theater owners soon learned that sex sold seats and they sometimes unscrupulously overstated the degree of eroticism in otherwise innocuous movies. One theater in Wakayama, for instance, described the Oscar-winning film *Anna and the King of Siam* as a "Picture scroll of lust and eroticism hidden deep in the palace" on a billboard featuring a scantily clad Asian woman.[68] This was not at all the kind of impression the Occupation authorities wanted to spread about the movie. The appeal of the movie to them, after all, lay in how a strong-willed independent British woman lectured the King of Siam about the need for democracy and the liberation of women in his kingdom. Unimpressed by this kind of erotic hype, the authorities suspended distribution to this cinema for a month.

As Bae points out, these strong, agentic female images were unlike the women previously seen on the Japanese screen since "[t]he filmic personae of these (Hollywood) stars were devoid of any sense of maternality or family purpose."[69] These Hollywood images were to do as much as any SCAP directive toward reevaluating Japanese attitudes toward the status and role of women. As Joanne Izbicki points out, the "new lustiness" in early postwar movies "gained respectability as the basis for marriage and hence was linked to the new legal recognition of peoples' right to choose their own partners on the basis of inclination."[70] Support for kissing movies was, then, part of wider Occupation policies encouraging democratic reform, an attempt to reform not simply Japanese institutions but also minds and hearts.

Tachiki Takashi notes how the close-up of the May Irvin/John C Rice kiss first screened in 1896 had sparked a "kiss revolution" in the United States after which film replaced literature as the primary means by which audiences learned about the arts of love.[71] Writing in 1936, Marcel Mauss had identified the cinema as the conduit via which "American walking fashions" had been taken up by Parisian ladies and emphasized the manner in which the cinema had emerged as a globalizing force in human culture. Hence, rather than being a "natural" consequence of physiology, Mauss argued that all such "techniques of the body" resulted from imitation and he identified the "prestige" of the model as a key factor determining the creation of a new habitus.[72] The "prestige" value of American culture, particularly that of Hollywood movies, clearly impacted upon Japanese ideas about courtship, as evidenced by contemporary media accounts. For instance, numerous articles in the Japanese press, particularly in movie magazines, discussed not only the techniques of lovemaking now visible on screen but also the etiquette of taking one's date to the movies[73]—a discussion rehearsed endlessly during the first postwar decade.[74]

Americans were, of course, convinced of the important role they played to their Japanese "wards" as instructors in democracy; as was pointed out in the 1947 book *Star-Spangled Mikado*, "the Japanese must be taught to walk, talk, think and play all over again."[75] The role that American culture should play in "educating" the Japanese was thus taken for granted. Lucy Herndon Crockett, an American resident in Japan at the time, reported that a Kyoto Imperial University student had told her that "he and his friends learn from the American pictures how to light a cigarette for a girl, hold her coat, open a door for her."[76] A young female acquaintance also confessed that she loved to see American movies since "men's behavior to women is especially refined," going on to speculate that "these things are now influencing our social life, and also our private feelings."[77] Hence, kissing, along with other courtship behaviors, were further techniques of the body popularized via American popular culture. Indeed, writing in 1953, columnist Junsei Ijichi argued that "nothing, it seems to me, is exercising so potent an influence on the minds of young Japan as Hollywood." He went on to outline how "American culture is now affecting native manners and morals," especially "love-making."[78]

In a curious episode in the history of censorship, it was "strongly suggested"[79] by the Occupation authorities that Japanese filmmakers should take steps to include kissing scenes in their own productions. As we saw in Chapter 1, in the 1920s the popularity of American movies had been singled out as a major factor contributing to the "shocking" behavior of "modern boys" and "modern girls" out and about on the streets and in the cafes of Tokyo. David Conde, head of the Motion Picture and Drama branch of the CIE, the agency entrusted with encouraging democratic thought in Japanese minds, had worked for the Psychological Warfare Branch during the war, and was well attuned to the usefulness of film for propaganda purposes. "The CIE was determined to remold Japanese cinema in ways that served SCAP's reconstruction efforts"[80] and Conde himself had "preached that kissing was liberating and democratic and literally ordered passionate Hollywood-style scenes included in feature films."[81] However native kissing movies got off to a false start in 1946. *Aru yoru no seppun* (A certain night's kiss) was the first Japanese movie to entice viewers with the word kiss (*seppun*) in the title, but the meeting of lips was obscured at the crucial moment by the unfurling of an umbrella. This did not stop advertisements for the movie playing up the sexual innuendo of kissing. One newspaper ad, for instance, stressed that the kiss took place between a pair of "soaking wet lovers." The verb *nureru*, meaning to get wet, has strong sexual overtones that suggested the couple's damp state was not entirely due to the inclement weather.[82]

Despite the promise of a kiss scene in *Aru yoru*, it was not until *Hatachi no seishun* (A twenty-year-old youth), screened later that year, that audiences finally saw two *Japanese* kissing on screen. *Hatachi no seishun* met with the approval of the censors since its theme of two young people choosing their own spouse against the will of their parents was considered suitably "antifeudalistic." Hirano reports that Conde personally intervened to request greater eroticism in the script, in particular that the couple should be seen kissing.[83] Rumor had it that the two leads, Ōsaka Shirō and Ikuno Michiko, were less than enthusiastic and that Ikuno placed cellophane on her lips before the crucial moment resulting in a so-called dry kiss.[84] That kissing was not part of Ōsaka's daily repertoire is apparent in an interview he later gave where he stated that, "[b]efore the filming began, I walked around in the used book shop district in Kanda, bought many copies of *Screen* and *Eiga no tomo* [Movie friends] . . . and studied poses of kissing. I was so cautious."[85] Ōsaka was right to be cautious; since as late as 1950, when beau-part actor Abe Tōru was kissed at a garden party by a visiting Hollywood actress, he was accused of bringing shame on the Japanese people.[86] The fact that media reports described the party as a "kissing school" suggests that Japanese men, as well as women, were still considered to have much to learn regarding kissing technique.

Tellingly, the kiss that is said to have most deeply impressed the public at the time did not technically take place. It occurred in the 1950 movie *Mata au hi made* (Till we meet again), an "anti-feudalistic" tale of true love in the final year of the war. As the erstwhile chaste couple wave a final goodbye, he about to depart for the war, they each put their lips together on either side of a window, hence nicely expressing the sentiment behind the kiss without the messy exchange of body fluids.[87]

So exciting was it to see two *Japanese* kissing on screen that the success of these early "kissing films" (*seppun eiga*) gave rise to a locally produced genre that was well advertised in the mainstream press[88] and endlessly discussed in the plethora of movie magazines that had recently sprung up. However, the critics' response to these first cinema ventures into public eroticism was not enthusiastic, one critic noting, "the kissing seems forced, and it looks as though these scenes were included merely for the sake of showing kisses,"[89] which, of course, they were. Critics were also keen to point out how Japanese actors lacked skill in kissing technique, noting that "very few leading men seem to understand how it's done. They mash their lips against the heroine's as if they were tasting castor oil!"[90] As a consequence the kissing scenes seemed "childish" and "uncouth" to many.[91] Japanese actors' lack of skill in kissing was made fun of in the press as can be seen in Figure 4.2, a cartoon depicting the filming of a kissing

Figure 4.2 Cartoon depicting the filming of a kissing scene from the February 1948 edition of the magazine *Danjo* (Man and woman), p. 56

Note: Original in the Gordon W. Prange Collection at the University of Maryland.

scene in which the director has to intervene to show the leading man how it is done.

Perhaps in anticipation of these criticisms, one Japanese actress, at least, was reported as seeking instruction in kissing from an American expert. In March 1946, *The Washington Post* ran an article entitled "Yank Tutors Jap Actress in Kissing"[92] in which it was reported that the actress Mimura Hideko confided in her acquaintance, the journalist Ernest Hoberecht, that she had never been kissed. She further explained that "Japanese movies never had kissing before and I cannot go through with it." The gallant "Yank" reports that "I saw my obligation to democracy" and offered to tutor the guileless actress. The lesson was, apparently, a success. However, despite the intervention of such foreign experts, the initially hesitant approach to the screen kiss adopted by Japanese actors and actresses led some commentators to compare them unfavorably with famous "kiss combinations" (*kissu konbi*) from America and Europe such as Clark Gable and Jean Harlow who kissed with more evident passion. Indeed, the November 1947 edition of the magazine *Liibe* (Love) still felt it necessary to point out to its readers that "kissing isn't something done with the mouth but with the tongue, . . . you should insert your tongue into your partner's mouth and swirl it round."[93]

The Kiss Debate in the Press

The movies themselves were of course important in conveying a whole new repertoire of actions and ideas related to modern, democratic lifestyles. However there was also a vast industry dedicated to film commentary where a range of voices competed to interpret, critique, diagnose, and explain the true or real significance of American movies for Japanese life.[94] From January 1947 on, for instance, there were at least 21 movie-related magazines published in Tokyo alone.[95] Most of these magazines were pro-American and accepted the "educational" nature of the Hollywood stories on offer. *Eiga no tomo* (Friends of the movies), describing itself on the cover as a "magazine for American movies," encouraged its readers to visit the cinema in search of "cultural and intellectual nourishment."[96] The first postwar issue featured Deanna Durbin in her starring role in *His Butler's Sister* on the cover and announced in its editorial that "[t]he spring of reconstructing Japan should start with American movies! Bright and joyful and filled with democratic culture, American movies will surely provide insight for Japan's democratization."[97] The editors hoped to see copies of *Eiga no tomo* placed "in school libraries across Japan." Through sponsoring region-based fan clubs, letters' pages, and a Q&A section,

Eiga no tomo was able to foster a sense of community among its readers who came to see their movie-viewing practices as much more than idle amusement. Indeed, some fans employed methods of exegesis when interpreting movie plots and dialogue that were more suited to religious texts. "Methods of spectatorship" were much discussed in the letters' pages[98] and for many readers, their active engagement with American movie culture was an important technique of the self through which they aspired to become modern, democratic citizens of the world.

The extent to which romance and kissing in particular were linked with discourses of freedom, liberation, and democracy by movie critics and actors alike is striking. In 1951, actress Yamaguchi Yoshiko, returning from a study tour in the United States, stated in an interview that "there were so many men who wanted to be my kissing teacher. I learnt a lot about the art of love. Kissing has been separated from the lives of Japanese for a considerable degree, so we have to create it from now on."[99] Female critics in particular, such as Sakanishi Shiho, read American movies as textbooks on how to conduct family life. She was particularly sensitive to the various important roles that women were given in American movies and the "close relationship of husband and wife" that she felt was missing in Japan.[100] Hence, the wave of democratic reforms sweeping over the political, family, and labor systems was seen by many as also sweeping away restrictions on people's most intimate and private feelings and desires.[101] Indeed, one movie critic looking back on this period in 1972 wrote that "[t]his occupation order [to include kissing scenes in movies] startled moviemakers. It was like a blessing from heaven. For how many decades have we aspired to this!"[102]

Audiences apparently responded in a very visceral manner to the lip action on the screen, by "gulping, sighing and yelling."[103] Indeed the behavior of couples while at the cinema was considered of such import that an ethnographic article reporting on "The state of couples in the movie theater" was even published in *Chūō kōron* (Central review).[104] The author observed that the couples under inspection responded with considerable excitement whenever a scene with "sex appeal" (*sei teki appiiru*) appeared on screen. It is worth noting that according to the author, these scenes included "dialogue containing the words 'I love (*ai*) you,' 'I like (*suki*) you,' 'marriage,' 'body,' and 'pregnancy,'" or scenes that "rush toward a kiss or some other physical resolution."[105] Just some of the physical manifestations of excitement that the author observed included "indiscreetly touching their partner's face; grasping their partner's shoulder; twitching fingers; tapping fingers; stretching out their legs; [and] mouths opening and gasping." That the behavior of other couples in the cinema could be as entertaining as the love scenes on screen was suggested by a cartoon that appeared in the April 1949 edition of the magazine *Jitsuwa to shinsō* (True tales and truth). The illustration depicts a couple on screen locked in a close embrace but all eyes in the cinema are turned to the back where a Westernized young couple is kissing passionately. Someone in the audience shouts out, "That's it! This is the best so far!"[106]

These responses might seem adolescent to contemporary readers,[107] and this was a point also noted by the critics at the time, numerous articles arguing that the Japanese people had been "robbed of their adolescence" by the war and by the previous feudal social system. Yamamoto refers to an essay entitled "On kissing" that appeared in the November 1947 issue of *Riibe* (German term for "love") that argued "new life is aflame in the shadows of the burned out buildings . . . after having endured injury for so long, now is the time to return to our adolescence under the blue sky of freedom."[108] The exuberant tone of this and other reports gives a sense of how fresh and optimistic a symbol kissing seemed to many Japanese people at the time and helps us understand how prominent sexologists such as Takahashi could have understood the practice to be a "symbol of democracy."

However other commentators were unsure whether the Japanese public would accept this "foreign" practice.[109] After all, as recently as 1938, film critic Tajima Tarō had written that "anyone would laugh at the idea" that young couples might kiss goodbye on the platform at Tokyo station since "we don't have that custom in Japan."[110] An article in the September 9, 1946, edition of the *Asahi* newspaper pointed out that although it did not seem unnatural to witness a kissing scene in a foreign movie, when Japanese actors were involved the scene quickly became "unpleasant to watch." The author put this feeling of discomfort down to the fact that "kissing has no cultural history in Japan."A *Yomiuri* newspaper survey published on August 14, 1946, also indicated largely negative audience responses to the first movie "love scenes" with almost two-thirds of the 411 respondents registering negative attitudes. Rural readers, as well as those in professions suggesting lower educational backgrounds, were particularly negative. Respondents mentioned various reasons for their negative response to on-screen kissing. Of particular concern was the fact that kissing was "not a Japanese custom" (*Nihon no fūzoku*) in real life and so to witness it on screen seemed "unnatural."

One of the difficulties in reaching agreement over the meaning and significance of the newly visible practice of kissing was that the two sides of the debate tended to interpret the act of kissing differently. The pro-Western reformers who wished to "open up" Japanese displays of eroticism tended to stress the "spiritual" lineage that the kiss had acquired in the Western romantic tradition as a symbol of affection between equals.

Japanese traditionalists, however, tended to view kissing as a carnal act, the first step toward a loss of chastity, and a prelude to intercourse. This was not an unreasonable assumption to make given that Van de Velde's marital guide, which we have seen was the most influential sex guide in the early postwar years, identified kissing as the first act of foreplay. Hence commentators were keen to warn of the dangers of kissing when it took place outside of the conjugal relationship. The participants in a roundtable discussion on "marital problems and sexual love" published in a 1949 edition of the women's magazine *Josei raifu* (Women's life), for instance, seemed to believe that sexual desires were exogenous to young unmarried women. They pointed out that before the war most young unmarried women were "untroubled by sexual desire" since "daughters of good families," at least, were protected from sexual stimuli.[111] In the postwar period, however, sexual stimulation was everywhere: at the movies, in the press, and on the streets and in the parks. Now young women "progressed" through the stages of walking alongside their male partner, to holding hands, to kissing. These activities awoke all sorts of unruly sexual desires that normally would only have been expressed in the context of marriage. Hence it was in this new context that "the sexual desires of unmarried women" were suddenly in need of a "solution."[112]

Many of these commentators, then, were not so much worried about the act of kissing itself, but about the unruly desires that kissing might give rise to in unmarried women. Invoking the long-standing distinction between "girls who are from good families" and "girls who aren't," those worried about Japan's developing dating scene asked what would happen to Japan's "good girls" if they began to feel that they had a right to explore their sexual desires prior to marriage, and to say such things as "a date that doesn't end in a kiss is boring?" These sentiments might have been considered unavoidable among "factory girls," but what would happen to morality if they began to be shared by women in general?[113] Hence the kiss debate was heavily inflected with class assumptions and biases—which for reformers was yet another example of the remnants of "feudal" thinking.

Many conservative-minded writers argued that the Japanese were unfamiliar with the types and the techniques of kissing and, displaying their class bias, feared that "the masses" were likely to misunderstand its significance, leading to a decline in public morals. Many felt that through championing kissing in the movies, the industry was simply pandering to "base instincts" and "commercialism." Rather than viewing kissing and other open displays of affection between the sexes as an aspect of democratization, these critics insisted that the movie studios were simply pandering to "sensationalism" in pursuit of profits.[114] Some American commentators agreed with this position and an article that appeared in a May 1946 edition of *Stars and Stripes* accused those movie makers of irresponsibility who "unnecessarily" included scenes of kissing, hugging, and touching.[115]

Acting on these concerns, in Taira, a town not far north of Tokyo, the local juvenile delinquency prevention committee went so far as to request local cinemas not to screen kissing movies on the grounds that kissing scenes were "bad for Japanese youth."[116] A 1952 report by the Education Ministry into 82 junior high schools concluded that "at least 30 per cent of the girl students had been 'subjected to indecent influences' by movies"[117] also giving rise to fears of delinquency.[118] One female student who wrote in for advice about kissing to the *Yomiuri* newspaper confided that despite her request for a platonic relationship her boyfriend had once kissed her on the lips. The advice was that kissing definitely fell outside the bounds of a platonic relationship and that she should take better precautions in the future and not go outside unaccompanied.[119]

In response to these concerns, those in favor of movie kissing argued that it was important to counter the understanding that kissing had an exclusively sexual connotation. If Japanese people were to cast aside their "bumpkin" (*inakamono*) reputation then it was important that kissing be expressed in broad daylight as a symbol of romantic affection.[120] Yet, writing in 1952, film critic Hayashi Fuyuko noted that kisses that went on "too long" could still provoke embarrassment and laughter,[121] suggesting that when watching couples kiss on screen discomfort was still experienced by many.

Interest in a lost or postponed adolescence as well as a new emphasis on the necessity of sex instruction for young people may explain the sudden run of Japanese movies dealing with the topic of first love. Several such movies were discussed in an article by Nanbu Kōichirō entitled "Adolescence, marriage, and sexual desires of movies celebrities" published in *Abekku* (Couple) in July 1948.[122] However the author is somewhat skeptical of the extent to which movies are an accurate reflection of real life. He notes for instance that "lovers in most movies get married less than five minutes before the end." Why is this so? "It is perhaps because we know that regret and disappointment follow a marriage." He goes on to argue that the actual lives of movie stars hardly reflect the beautiful images of romance that they portray on screen, noting that Tanaka Kinuyo married at 18 and divorced only three years later and that Mito Mitsuko divorced her husband shortly after giving birth, and that Yamada Isuzu had repeatedly divorced and remarried. Yet for the author the discrepancy between actresses' on and off screen love lives do not really concern him since both portray the complexities of sexual life that he finds "intriguing."

The author does note several American movies recently screened in Japan "in which we find a considerable number of depictions of sexual desires" and goes on to praise Japanese movies such as the 1947 *Yottsu no koi no monogatari* (A tale of four loves) and *Subarashiki Nichiyōbi* (Wonderful Sunday) that "present vivid motion pictures of sexual desires." As if to refute charges of obscenity once used to excise kissing from Japanese screens, he concludes that "sexual desires that are expressed in movies are by no means dirty. In fact, they are beautiful."[123] The movies in question were just two of a whole series of films that, under the guise of offering "sex education," were able to address a range of sexual attitudes and behaviors that had been off limits during the militarist period.[124]

Social commentators often used love scenes from movies from the United States and Europe as starting points to launch into general discussions of sex. One particularly influential film that fed into debates about the need for greater sex education was the 1949 Italian movie *Domani e troppo Tardi* (Tomorrow is too late) screened in Japan in 1951 as *Ashita de wa ososugiru*. The movie featured an Italian schoolteacher who was keen (against Catholic interference) to teach the facts of sex to his students. The movie received mainstream attention in an article in the *Asahi* newspaper published on January 17, 1952. Because of the frank discussion of sexuality in the plot, it was reportedly being received by audiences as a "sex education film." Interestingly, the article, which contained perspectives from educators, parents, and young people, came to the conclusion that a conservative approach to sexuality education, as opposed to a more frank approach, was more likely to lead to delinquency.

The potential impact of the movie was also debated in a 1952 issue of popular sexology magazine *Ningen tankyū* (Human research). It featured a roundtable between three high-school teachers who, on the whole, recommended that the movie be viewed by middle-school students. They pointed out that such was the state of sex-education before and during the war that students as old as 17 or 18 still had no idea about the biology of sexual reproduction and it was common gossip among girls, in particular, that even kissing could result in pregnancy.[125] Given this state of ignorance, they felt it important that movies such as *Ashita de wa ososugiru* should be viewed by young people, a recommendation also supported by some parents. In this discussion increased sexual knowledge emerged once again as an important corrective to the "feudal moral complex"[126] instilled in students during Japan's militarist period.

Although it is difficult at this remove to draw clear lines between this increase in representation and the actual practice of kissing,[127] research conducted in two separate studies conducted in 1948 and 1952 by Osaka University Professor Asayama Shinichi suggests that the sexual attitudes of Japanese young men and women were rapidly changing. In a survey of his findings published in *Sandē Mainichi* (Sunday Mainichi) in October

1953,[128] Asayama helpfully tabulated his results in a series of diagrams. Although he only included the results of experiences up to the age of 18, the 1952 sample showed significant increase in the number of both young men and women who had experienced kissing or who experienced the desire to kiss when compared with the 1948 sample. Indeed the number of informants who expressed a "desire for kissing" had tripled in the later survey, albeit, as Asayama pointed out, the number with actual experience was still far below the rate for American men recorded in Kinsey's 1948 survey. Interestingly, the Japanese figures were repeatedly related to Kinsey's 1948 findings, as if American sexual behavior somehow set the benchmark against which the Japanese themselves needed to be measured. In these discussions American women were often presented as "one step ahead" of Japanese women in terms of sexual liberation and in experiencing "extremely liberated feelings" with regard to sex.[129] Once again the supposedly liberated expression of female desire in the US context was used by progressive thinkers in Japan as a means of bolstering their own demands for sexual reform.

Kissing as a Symbol of Democracy

It may strike contemporary readers as odd that late 1940s' American film culture that now seems hopelessly staid and old fashioned in its portrayal of relations between the sexes should have seemed such a beacon of liberation to the Japanese. To an extent this is due to the fact that US popular culture endorsed and encouraged the expression of intimacy between the sexes that in traditional Japanese culture had been disavowed or expressed only in private. SCAP advisors "encouraged [love] scenes purposely to force the Japanese to express publicly actions and feelings that heretofore had been considered strictly private."[130] Kissing thus became part of wider Occupation policies encouraging democratic reform, an attempt to reform not simply Japanese institutions but also psychology.

The extent to which sexual liberation, romance, dating and kissing in particular, became symbolically linked with discourses of freedom, liberation, and democracy in the minds of many Japanese people is striking. Yet, this should not be surprising given that statist interventions into people's private lives, in particular the repression of sexuality, had been cornerstones of the old militarist system.[131] The wave of democratic reforms sweeping over the political, family, and labor systems was seen by many as also sweeping away restrictions on individuals' most intimate and private feelings and desires and helps us understand how prominent sexologists such as Takahashi could have understood kissing to be a "symbol of democracy." Although it seemed odd to some Japanese that the American authorities required kissing scenes to be inserted into movies when the practice of kissing was not a spontaneous or natural part of the Japanese "national lifestyle,"[132] such was the prestige of American culture and so engaging were the models portrayed on the screen that there was widespread support in the community for this new "technique of the body."

In part, this was because Japan's defeat had been so spectacular that the ideology supporting the wartime social system had collapsed along with the regime that enforced it and American culture moved in to fill the gap. Although the United States's "imposition" of democratic principles might now seem heavy-handed, in an important essay on the symbolism of "America" as "desire and violence" Yoshimi Shun'ya argues that "'America' appears not so much as a 'prohibiting' presence but as a 'seducing' presence in the everyday consciousness of the times."[133] As Yoshimi points out, "numerous powerful cultural influences—jazz, fashion, sexual culture—spread out from the American bases and took root very soon after the beginning of the occupation."[134] He goes on to suggest that American popular culture could not have exerted such a strong influence were it not so attractive to the population at large. Despite critics who accused the Japanese culture industries of giving way to American cultural imperialism through pandering to sensationalism, "many Japanese welcomed the liberation of sexual expression."[135] Indeed, as Hirano points out, if the increased openness of affection between the sexes had not been acceptable to the Japanese populace at large then these expressions would have withered away naturally after the Occupation ended.[136] However, on the contrary, for many people, the rhetorical alignment of democracy with music, fashion, romance, and sexual freedom was welcomed. The clear connection made in the Japanese press of the period between the loosening of "feudal" strictures restraining people's bodily behavior, particularly between the sexes, and the process of "democratization" was seen as a positive step.

However Japanese people were never purely passive in relation to this process of "seduction." Whether it was through the purchase of an aloha shirt, the perming of the hair, a visit to a dance hall, or a Deanna Durbin movie, young Japanese people actively constructed their own meanings around these new activities, determined to discover new ways of living in the face of everyday privation. For Japan's ex-soldiers and female factory workers for whom the war had brought nothing but humiliation, loss, and hardship, the new opportunities to mingle together "democratically" while "cheek dancing" to the seductive rhythms of a jazz band could be construed as a rejection of feudalism and an embrace of progressive, democratic ideals. For many young people, participating in these new American-style recreation activities was a way to become "instant democrats."[137] It is in this context, then, that kissing could be proclaimed a symbol of democracy.

In conclusion, the introduction of kissing—on screen and in life—cannot be understood in isolation. The act of kissing was just one particularly potent symbol of a much broader change that was taking place in the "cultural scenarios" structuring heterosexual courtship, scenarios that will be explored further in the next chapter. As we will see again through a discussion of marital sex guides, "democracy" proved a remarkably flexible sign that could be invoked in support of almost any kind of action or belief that was counter to the perceived groupism and feudalism of the past. Making claims to democratic principles was a useful tactic for reformers who wished to open increased space for sexual expression in Japanese society.

5

The New Couple

It seems to have been taken for granted by Japan's defeated rulers that the arrival of the Allied forces would require the Japanese people to reform aspects of their behavior, particularly pertaining to male-female relations. Indeed, only two days before they were ordered by SCAP to disband, the Special Higher Police prepared a document entitled "Various aspects of American personality characteristics" that was intended to help Japanese interact in a friendly manner with their new foreign rulers. The report encouraged Japanese people not to be "overly polite" (which Americans, apparently, found annoying), to shave and keep their hair properly managed, not to expose themselves (especially women), for men to give women priority seating on transportation, not to smoke in front of women, to take their hats off in elevators, not to urinate in public, not to pick flowers from public gardens, not to spit on the streets, not to talk too openly about their mistresses, and not to be afraid to sit next to Allied forces on public transportation.[1]

The number of guidelines specifically directed at reforming the way Japanese men behaved toward women suggests that the Japanese male populace was acutely aware that their manners in regard to women might be found wanting. This became only more obvious as people began to realize that "the American ladies-first custom is followed everywhere by foreign men."[2] The behavior of American men toward Japanese "ladies" helped Japanese men "to understand that to be courteous and friendly toward women is neither a detriment to masculine dignity nor to feminine chastity."[3]

However, demonstrations of the "ladies-first" principle by GIs must have at first appeared bewildering, as Yukiko Koshiro points out:

> The practice of "treating ladies with respect"—one that GIs frequently were happy to demonstrate in public toward Japanese women despite the

antifraternization regulation—was in many cases ridiculous to the Japanese, not only because of cultural differences but also because of its flirtatious nature.[4]

For instance, one incident reported in the May 1946 issue of the magazine *Modan Nippon* (Modern Japan) described how a hulky GI had ordered all passengers off a train carriage and then, shouting "ladies first!" had ordered the women to board first to ensure that they all got seats.[5] As one American serviceman pointed out, "Being deferred to by a person who has power is a new experience and one which in some cases terrified the recipients."[6] Yet, despite the bizarre nature of these theatrical spectacles, there was widespread agreement in the popular press that the very foundations of male-female interaction in Japan needed to be reconsidered. In particular, writers were keen to outline how new norms and behaviors consistent with democracy needed to be encouraged for Japan's "new" or "modern" couples.

According to Tsurumi Shunsuke, "for people at large, the most durable influence of the Occupation was on the Japanese lifestyle, especially with respect to relationships between women and men."[7] There had, as previously described, been a period in the 1920s when the Japanese (or rather, those able to visit some of the fashionable areas in Tokyo and other large cities) had seemed to be moving toward the development of more "modern" dating customs. However, according to postwar commentators, the main difference between pre- and postwar developments in sexual customs was that eroticism became "democratized" (*minshuka*) and men were able to seek out "regular" (*ippan no*) and "amateur" (*shirōto*) women as partners, as opposed to "professional" sex workers.[8] This was partly due to the ubiquitous displays of the pan pan girls and their partners that helped normalize the sight of young men and women consorting in public. The activities enjoyed by the pan pan girls and their foreign lovers—dancing, day trips, movies, and coffee—soon came to be sought-after pastimes among young Japanese men and women in general.[9]

Before Japan's defeat, "women from good families" had been extremely constrained in their heterosocial activities and it was difficult for them to associate freely with men outside the family. During wartime the "taboo on social intercourse between the sexes"[10] had only intensified. Train stations and other public gathering places emerged as major sites of surveillance as Japan descended further into militarism and the police had the power to detain unmarried couples out together in public.[11] Male students caught associating with women outside of designated brothel areas risked expulsion from their schools. Even for husbands and wives, "it was a shame to be seen walking together in the street."[12]

These restrictions between men and "non-professional" women (*shirōto onna*) did not arise from prudery about sexual expression per se but were aimed at "preserving the purity of the home."[13] Men did have some freedom to associate with "professional" women of the pleasure quarters (known as "public" prostitutes), or "semi-professional" (so-called private prostitutes) such as the café waitresses, "taxi dancers," and "stick girls" of the Ginza. For instance, under restrictions regulating dance halls (before they were closed down completely in November 1940) "'professional female dancers' and 'adult male customers' were the only legally sanctioned couples that could engage in social dancing."[14] There were very few contexts in which men could spend time recreationally with "ordinary women" or go on a "date," at the cinema (where seating was sex-segregated), theater, or milk bar as was common in the United States. "Mixed society" was very much "a commercial affair" in Japan and remained so into the postwar period.[15]

In an effort to shrug off such "feudal" thinking about male-female relationships, writers in the early postwar press rapidly embraced the idea that women's new right to choose their own marriage partners required that *ippan no josei* or "women in general" should have the right to exert agency during courtship and that women, too, had romantic and sexual needs. As John Dower notes, "to esteem genuine reciprocity in the conjugal relationship, including not only 'love' but also mutual sexual gratification, became one way of defying authority and elevating the primacy of individual feelings."[16]

To a large extent the emphasis on women's emotional and sexual rights within heterosexual coupledom represented a new "cultural scenario,"[17] the parameters of which had to be negotiated and defined. Hence, multiple authors stepped in to offer advice on how courtship might proceed and to define the new meanings associated with dating practices and lovemaking techniques. Indeed, such was the importance of men developing the skills to court "regular women" that men whose only sexual experiences had been of a commercial nature later came to be regarded as "*shirōto dōtei*," that is, virgins in regard to nonprofessional women. An alternative designation posited these men as "half virgins" (*han-dōtei*), suggesting that sex, in order for it to count, had to be freely given by a woman unconnected with the floating world of bars and prostitution. That experience of the sex act itself was no longer considered sufficient for a loss of virginity among male youth points to the heightened value that was placed upon the need for courtship and the establishment of more equitable male-female relationships among men of the postwar generation.[18]

The didactic manner in which writers and editors sought to initiate young men and women into these new, more "modern" forms of coupledom and new, more "democratic" expressions of desire is particularly striking. In this chapter we will consider some of the ways in which early postwar authors sought to differentiate the "new" or "modern" couple from previous patterns of courtship behavior.

The "Democratic" Reform of Male-Female Relationships

In an article entitled "The sexual act and social evil: sexual acts are not wicked" in the December 1947 edition of the magazine *Sūingu* (Swing),[19] Goda Tadashi bemoaned the lack of a proper understanding of sexual acts among Japanese people. He argued that the Japanese still associated sex with "feelings of guilt" due to the ideas that too much interest in sex might lead to addiction or an emphasis on sexual pleasure might distract from the proper emphasis on reproduction. He suggested that instead of feelings of guilt, there should be a feeling of "rightness" about sex that took place with a partner with whom one was in love. Goda did note that the postwar "liberation of sex" had led to some social problems, not least an increase in prostitution. However, his response to this situation was to call for greater sex education that should include the new understanding that social and sexual interactions between men and women are not "social evils." He went on to claim that parents interfered too much in the lives of their children and that young people should be left alone to seek out their own "eye opening" sexual experiences.

Despite these calls to let young people develop their own relationships, there was still the strong feeling that the young should not be allowed out in mixed-sex company without chaperones. How then could the democratic mixing of the sexes be achieved? The neighborhood societies that had been coopted by the militarists to ensure that everyone fulfilled their patriotic duties during wartime were not disbanded after the war since they were the only effective means of distributing food rations. They were, however, expected to reorganize themselves in a "democratic spirit." What better way to advance democratic ideals than involve young people, especially young women, in social life? Hence "'young people's social meetings,' where boys and girls practiced social dancing and English conversation" were organized by some neighborhood committees[20] allowing young men and women to get to know each other but under the watchful eyes of their neighbors. Given the strong social prejudice that still existed against mixed-sex intimacies, there soon developed a "country-wide mania for social dancing"[21] since this provided an acceptable opportunity for barely acquainted young men and women to touch each other in public. Dancing and practicing English were also two important skills for those girls who wished to get better acquainted with the foreign Occupiers. One Allied serviceman recalls: "One evening a friend of mine and I were stopped by two fairly good looking girls who propositioned us thus: they would go anywhere, do anything, if we would in turn teach them to dance and also teach some conversational English."[22]

Increased opportunity for male-female interaction, especially among young people, was indeed a pressing concern in the early postwar years, partly due to Allied reforms of the education system that introduced widespread coeducation in public schools and universities. As Takemae Eiji points out, prewar education had been segregated by sex, with boys and girls attending separate institutions. "It was also male-centered, elitist and multi-tracked, with five different orientations reflecting gender and class distinctions."[23] American reforms not only extended the scope of compulsory education from six years to twelve, but also made public elementary and middle-schools coeducational. The former imperial universities, too, were required to admit women, albeit this got off to a slow start with women undergraduates making up only 5 or 6 percent of the student body in 1949.[24]

Hence, for the first time in Japanese history, young male and female students were studying at the same institutions and in the same classes and yet had very little experience of how to negotiate heterosexual relationships. Even though attitudes toward mixed-sex interaction were changing, a survey found that only 16 percent of respondents considered it acceptable for a young man and a young woman to walk the streets arm in arm.[25] A contemporary American observer noted that "the relationship between the predominantly male students and the coeds is still very immature."[26] This was largely, as Ronald Dore noted, because "there [were] no established patterns of behavior in such relationships and embarrassment and frustration mixed with guilt [was] a frequent result."[27] That the new social mix at coeducational institutions was the source of much humor in the press can be seen in the cartoon in Figure 5.1, where the father's reply to a passerby outraged at the sight of his daughter strolling "arm in arm" with a young man is, "It's OK, she's just preparing for entrance to a coed university."

This new environment no doubt proved bewildering for many. As Bae notes, "Living in the new era of peace and democracy, the *shōjo* (young girl) . . . experienced the physical maturation of her body in a newly legitimized coeducational environment."[28] Yet despite the fact that increased space had opened up for male-female interaction, many young people were still confused about how to behave with the opposite sex. Bae notes how "boys . . . emphasized the difficulty of associating with girls due to outside social pressures."[29] Indeed, in the early postwar environment, the label *furyō* or delinquent was often used to describe those who

Figure 5.1 Cartoon depicting a young couple strolling arm-in-arm in preparation for entry to a coeducational university from the July 1946 edition of *Modan Nippon* (Modern Japan)

Note: Original in the Gordon W. Prange collection at the University of Maryland.

had met with disapproval by socializing too closely with members of the opposite sex.[30]

However, by the end of the Occupation relations between the sexes among the "*apure*" generation had "settled down" according to a roundtable of male and female university students published in *Fujin Asahi* (Women's *Asahi*) in 1953.[31] The students mentioned that at the beginning of the coeducation system, relations between the sexes had been quite strict, with the girls socializing in groups with other girls. If a boy wanted to communicate with a specific girl he had to do so through the passing of notes. Yet, after two or three classes of women had entered the schools, the students were thought to have gotten much better at "differentiating between feelings of friendship and love."[32] It was now "no problem at all" to be seen strolling hand in hand with one's partner on campus.[33]

Increased opportunities for liaising with the opposite sex were available to older people, too. "Mass introduction events" (*shūdan miai*) quickly gained in popularity. In April of 1947, some 300 men and women between the ages of 20 and 50, each wearing a number, strolled around the banks of the Tama River in southern Tokyo. If a person caught their eye, they were able to drop by an office that provided a copy of that person's resume.[34] For those preferring even more anonymous modes of introduction, "marriage introduction magazines" appeared where interested parties could advertise for suitable spouses. Readers interested in making the acquaintance of a lover or sweetheart (*koibito*) for the purposes of correspondence could send in their details, and for a fee of 20 yen could receive multiple introductions.[35] Perhaps as a result of such ventures, a survey published in 1951 announced that so-called love marriages had increased from 15 percent before the war to 40 percent.[36]

Despite the continued social stigma against young men and women mixing together, attitudes toward courtship and marriage were slowly shifting. For instance, a 1949 survey of 2,500 Japanese men revealed that 33 percent of respondents felt that it was the individual who should personally decide the selection of his marriage partner whereas 40 percent felt that the decision should be made jointly between the son and his parents. Only 20 percent were happy to leave the decision entirely in the hands of the parents.[37] The survey found that younger people felt more strongly that the individual should have the final decision and that the individual-oriented respondents also tended to be urban and better educated. A later 1953 survey of 3,000 men and women returned similar results with 44 percent of respondents believing it to be the individuals concerned who should choose their own marriage partner with only a slight majority believing that the family should have some say in the choice of spouse.[38] Among educated young people in particular, there was also a growing "individualism" (*kōjinshugi*). University students expressed their intentions to seek the opinions of their close friends, senior classmates, and other respected figures on choice of marriage partner, and not rely solely on the advice of parents.[39]

Courtship Advice

The development of "free relations between men and women" (*jiyūna danjo kōsai*) was one of the most visible changes in Japanese society brought about by the Occupation. Women's new relations with potential suitors were said to be symbolized by the "Three Ds," that is, dating, dancing, and driving. Sometimes this list of D words was extended to five with the addition of "drinking" and "going Dutch" (*dacchi akaunto*)—the latter gesturing toward women's improving economic as well as social freedom but also indicating reluctance on the part of some women to be indebted to men.[40] The opening up of social relations between the sexes meant that young men and women needed to learn how to behave in these new environments.

Although it has now dropped from common currency, in the immediate postwar years, the foreign loanword *abekku* (from the French *avec* or "with") was widely used for a dating couple.[41] The term frequently appeared in the title and body of articles about dating and courtship and was also used as the title of a popular magazine—*Abekku*. The term *abekku* had been in circulation in Japan as early as the 1920s when it referred to *married* couples enjoying themselves in public as well as same-sex friends such as pairs of soldiers or students out to amuse themselves. However prior to the Occupation it was problematic for women to appear outside the home with men who were not relatives and so Japan did not have the Western custom of young dating couples taking to the streets in search of diversion. As columnist Junsei Idditie notes, "the sight in the streets and in parks of young men and women walking with their arms locked together [was] a sight unknown before the Occupation."[42] During the war years in particular, it was customary for women to walk a few steps behind men since to have walked alongside one's husband or partner would have brought down censure.[43] It was American GIs consorting with their paramours in public that helped normalize the sight of young men and women in close proximity. As Japanese couples, too, began to behave as did GIs and their dates, the term *abekku* began to crop up in other phrases such as *abekku sentā,* that is, couple "centers," such as parks, where many couples gathered. Indeed such was the increased traffic through Tokyo's parks that the pine trees were said to be endangered by the large number of couples trampling on their roots.[44]

One of the most popular *abekku* meeting places in Tokyo was Hibiya Park, directly across from GHQ as well as the adjoining grassy verges of the imperial palace moat. This area was and still is one of Tokyo's main financial and business hubs, and it saw a massive influx of workers during the day. An article based on a "study of *abekku*" noted that many of the couples picnicking on the lawn areas during lunchtime were workers from nearby offices.[45] The article provided a series of photographs with commentary on *abekku* in various poses as they sat on the grass. This particular location clearly had symbolic significance for many. As the author pointed out, the couples completely ignored the "keep off" signs on the lawn areas and, sitting with their back to the old authority (the Emperor), sat facing the new one (GHQ).[46] Couples were depicted idly chatting while plucking away at the grass, sitting back-to-back reading magazines, lying down on the grass with their legs touching, and even one particularly daring couple was lying side by side with a single handkerchief covering their faces (to protect from sunburn or to hide their kisses, the author couldn't be sure). It would, of course, have been inconceivable for young couples to have behaved in such a casual manner in front of the palace during wartime and the opening up of this area as an *abekku* "center" was a potent reminder of the regime change.

Other popular *abekku* phrases included *abekku taimu*, that is, special couple "times" at dance halls when couples could enter for a reduced price and *abekku hoteru* (hotels), precursors of today's love hotels, where couples could rent a room for just a few hours. Hence in the postwar period the nuance of *abekku* changed, coming to denote an unmarried couple out on a date. The term also developed a sexual charge, perhaps explaining why in subsequent decades it dropped out of use and was replaced by another loanword—*kappuru* (couple).

The sudden rise in the number of young male-female couples seen about town led to a spate of crimes perpetrated both by and against *abekku*, including a series of robberies. In 1948 a particularly fashionable *abekku*, he sporting a "rockabilly hairstyle," and she a "young beauty with permed hair," robbed a tobacco shop in Shibuya right next to the police station. Newspaper reports about this incident noted that it was the female partner who seemed to incite the crime.[47] Another pair of *abekku* robbers, also identified as dressed in Western clothes, was reported as targeting homes guarded by elderly relatives. The female partner would distract the elderly residents while her boyfriend climbed in through the window and stole items.[48] *Abekku* themselves were also the targets of crime, there being numerous reports of gangs hiding out in parks and other solitary locations favored by courting couples. These gangs would threaten the female partner in an attempt to get the male to part with his cash. A particularly serious series of incidents unfolded across 1950 when a serial killer known as the "*abekku* assassin" murdered women out on a date with their boyfriends by stabbing them in the neck with a jackknife. *Abekku* were easy victims of crime given that they deliberately sought out dark and private spaces and were usually too distracted by the goings on between them to pay much attention to their environment. Indeed one unfortunate couple who were making out in a narrow alleyway late at night were shot by a nearby householder who suspected them of trying to break in.[49] A humorous cartoon in the *Asahi* newspaper that depicted a couple sitting on opposite sides of a tree suspiciously eyeing passersby played up this atmosphere of apprehension in the wake of the *abekku* murders.[50] However, whether positive or negative, the volume of coverage given to *abekku* and their activities helped establish the dating couple as a permanent fixture of Japan's cityscapes.

Since for most couples going on a date was a newly discovered, if at times perilous, freedom, many articles appeared in the *kasutori* press not only documenting the phenomenon of "dating couples" but also proffering advice on how to behave on a date. A 1948 article on "dating couples on the street" analyzed different kinds of *abekku* according to their clothes and accessories.[51] The oddness of seeing men and women walking around the city streets in close intimacy was registered by the fact that the number of centimeters separating these different couples was recorded, as was the potential difficulty of maintaining a proper "gait" (*ashimoto*) while walking alongside or arm in arm with a partner. The attention to detail that these articles gave in their descriptions of the *abekku,* extending to the minutiae of their dress and behavior, shows that the notion of "promenading" with a loved one around the city streets was a new and fashionable practice in need of elaboration. It was via these articles that readers and potential *abekku* were thus being inducted into what Marcel Mauss would have called "techniques of the body,"[52] that is a new *habitus,* or way of being with a loved one in public space. While in the American context, teenage youths would gradually have learned the body language of dating through trial and error and from cues in their environment such as older friends and siblings and romance movies, in Japan in the early postwar period, young men and women had to have practices such as walking arm in arm, kissing, petting, and even techniques of lovemaking explained to them in great detail. These new techniques of the body were thus brought into play in the context of broader techniques of the self, that is, ways of understanding one's body and desires in relation to wider systems of thought that explained, contextualized, and naturalized ways of acting and thinking that were, in fact, highly artificial and contrived.

In the now discredited feudal model of marriage, there had been little or no place for courtship. For the middle and upper classes especially, marriage partners had been decided by or in consultation with parents and other senior family members and the family patriarch had effectively been given the power of veto over unions of which he disapproved since his seal was necessary for the issuing of a marriage certificate. Since a new spouse (almost always the bride) was entered into her husband's family register, marriage was not seen as a union between two individuals so much as the addition of a new member to the family. Hence other family members had a vested interest in vetting any potential brides and a new bride's status in the family was insecure, at least until she bore her first child, preferably a boy.

In the old system, it was not uncommon for the bride and the groom to have had little contact before the wedding and it certainly was not an expectation that they should be in love. Hence, everything about the newly recommended courtship process needed to be analyzed and explained in great detail, starting with the initial overture. For instance, a "romantic-love studies seminar" offered in the December 1948 edition of *Bēze* (Kiss) proffered advice on how to write a love letter.[53] Having sought advice from "a member of the intelligentsia with experience in such matters," the author provides examples of an appropriate letter and response. His use of the term *retā* (letter) throughout, as opposed to the more familiar Japanese term *tegami*, indexes the way in which this kind of communication was considered part of a wider, and US-inspired, envisioning of courtship. However, despite the US influence, the author remained wedded to traditional Japanese notions about women's character. For instance, due to the "passive" nature of Japanese women and the fact that to receive a love letter from a woman would seem a little strange, the author suggested that the first letter should always come from the man. The author also recommends restraint, arguing against dwelling too much on feelings and suggests that terms such as "love" (*ai*) or the slightly stronger "love/yearning" (*koi*) should not be used. Instead, he encourages the male suitor to dwell upon the virtues of the woman and stress the positive impression that she has made upon him.

The above article was typical of a whole genre of advice that instructed men and women on how to make an initial advance, gave pointers toward appropriate venues for a date, and cautioned on when and how to walk, hold hands, and, frequently, to kiss. As Yamamoto Akira points out, "these instructions about kissing always made it a rule to declare the principles of anti-feudalism and modernism"[54] thus reinforcing the linkage in people's minds between liberation of the body and of democracy. Through directly linking sexual liberation with liberation from feudal values, authors and publishers were of course also better able to defend themselves against charges of obscenity.

The US authorities, too, were keen to stress the connection between the "liberation" of women and democracy. For instance, the NHK radio show "Twenty Questions," which was used by the Occupation authorities to promote discussion of democratic topics, often featured questions relating to women's new rights and status alongside discussion of the etiquette of opposite-sex relationships. Indeed, "recently enfranchised Japanese women were . . . encouraged to broadcast their concerns and thoughts" and these programs helped bring about "a new consciousness among women and increased their recognized importance in Japanese society."[55] One such program, featuring a roundtable on romantic love versus arranged marriages, was apparently so popular that it "led to the setting up of receivers in public parks for those who didn't own sets."[56]

As well as the more philosophical foundations of romantic love, the techniques of courtship, too, were in need of elaboration, and "romantic-love classroom" (*ren'ai gakkō shitsu*) discussions were featured in many magazines. One such "class" in the October 1948 edition of *Bēze* (Kiss), offered by a writer using a name that can be translated as Professor Loves Women, explained the "psychology of the lover."[57] The professor's advice on how to discover the true feelings of one's object of affection was directed separately to both male and female readers, and was broadly concerned with matters of etiquette. Whereas his advice to men was more concerned with social interaction, it being suggested that male readers address their female partners by name without the polite suffix "-san" in order to gauge their response to this intimate gesture, his advice to women was more centered on bodily functions. For instance, he notes that if, in advance of a "rendezvous"[58] with her beloved, a lady has eaten too many sweet potatoes (a staple food in the early postwar years), thus giving rise to the urge to pass gas, "there is no need to persevere but just let rip with a 'buuu' sound." The woman should then pay careful attention to her partner's response. If he responds with "an unpleasant regard," then the relationship should not proceed since it is evident that the man "does not love you from his heart"; Jean Paul Sartre having argued that if a man loves a woman he loves even her intestines. The appropriate response from a man with real feelings of romantic love was, apparently, to inquire tenderly after his date's health. This juxtaposition of scatology with philosophy was a characteristic of much popular literature of the time. Writers emphasized the importance of the material body and its desires and needs as an antidote to wartime propaganda that had insisted on the unique spiritual qualities of the Japanese and which had brought about such misery and privation.

The Importance of Sex Instruction

Japan's newfound "sexual liberation" was not without its manuals. In June of 1946 a complete translation of Van de Velde's sex guide was reissued under the title *Kanzen naru kekkon* or "Perfect marriage" and was soon released in abridged versions by several publishers,[59] becoming a best seller. Popular magazines and newspapers ran excerpts and there was much discussion of his advice in the context of the "new" or "modern" couple. The term *sei manzoku* or "sexual satisfaction" began to be widely discussed and written about. Indeed, "sexual satisfaction" can be said to be one of the defining characteristics of discourse surrounding "modern" as opposed to traditional forms of coupledom, the latter being dismissed in these accounts as "feudal." Despite the obvious deficiencies in Van de Velde's construction of men's and women's complementary but "opposite" roles, his text did serve as a springboard for more wide-ranging discussions of sexual activity and, importantly, psychology.

Early postwar sex writers such as Takahashi Tetsu criticized Van de Velde for focusing too much on the "debate over positions."[60] Takahashi had read widely in psychology, including Freud, as well as anthropology and ethnography, and argued that sexuality was an extremely complex cultural construct and that sexual compatibility demanded more than the adoption of appropriate positions. Van de Velde's recommendations that couples try out a range of positions until they found one that enhanced mutual stimulation while also optimizing opportunities for pregnancy supported a model of marital sexuality in which reproduction was the goal of sexual interaction, a model that now seemed "feudal" to progressive thinkers like Takahashi. As a good Freudian, Takahashi believed that sex existed as much in the mind as the body and hence he argued that Van de Velde, in reducing sex to a matter of "friction," overlooked more significant cultural and psychological factors.[61] Indeed Takahashi's 1953 book *Arusu Amatoria* (*Ars amatoria*) was subtitled in English as "coital postures and a sexual atmosphere," and specifically addressed the need for establishing a proper mood prior to lovemaking.[62] Most important, according to Takahashi, were the psychological and emotional compatibility of the partners, considerations that had not been paramount in the previous family system but that in the postwar period became the defining characteristic of the "modern couple."

Takahashi was also more understanding of sexual variety, refusing to condemn practices such as masturbation, homosexuality, and a variety of "fetishes."[63] Takahashi's use of Freudian theory thus contrasted starkly with the trend in Japanese academic psychology influenced by the United States that used psychology to explain or treat a number of "pathological" human conditions including abnormal sexual behaviors.[64] In fact, Takahashi encouraged his readers to discuss these issues with their partners, going so far as to include a range of "abnormal" practices and desires in his "Marital conversation dictionary."[65] The dictionary included an eclectic choice of sex-related vocabulary derived from European and Asian languages as well as from Edo-period texts. Takahashi suggested that a "coed climate" should be established at home through husbands and wives studying and discussing the arts of love together.[66] Takahashi also frequently criticized Western sexology for being overly scientific and encouraged Japanese people to explore the many erotic classics of the Edo period that contained "words of beautiful sound and meaning."[67] Edo-period erotic culture depicted a wide range of human sexual interaction,[68] including many nonprocreative practices, and Takahashi argued that contemporary Japanese had much to learn from their own past sexual traditions.[69]

Takahashi's critique notwithstanding, Van de Velde's book did help consolidate the new idea that sexual satisfaction of *both* partners was a core principle for a successful marriage. In the early postwar years, endless articles addressed both male and female readers on how to conduct a "proper sex life" (*tadashii sei seikatsu*), the key foundation of which was the satisfaction of both the male and female partner. For instance, in a 1949 article in *Fujō kai* (Women's world) aimed at "dissatisfied wives," medical professor Miyata Shigeo asked the question, "What to do about sexual dissatisfaction among married couples?"[70] In the article he explored a range of problems, including men's selfishness and "egotism," arguing that "it's not enough to attend only to your own satisfaction and then fall asleep and snore." Miyata pointed out that although it was commonly supposed that it was women's place to follow a man's lead, in fact "coitus is an act that a couple does together" and both men and women needed to be better educated about female sexual responsiveness. Like Van de Velde, Miyata also took orgasm (*orugasumusu*) to be the key indicator of both male and female satisfaction but argued that women were held back from experiencing the climax of the sex act, not only due to men's lack of skill but also ideological conditioning stressing women's "chaste nature." Just as Van de Velde had stressed the necessity of extended foreplay to excite the female partner, Miyata also pointed out that for women orgasm was "not an easy thing" and that the solution was to be found in the development of an "*ars amatoria*" (*ai no gikō*), that is, a knowledge of sexual techniques shared between couples. Knowledge and understanding of each partner's sexual needs was important for a marriage given that Miyata considered the ultimate goal of coitus—simultaneous orgasm—to be the moment when a couple's physical love and spiritual love were united, hence reinforcing the idea that the sex act was ultimately a democratic exchange.

The Science of Sex

In his article for *Fujo kai*, Miyata suggested that it was insufficient to pick up sexual knowledge from the pages of the "carnal literature" then in circulation, arguing instead that proper sexual knowledge must be derived from a "scientific" basis. As seen in Chapter 3, the idea that sexuality was the proper provenance of scientific experts had been reinforced in 1948 by the widespread media discussion of the first Kinsey report on the sexual behavior of American men. In 1953, Kinsey's status as the preeminent sex expert, a man whose name "has become synonymous with sex,"[71] was further consolidated by the media discussion that surrounded the release in America of his second report, this time on the sex lives of American women.

Although still widely reported upon in the Japanese press, *Sexual Behavior in the Human Female* caused slightly less excitement than did the earlier 1948 volume on the male. This was because, first, by 1953, the Japanese reading public was already acculturated to discussion of intimate sexual details in the press. In particular, the idea that women had independent sex drives, albeit with different interests from men, was now widespread and unlikely to raise eyebrows. Second, the more stable publishing environment of the early post-Occupation years made it possible to present extended features by reputable authorities that described the scope and content of Kinsey's new report in a balanced and objective manner. The kind of breathless expose of the more salacious details of the male report was largely absent this time.

Throughout 1953, both the *Asahi* and *Yomiuri* newspapers ran regular updates on the reception of the female report in Japan, including details of the publishing houses that were vying to obtain the translation rights. These negotiations were complex because the Kinsey team had placed strict restrictions on the format of the translation as well as the back catalogue of the publisher, preferring an academic or scientific press. The female volume was eventually released in Japan in 1954 by the Kosumoporitan publishing company and advertised in the press as "opening a new door onto sexuality" and "uncovering the depths of women's sexual lives."[72] However, given the astonishing scope already covered by the Japanese sex press of the preceding decade, there was relatively little left to reveal that would have proven shocking.

Detailed reports in the mainstream press included a seven-page article in the October 1953 edition of *Fujin Asahi* (Women's Asahi), reproduced from America's *Time* magazine, that outlined Kinsey's major findings, including detailed discussion of rates of women's premarital intercourse, sexual experience outside of marriage, onset of awareness of masturbation, and homosexual experiences.[73] Other articles helped readers contextualize Kinsey's findings by offering detailed breakdowns of his data by age of respondent, pointing out that there had been a "revolution" in sexual mores in America following on from the First World War. It was noted that the Second World War, too, had done much to liberate American women and that servicemen returning home had been surprised by the sudden upsurge in women's agency as evidenced by women's increased presence in the workplace, at the bars, and on the streets.

Hence Japanese readers were led to reflect upon the manner in which recent events had impacted on Japanese women's roles and behavior. This line of argument suggested that human sexual behavior was in large part a social construction. However another line of argument sought to establish human sexuality "in nature." For instance, one article in a popular weekly concluded that Kinsey's research proved that human beings were in essence animals. As such all human sexual behavior had a basis in nature, and even acts that society might condemn as "perverse" (*hentai*) "must be considered natural and proper from a biological standpoint."[74] The implications of both these approaches were, of course, troubling to many.

Some commentators on the new report were skeptical of Kinsey's "scientific" approach, wondering if it were appropriate to study sexuality simply as a "behavioral system" taking no note of the wider legal and value systems of a society.[75] It was noted by some that moralistic terms such as "natural" (*shizen*), "unnatural" (*fushizen*), "correct" (*seijō*), "perverse' (*ijō*), and, importantly in the context of discussions of women's sexuality, "pure" (*seijun*) were conspicuously absent in Kinsey's analysis, thus providing a stark contrast to wartime sexual rhetoric. Yet, despite the fact that some experts criticized Kinsey's biological approach, the publicity concerning the report did further reinforce one tendency in postwar sex journalism to *describe* actual behaviors rather than *prescribe* ideal codes of practice. Japanese women, in particular, were recommended to read the report, not only to dispel the remaining "taboos" that surrounded discussion of women's sexuality, but also to better comprehend the difference in the "degree of sexual liberation" between Japan and the United States. Many of these commentators, clearly unaware of the double standard that pertained in the United States regarding attitudes toward male and female sexuality, tended to read Kinsey's "scientific" approach as indicative of the sentiment of the American public in general. Indeed the supposedly widespread availability of sexological as well as psychological information about human sexuality in the United States was offered as the reason for the success of American couples in making appropriate "sexual adjustments"—unlike couples in Japan who were still considered to be "separated by a valley."[76] Hence the second Kinsey report became an important rhetorical device for progressive thinkers who sought to further discredit the Japanese authorities' unscientific and moralistic approach to sex through comparison with the supposedly more objective and "scientific"-minded Americans.

Kinsey's second volume also did much to reinforce the now widespread idea that the sexual satisfaction of women was a key problem in marriage. Even prior to the book's official launch, the Japanese press had been reporting on some of Kinsey's key findings, not least that women maintained a strong sexual capacity across a longer period of the lifecycle than did men. Hence, some of these reports stressed that rather than women's lack of interest in sex being a cause of miscommunication, it was often the case that men's declining ability to perform lay at the heart of marital instability.[77] Not surprisingly, advice on how to "rejuvenate" male sexual organs and appetites was eagerly proffered in a new genre of "couple magazines" that first appeared in 1949 and maintained a popular following until 1955.[78]

Reinventing the Conjugal Couple

The Japanese term for conjugal couple is *fūfu*, consisting of the characters for husband and wife. The changing nature of coupledom was registered in the titles of several popular magazines first published in 1949, such as *Fūfu seikatsu* (Conjugal couple lifestyle),[79] the most enduring and well-read, and its competitors *Shinfūfu* (New conjugal couple), *Modan fūfu seikatsu* (Modern conjugal couple lifestyle), and *Fūfu tokuhon* (Conjugal couple reader).

As noted in Chapter 1, during the long war years, marriage and family-rearing had been portrayed as patriotic duties and pleasure and eroticism had been downplayed. From the mid-1930s it was women's roles as *mothers* that had been emphasized; they were depicted as "married, as it were, to the nation."[80] The "new couple" however was exhorted to enjoy time alone, away from the pressures of work and family. In particular couples were encouraged to take a honeymoon to a romantic destination soon after marriage. Trips to hot spring resorts (long associated with the commercial sex trade) were particularly recommended. Such trips were considered important because privacy was hard to come by for many couples. In fact the very idea of "privacy" was difficult to communicate using existing Japanese terms, leading to the widespread Japanization of the English word *puraibēto* (private) to designate aspects of one's life that required seclusion and secrecy.[81]

The mostly wooden houses in Tokyo and other strategic cities had been largely destroyed by the incendiary bombs in the closing months of the war, and what remained of Western-style brick or concrete housing was often requisitioned for the use of senior SCAP personnel and their families. What accommodation could be found in the cities was flimsily constructed and overcrowded with entire extended families often sharing the one room where they slept "like fish in a basket."[82] It was no surprise then that for many couples, "in postwar Tokyo, a house was longed for more than a heap of jewels."[83] Those living in the countryside often did not fare much better because of the custom of three generations of a family living together. As one account of 1950s living conditions in a farming village noted, "The house is small and crowded. [It] offers almost no privacy for intimacies, nor is there much opportunity for wandering unobserved on the hill or in the fields."[84] The cramped conditions under which many families were required to live necessarily affected a couple's sex life, which was prone to be a "brief, businesslike affair, with a minimum of foreplay."[85]

Japanese housing was also sparsely furnished and usually did not provide separate sleeping spaces. It was common for the living room (often the only room) to also serve as dining room and bedroom for the entire family. Beds, chairs, and sofas were uncommon items of furniture except among the wealthy who could afford a separately furnished Western-style space. Bedding consisted of futon mattresses that could be folded up and stored in the closet during the day and it was common for parents and children to sleep side by side. The impossible situation that many young lovers found themselves in due to lack of privacy was explored in Kurosawa Akira's 1947 movie *Subarashiki Nichiyōbi* (Wonderful Sunday) that featured a young married couple unable to live together due to lack of funds and suitable accommodation. Their married life is thus reduced to regular Sunday meetings where the husband's sexual frustration is subtly alluded to. On one of these meetings they wander wistfully through a model home.

Given this background, the reality of postwar overcrowding was addressed in many articles that proffered solutions for obtaining privacy.[86] One article suggested making a bed for the children in the closet of one-room apartments, or, if space allowed, constructing a platform under the eaves where the parents could lay their futon. Although the phrase "my home-ism," signifying a desire to enjoy the comforts of family life, is regarded as an aspiration that only took hold for most Japanese couples in the early 1960s,[87] we can already see an increased desire for private space in the couple-magazines of the late 1940s. The magazine *Fūfu seikatsu* in particular often carried advertisements for bedroom furniture and the back cover was given over to full-color ads for different styles of house construction. "Even though small, it's fun: a couple's escape" declares an ad on the back cover of the October 1949 edition illustrating a small tatami-style room that could be separated from the rest of the house by screen doors.

Numerous articles rehearsed the need for a "couple only space" where intimacy could be shared. Colorful illustrations, often at the very front of the magazines, showed young, Western-looking couples in various states of undress relaxing in Western-style bedrooms including soft beds, lush draperies, bedside tables stacked with whiskey and cigarettes, standing lamps, and mirrors.[88] Children were never featured in these images and representations of the extended family—still very much a reality of everyday existence for most couples—were also absent.

The need for a "couple-only space" was not simply due to modesty. As we saw in Chapter 1, the constant display of affection between husband and wife that was so central to the romantic love marriage among Americans was not part of Japanese tradition. Part of the resistance to the love scenes in postwar movies was the idea that in Japan the national character required that "expressions of love between husband and wife be hidden at the back of the house, a place absolutely untouched by public scrutiny."[89] Even in the late 50s one anthropologist noted that "[t]he expected pattern of daily behavior, during the first year [of marriage] especially, tends to curb any show of affection." The reality for many couples, then, was that they were "chaperoned within the home by their elders and outside by their neighbors"[90] and couples who showed too much amorous interest in each other risked disapproving glances. It is not surprising then that by 1949 a large number of "couple hotels" (*abekku hoteru*) had sprung up to cater to young couples in search of privacy who needed to rent a room by the hour or were just looking for the opportunity to share a bath together.[91] It was estimated that as many as one-third of the customers frequenting such hotels in the Ueno and Asakusa areas were married couples.[92]

The couple magazines were also instrumental in encouraging partners to reflect on their married lives, particularly their sex lives, thus contributing to an increased sense of interiority surrounding the "couple relationship." One way in which this was achieved was spelled out in an article in a special edition of the magazine *Kōdan hiwa* (Secret stories) dedicated to "perfecting sexual intercourse" that encouraged newlyweds to keep a diary reflecting on their experiences of married life, something they would be able to look back on fondly in old age. Both spouses were encouraged to keep separate diaries and to record their every thought and feeling during the first few months of marriage. The article stressed that the honeymoon was an essential start to a good sex life since it was only in the context of a stay at an inn that a couple's sex life could be commenced in a suitably leisurely (*burabura*) manner.[93]

That the sex act should not be rushed was fundamental to the basic "etiquette" (*echiketto*) of sex described at length in these magazines. "Petting," a term that was popularized via the 1948 Kinsey report on the human male, and supposed to be characteristic of American-style love-making, was described as the "ideal" method of foreplay (*zengi*) because it could be practiced equally by both partners.[94] Indeed "give and take" was now being promoted as the absolute foundation of sexual satisfaction in a happy marriage. Not content with itemizing ways of exciting one's partner through foreplay, the importance of postcoital intimacy (*kōgi*) was also discussed. However, in case the sex act should seem to be too complex and burdensome, sexologist Takahashi Tetsu pointed out that simply falling asleep with hands entwined was sufficient postcoital intimacy.[95]

Hence, these discussions played an important role in challenging traditional ideas that had de-eroticized the married couple. The magazines, issued in B6 pocket-size format, were highly popular; *Fūfu seikatsu*, the most long-lived, sold between three-hundred and four-hundred thousand copies monthly.[96] Ronald Dore, who was researching married life in Tokyo in the early 50s, noted that one of the couples he surveyed subscribed to the magazine.[97] He also mentions that among his informants, "*fūfu seikatsu*—the word translated married life—is one commonly heard and has primarily sexual connotations."[98] Indeed, even today its mention provokes laughter and smiles from Japanese of the older generation. That *Fūfu seikatsu*'s contents were meant to provide talking points between couples was made clear on some of its covers, which described the magazine as "a practical household magazine [meant] to be read together." Whereas marital sexuality had been beyond the bounds of discussion in prewar print media, what distinguished the "new," "modern," or "*apure*" couple from the now discredited feudal model was an emphasis on the need for shared sexual knowledge.

There was, of course, an extremely masculinist bias in these magazines, which frequently opened with a photo section featuring female (never male) nudes.[99] In the vast majority of cases, the reader being addressed was the male partner as signified by the use of the casual second-person pronoun *kimi*, most frequently exchanged between men.[100] That men were the target audience was also suggested by the covers, which always featured close-up artwork of young, beautiful, Japanese women with Western-styled hair, make-up, and jewelry, albeit sometimes wearing kimono. The covers featured these women's male partners, too, but it was the women who were foregrounded looking out at the reader seductively.[101] The men in the pictures, attired in smart suits and ties, usually stood behind or to the side of the woman and gazed at her approvingly (see fig. 5.2).

Inside the magazines, too, it is the many illustrations of women that are foregrounded, with men in the background looking on. Women's bodies were very much the center of attention in these magazines and little effort was made to present seductive images of men. Although women may, of course, have engaged with these illustrations, imagining themselves to be the object of these loving and approving gazes. One particular problem with the focus on women's bodies was the emphasis contributors placed upon Western standards of beauty. Depictions of both men and women in their pages were highly Westernized, with women in particular being encouraged to undergo makeovers to "improve" their appearance. Articles on how to achieve this end were not limited to hair, makeup, and fashion

Figure 5.2 A husband gazes at his wife lovingly on the cover of the March 1950 edition of *Fūfu seikatsu* (Conjugal couple lifestyle)

advice but also extended to reworking the body itself. For instance, one article in the July 1950 edition of *Fūfu seikatsu* authored by a medical professor asked "What are the ideal type of breasts?" and explained in detail how to measure the dimensions of one's breasts in order to ascertain their level of beauty.[102] For breasts found wanting the article that followed recommended a range of therapies including massage, exercises, hormone treatment, and surgery.[103] A similar article authored by two "Ginza surgeons" in 1952 announced "The birth of a beautiful wife" through a range of reconstructive surgeries aimed at correcting "imbalances" in a woman's bodily proportions.[104]

There was, however, some attempt to address the needs of women. The September 1952 issue contained 25 letters, purportedly submitted by wives, under the heading "25 sexual techniques that wives would like their husbands to practice."[105] Women asked, among other things, that their husbands not limit their sexual attention to bedtime, but be more spontaneous during the day. One wife asked that her husband "mess me up a bit so as to get my blood boiling" whereas another suggested that it would be nice if her husband performed cunnilingus while they took a bath together.

The male body was also objectified to a certain extent, the workings (and ideal size) of male sexual organs were discussed alongside diagrams depicting their physiology. Wives were instructed not to "just grab a hold of" their husband's penis since "it might cause pain." They were also informed that the penis wasn't the only erogenous zone on a man and that the area "between the scrotum and the anus is particularly important."[106] "Women's perspectives" were also acknowledged in the occasional article penned by female writers, albeit the "experts" who wrote for the magazines were overwhelmingly male.[107] Contraception advice was given and its pros and cons discussed from both male and female perspectives.

The couple magazines could be extremely explicit in their exploration of sex techniques since they did so with the aim of encouraging equality between the sexes and spoke of sex only in the context of promoting state-sanctioned marital harmony.[108] With titles such as "How to be a husband who makes his wife go 'buru buru,'" articles went into unprecedented detail about the mechanics of sexual stimulation.[109] "You must throw out the idea that the futon is the only place to express a couple's love" declared a 1952 article that encouraged couples to explore the possibilities for sex in every room of the house—particularly the bathroom and the living room sofa.[110] Changing the lighting could change the mood of a room, it was suggested, as could changing your routine.[111] Why, for instance, put your clothes on after a bath? Why not ask your wife to serve tea while naked?[112] Couples were also exhorted to be adventurous in their sexual activities and include sex toys as part of the foreplay process, or even a little bondage and sadomasochism.[113] Japanese couples were also chided for being too "herbivorous" in their sexual tastes, unlike the red-blooded French who, apparently, enjoyed conjugal pleasures twice a day—at lunch time as well as at night. Although it was acknowledged that the daily commute made this impossible for most husbands, afternoon sex could still be practiced at the weekend.[114]

For those couples who had to share their accommodation with others, it was recommended that they frequent hotels with the *onsen* (hot spring) sign. Some of the more enterprising short-stay hotels catered to the fad for Western furniture and offered rooms with exotic items such as sofas and double beds for an additional fee.[115] For those who could not afford a hotel stay, it was recommended that they rent a boat on one of Tokyo's many park lakes, row over to a sheltered spot and enjoy each other's company "under the sun."[116]

This detailed elaboration of marital sexuality was something new in Japanese print culture. As Mark Driscoll has pointed out, the prewar censorship system had been particularly obsessive about preserving the sanctity of the patriarchal home and depictions of "explicit relations between husband and wife" as well as adulterous relations involving wives were forbidden.[117] Japanese people were thus encouraged to think about the marital relationship in entirely new ways through their encounters with the couple magazines.

One of the ways in which readers were brought into the world of the magazine was through letters and articles purportedly written by readers themselves, often by wives, who described their own sex lives. The October 1949 issue of *Fūfu seikatsu* contained a special section dedicated to "Our conjugal lifestyle" contributed by readers. One article written by a person using the women's name Takeda Toshiko and entitled "Every morning before leaving for work: a hug and a kiss" described the "dreamlike" happiness that she shared with her husband of six years.[118] Significantly, the special "techniques" (*kufū*) that they deployed to ensure marital satisfaction would have seemed rather pedestrian to most American couples. These included sharing a kiss and a hug each morning before the husband's departure; ensuring that the two children slept in a room separate from the couple so that they could experience a "storm" of "loving feelings" in private; and the setting aside of Saturday evenings after the children had been put to bed for the sharing of special treats and intimacies. In 1949 these rather simple ways of sharing intimacy between couples obviously seemed sufficiently new and interesting to report upon.

Other contributions were, however, somewhat more sensational, such as an article bearing the male name Isehara Jirō and entitled "Our heavenly nights spent without a stitch on."[119] This young couple, yet to have children, enjoyed spending the evening together naked after having taken a bath, irrespective of the season, and made love every night of the week. The article is accompanied by a line drawing of a naked, full-breasted woman lying on a bed with her husband gazing on lovingly in the background. It would be easy to dismiss accounts such as these as having little more than pornographic intent. However when read in the context of 1949, only four years since the end of the war, the language is still startling. The author states that "you might think that it's because we don't have children [we act like this], but that's not the case. We really love each other. To outsiders it may seem a crazy infatuation or even perverted but we think this is a real couple's love." He goes on, "When we are alone together we think of nothing else . . . we just unite together our spirits and our flesh," concluding "[w]e think we are the most blessed couple in the world." This is a particularly extreme example of the common exhortation to set aside "couple time" and needs to be understood in relation to wartime demands of discipline, restraint, and civic duty—exhortations that were increasingly part of postwar discourses of "national reconstruction." Through the purple prose of the passage, the author luxuriates in the sensuality and obsession of his relationship. Here the everyday world of civic duty is reduced to jealous onlookers who simply don't "get it." *This* is what real love is, *this* is the liberation of sexuality, he seems to be saying. The husband's celebration of nakedness is not then, simply a titillating detail, but can be read as a rejection of emerging "salary-man" masculinity that Kathleen Uno describes as "a man in a dark suit commuting by train to a company, an actor in the public world, rather than a father or husband in the private world of the home."[120] It resonates also with the developing "literature of the flesh" that likewise celebrated nakedness as a metaphor for liberation. Sakaguchi Ango, one of its original proponents, encouraged readers to "rip off the various veils of deception . . . in order to start afresh as naked human beings."[121] The couple magazines were therefore important sites for spreading these new ideas and challenging state-sanctioned roles for both men and women.

On the whole, the couple magazines addressed themselves to young people, particularly those approaching marriage or who had just married. However, the encouragement to learn and practice "proper sexual technique" was by no means limited to the young. A range of articles addressed the importance of maintaining an active sex life across the course of a marriage, even into old age. The problem of maintaining "potency" (*potenshii*) was considered to be particularly acute for men. One article offered the diagram of a man's palm held out vertically with fingers extended illustrating the angle of erection that a man could expect to attain at different periods in his life. In his 20s a man's erection was expected to be near vertical like the thumb and with each decade the angle of erection decreased with each finger until in his 60s a man's penis drooped downwards like the little finger. Men were, however, encouraged not to accept this natural decline and to take advantage of a range of interventions, including hormone treatment and even surgery.[122] Seasonal foods that were thought to increase potency were also introduced.

To ensure that couples were engaging in the appropriate amount of sex, the couple magazines offered advice purportedly based on survey data in order to ascertain the "ideal" amount of sex for each age group.[123] The main "problem" for a husband with declining abilities was the sexual satisfaction of his wife, whose sexual responsiveness was thought to increase with age. Contrary to the prewar paradigm where, in pursuit of a "smooth" marital relationship, a wife was expected to "assimilate" to the needs of her husband,[124] the postwar companionate model of marriage required the "sexual satisfaction" of both parties. For middle-aged women whose desires were left unfulfilled, the consequences were thought to be dire, and included "nervous exhaustion" and even "hysteria."[125] Hence husbands were exhorted to take steps to avoid impotence (*inpo*) through paying attention to their health and diet.

Throughout the couple magazine genre, it was an unquestioned assumption that the new "liberation" of sexuality within marriage was a positive step and that with a little education and encouragement, wives would be willing to follow their husbands' lead into previously uncharted areas of sexual exploration. These articles in the couple magazines, then, had much in common with the literature of the flesh since, as Igarashi points out, they catered "to a male fantasy of women under male sexual tutelage."[126] The "good wife, wise mother" model of feminine virtue that had been promulgated via policy initiatives, the media, and education prior to the war was overturned. Instead, in the couple magazines the good wife was a *wise lover* who understood the role that sexual satisfaction played as a foundation for a happy marriage. However this was a role that was still very much crafted for her by male authorities. As Igarashi insightfully argues, "in rescuing female sexuality from the weight of history, Japanese men enabled women to leave the position of victim and join male members of society in celebrating the rejuvenation of Japanese society."[127] Japanese men, as "leaders" in the liberation of sexuality "thereby used female bodies to confirm [their] historical continuity from wartime into the postwar period."[128]

Hence, how this "sexual liberation" might have worked out in real life is not easy to discern. Women brought up during the long war years, in particular, had been indoctrinated by a system that downplayed sensuality and praised "virtue." Indeed, it was the virtuous and chaste nature of "girls from good families," as opposed to the supposedly libidinous and unrestrained sexuality of lower-class women (and Westerners) that had set them apart. How easily this austere mindset could be put aside and a new vision of a sensual and sexually agentic womanhood embraced is unclear. It was noted that unlike "factory girls," who, during their adolescence had been exposed to all sorts of deleterious sexual influences, "girls from good families" had been protected from sexual stimulation prior to marriage and thus had difficulty making the rapid adjustment to marital sex life.[129] As medical doctor Miyata Shigeo argued in his article aimed at "dissatisfied wives" discussed earlier, many women in whom an "instinct for chastity" had been instilled by family and religious training found the "first night experience" of marriage a shock. He urged his readers to consider that "there is no such thing as a married life without a sex life" and to cast aside the ideas that sex was vulgar, lewd, and dirty and to educate themselves in the "*ars amatoria*."[130]

No doubt, many women may have found these new demands on their time and energy to be traumatic and bewildering. The requirement to familiarize themselves with an ever expanding body of sexual knowledge and techniques may also have induced anxiety among men. The failure to make one's wife "go 'buru buru'" may have been experienced as a failure of masculinity. After all in the commercial sex scene with which men who came of age before and during the war would have been familiar, it was male pleasure that had been central, women had simply been service providers. Men's new responsibility to take the lead in sexual exploration, maintain "potency" into old age, and ensure the proper rate of sexual intercourse for their age group no doubt proved difficult for some. Not surprisingly sexual problem pages where readers wrote in to express their anxieties were staples of these magazines.[131] One worry that can be directly traced to Van de Velde concerned penis size. The "ideal" size of an erect penis, according to Van de Velde, was between 14 and 16 centimeters. However, the average Japanese penis was somewhat shorter. Takahashi Tetsu felt he had to point out that for Japanese men "ten centimeters is good enough" since Japanese vaginas were shorter, too.[132] Given these concerns, it may well have been the case that the mutual exchange of pleasure recommended by the couple magazines was as much a fantasy aspiration as were the luxurious and exotic Western-style bedrooms in which these fictions were sometimes set.

However, despite their evident drawbacks, the couple magazines were innovative in a number of ways. First, they elaborated a new "cultural scenario" that established a clear connection between love and sex. It is in the early postwar period that we see the idea that one's *hatsu taiken* or "first experience" of sex should be with a partner that one has romantic feelings for gain in importance. The sharing of mutual pleasure during the sex act came to be seen as an expression of a couple's love and commitment. Furthermore, the couple magazines offered an induction into a new style of "self-other relations," offering detailed instruction "in times, places, sequences of gesture and utterance"[133] that aimed to establish male-female sexual relations on a properly "democratic" basis. This was in sharp contrast to the prewar family system that had downplayed the value of romantic love as the basis for the marital relationship, tended to prioritize only the husband's satisfaction, and spoken of sex only in relation to reproduction. Even Van de Velde's detailed marital sex guide that was so influential in the early postwar years had taken pregnancy to be the ultimate object and aim of all sexual relations. Yet the couple magazines also presented a range of nonprocreative sexual acts whose only purpose was to provide pleasure. Importantly, too, the magazines discussed contraception.[134]

As noted earlier, the authorities from the Meiji period onward had not supported birth-control measures since their goal had been to increase the population so as to strengthen the army and provide settlers for Japan's vast newly conquered territories in Manchuria. From the late 1930s it had become increasingly difficult to speak of the positive benefits of contraception and family management since discussion of birth control was targeted by the thought police who considered it contrary to the war effort. The early postwar government however, faced with a population crisis as over 5 million overseas Japanese were suddenly repatriated from the former colonies, cautiously welcomed "appropriate" birth control while at the same time cautioning against the "decay of sexual morality."[135] Official statements concerning birth control often carried highly moralistic overtones and "family planning groups remained small, factionalized and ineffectual."[136]

The couple magazines were therefore an important source of family-planning advice. It was common for *Fūfu seikatsu*, for instance, to advertise contraceptive methods—condoms, pessaries, and creams—on the inside cover. Couples were encouraged to discuss the methods that were most appropriate for them. Husbands were warned not to simply slip on a condom without discussing it first since in the prewar period condoms had been marketed as disease prevention devices and a wife might mistake the act of wearing a condom as a confession on the part of her husband that he had been playing around.[137] Contraception was presented not simply in terms of women's health, or a family's economic circumstances, but as a planned strategy designed to enhance the relationship between husband and wife. Procreation, although still seen as an important aspect of marriage, was no longer presented as the be all and end all of a relationship, and certainly not as the necessary or only outcome of shared sexual intimacy. The "modern couple," despite maintaining a range of responsibilities to state and family, was primarily conceived as a pair of lovers, held together by mutual affection and concern for each other's welfare and pleasure. Hence, the couple magazines' championing of contraception was quite different in tone from that of Government-sponsored advice. As Christiana Norgren points out, "elites continued to ascribe to a reproductive ideology that centered on the national interest."[138] In this context, then, family planning aimed at enhancing the sexual relationship between husband and wife was indeed a new idea.

Although as we saw in Chapter 1, there had been widespread debate about the supposed benefits and demerits of the "romantic love marriage system" throughout Japanese society for decades, love was not the basis on which most marriages were contracted. Significant structural impediments made it difficult for young men and women to get to know each other well before entering into marriage. Those who came of age in the immediate run-up to war, in particular, were subject to a particularly eugenicist notion of the marital relationship that recognized the couple only to the extent that it served the nation as a reproductive unit. The notion of "couple time," or the exploration of nonreproductive pleasure in the name of marital harmony, would have seemed a selfish and perhaps unpatriotic notion during the war years. It was then, in the couple magazines of the early postwar years, that we first recognize what has now become the generally accepted understanding of the "love marriage" in Japan.

It was the couple magazines that first insisted upon the necessary connection between love and sex and love and marriage. Sex without love (for example, when paying for it) had been an accepted mode of behavior for men in Japan for centuries; however, in the postwar climate it was viewed as problematic. Similarly, sex for any reason other than as an expression of love (for example, solely for the purposes of procreation) was similarly problematized. This had the effect of positing children as the ultimate goal and product of love (as opposed to mere continuance of the family line). In the prewar system where only adultery on the part of wives had been a criminal offence, there had been provisions to integrate a husband's illegitimate children into his marital family. After the war, this imbalanced legislation was removed. However, the change in mindset was not so much a result of the transformed legal situation but rather of the rise to prominence of a new ideology structuring family relations, an ideology that made love the basis for marriage, for sex, and for children.

So far we have looked at how the discourse of romantic love was closely associated with wider debates about the progress of democracy as these themes played out in the context of heterosexual, particularly conjugal, unions. Rather than endorse a model that limited sexuality to its procreative function, many of these accounts encouraged sexual exploration and even went so far as to suggest that unorthodox kinds of sexual experimentation could play a role in the marital relationship itself. Indeed Miyata in his address to "dissatisfied wives" noted that among couples there were no small number of "perverts" (*hentai seiyokusha*), particularly partners with a predisposition toward either sadism or masochism. He suggested that these predispositions could, with the right expert advice, be integrated into a couple's "*ars amatoria*."[139] Takahashi, too, when replying to a young man worried that his marriage might be affected by his sexual fetishism, replied that "most of us are some kind of fetishist anyway," and encouraged him to keep a journal of his fantasies—even offering to publish some of the entries in his magazine.[140]

Although the couple magazines took as their focus heterosexual sex, the early postwar sex press had much to say about other, less conventional sexual relationships, including a range of "perverse" acts and identities such as homosexuality. Yet rather than repudiate these "abnormal" practices in the interest of promoting the marital relationship as the key and only proper site for the expression of sexuality, many authors endorsed sexual "curiosity hunting." Some of these "strange" sexual subcultures are explored in the next chapter.

6

Curiosity Hunting

Recent English-language accounts of the impact of the Occupation upon Japanese sex and gender policies and practices have helped us understand the connection that was made in the minds of the Occupation authorities themselves, as well as the Japanese government, between the proper management of male-female relations and the nation-building project. In some of these accounts, the largely American authorities are afforded a great deal of agency in shaping postwar sexual mores both rhetorically as well as in terms of day-to-day relations. For example, Sonia Ryang has stressed how policies concerning sexual ethics in Japan were among a range of initiatives drafted "under tutelage from the concerned offices of the Occupation."[1] She points out how the Japanese government, like the Occupation administration, saw "purity and sex education" as a necessary foundation for national security. This point is also stressed by Mire Koikari who considers the restrictive sexual dynamics between Americans and Japanese during the Occupation to be symptomatic of Cold War containment politics.[2] Igarashi Yoshikuni, too, notes how "American medical discourse" was instrumental in the process whereby Japanese bodies were "cleansed, normalized and democratized by the victor's hands."[3]

In these previous studies of gender and sexuality during the Occupation period, sexuality has tended to be discussed exclusively in terms of heterosexuality and gender has been accepted as binary. Most studies, albeit sensitive to issues such as race and class, have tended to accept the categories of "men" and "women" as self-evident. Diverse forms of same-sex sexuality (including cross-dressing prostitution) as well as a range of heterosexual "perversions" are not mentioned, despite the fact that some sections of the Japanese media in the late 1940s were interested in these issues. John Dower does acknowledge the existence of same-sex sexualities when he notes that "although male prostitutes also emerged to cater to the GI trade, little public mention was made of them."[4] However when he goes on to argue that "[male prostitutes] failed to capture the popular imagination," this is true only in relation to their interaction with GIs, discussion of which was impossible due to the stringent precensorship regime relating to "fraternization." As this chapter demonstrates, cross-dressing male prostitutes, or *danshō* as they were termed, were in fact widely discussed in early postwar media, including popular daily newspapers, as were a range of other nonheterosexual identities and practices including female-to-male cross-dressing. The *kasutori* press in particular was full of stories of sexual instability and confusion. Within the *kasutori* genre stories and accounts dedicated to *ryōki* or "curiosity hunting" that detailed "strange" and "abnormal" sexual desires were prevalent. Yet, despite the popularity and ubiquity of such reports in the press at the time, they have largely been overlooked in the English-language scholarship on the Occupation.

Also, much previous scholarship has understandably emphasized the importance of the interracial dynamics that structured official Occupation policies regarding Japanese sexuality in general.[5] Less attention has been paid to the various discourses informing the relationships between Japanese men and women. As outlined in Chapter 2, the "paranoia"[6] concerning fraternization between Japanese women and the men of the Occupation forces led to the censorship of even the most innocent of juxtapositions that might be taken the wrong way. Yet, despite the absolute prohibition of mention of the sexual behavior of Allied personnel, a voluble discourse about the sexuality of the local population was enabled (rather than silenced) by early Occupation initiatives that dismantled the previous censorship system. Hence "the heavy handed nature of sexual regulation imposed by the occupiers"[7] was only ever partial in its scope, focusing mainly on interracial heterosexual liaisons in both practice and in print. The *ryōki* genre, which focused on "strange" goings on between the Japanese themselves, was largely overlooked by SCAP's censorship regime.

Previous studies all present important bodies of evidence that testify to the effects of "top down" management through bureaucratic processes and the ideologies that they instantiate. However it is important that we do not ascribe too much influence to US policies or to the eagerness of the Japanese government to reintroduce "purity" into contemporary sexology debates. Occupation initiatives were never comprehensive and totalizing in their effects, as can be seen in the agency that the Occupation censorship policy afforded a wide range of voices to speak about sexual matters—an unforeseen consequence of the lifting of limitations on freedom of expression. As we saw in Chapter 2, also, despite renewed efforts at pursuing obscenity cases on the part of the Japanese police from 1947 on, the material targeted reflected local Japanese concerns about extramarital sex and was not influenced by developing Cold War paranoia about homosexuality.

Through emphasizing policy directions it is possible to create the impression that there were few aspects of life outside the discursive reach of the authorities during the Occupation. This is certainly not the case when we consider the complex nature of sex and gender relations on the ground in the chaotic postwar period. It may well be the case that various initiatives sponsored by the Allied authorities and the Japanese government alike were aimed at "educating" the public about sexual matters but to what extent did the public accept such tutelage? What other competing narratives were also available at the time?

I argue in this chapter that during the Occupation, sexuality, although it remained a site of intense surveillance and discipline, was also the source of popular resistance to both Occupation and Japanese government attempts to establish normative, state-sanctioned parameters for desire, practice, and identification. Perhaps the most startling feature of Japan's early postwar press from a contemporary perspective is the widespread discussion of "perverse sexuality" (*hentai seiyoku*) that took place. Under the blanket term *ryōki*, or "curiosity hunting," numerous publications sought out strange and bizarre stories that had much in common with the 1920s' and 30s' preoccupation with "erotic, grotesque nonsense" and points to the continuation of prewar interests into the Occupation period. Hence, a "bottom-up" reading of sentiments expressed in the popular press complicates the notion that the Occupation period saw the imposition of a unitary, normalized, and sanitized understanding of sexuality on the population at large.

The *Ryōki* Boom in the Early Postwar Press

As we saw in Chapter 1, *ryōki*, or seeking out the bizarre and unusual, was a genre of storytelling popular in the Japanese press of the late 20s and early 30s that was closely related to the fad for "erotic, grotesque nonsense." *Ryōki* is made up of the characters *ryō* 猟 with a base meaning of "hunting" and *ki* 奇 signifying "strange" or "unusual." The term has sometimes been rendered into English simply as "bizarre" but *ryōki* is better translated as "curiosity seeking" or "curiosity hunting" since it indicates an active propensity to seek out the unusual. As Jeffrey Angles has shown, *ryōki* did not involve a purely passive "armchair" consumption of strange stories but "also entailed firsthand exploration of areas beyond the bounds of ordinary life."[8] As he notes,

> With a minimum of time and money, one could engage in mini-*ryōki* adventures simply by walking through unfamiliar territory in search of unusual places, people, and things . . . the majority of the accounts of

> *ryōki* adventures are set in the more densely populated regions of Tokyo because . . . the size and flux of the metropolis allowed for many possibilities for interesting encounters.[9]

The term was popular in interwar detective fiction where many stories were characterised by *ryōki tan'i* or "hunting for the strange and indulging in the peculiar."[10] But *ryōki* also carried a sexual charge. As Angles shows, the development of the term was closely related to the spread of sexology that excluded certain kinds of acts and people from the world of the civilized and the normal. Yet, "[b]y labelling certain sexual acts and forms of sexual desire as strange, medical psychology and sexology helped turn them into precisely the kinds of 'curiosities' curiosity-hunters might seek out."[11] Hence, despite its emphasis on prohibition, sexology was never simply restrictive in its effects; it was also a highly productive discourse that inadvertently stimulated interest in precisely those aspects of sexuality that its authors stigmatized.

In the early postwar context, the term was often seen as part of the phrases *ryōki shumi* and *ryōki shisō*. The former is best translated as "an interest in seeking out the strange" rather than as a "strange interest" and the latter as a "curiosity-seeking mentality." Tokyo during the early years of the Occupation was a chaotic and unstable place, and the possibilities for witnessing strange and unusual scenes were multiple. As a consequence *ryōki* accounts were a staple of the *kasutori* press. In a search of the online database of Occupation-period magazine and newspaper headlines and titles contained in the Prange collection, *ryōki* appears in the main heading or subtitles of 650 articles, spanning both the mainstream and *kasutori* press, as well as in 3 advertisements for membership of "*ryōki* clubs." This figure does not include the large number of other articles that featured *ryōki* as a theme without including the term in a heading. In contrast, the popular prewar term "*ero guro*" appears only 86 times suggesting that *ryōki* had narrowed its focus to cover much the same ground as the "erotic grotesque" of the prewar period.

Angles has described the prewar *ryōki* boom in part as an "ethnography of the strange"[12] and has attributed its popularity to the homeland population's growing interest in "exotic" happenings in European capitals and on the fringes of Japan's empire. However, while the urge to seek out the strange had sometimes taken writers outside Japan, in the early postwar chaos the strange was suddenly brought much closer to home. This may, in part, have been an attempt to avoid censorship since as we saw in Chapter 2, any reference to behavior in an Allied nation (and this included China) that could have been construed as implying "criticism of the Allied forces" was liable to be censored. Rather than look overseas, the new *ryōki* discourse emphasized what has been termed the "real time" situation on the streets of postwar Japan. Sex crimes, prostitution, sex problems, sexual disease, "perverse desires," sex instruction—all these featured as topics of interest in both documentary and fictional formats. The tone of these accounts was also much more erotic and "indecent" than had been possible under the prewar censorship environment.[13]

The extent of the discussion of "perverse" or "abnormal" sexual issues is clear from a search for key terms related to same-sex sexuality in the titles and subheadings of magazine and newspaper articles in the Prange database. The database contains 89 articles with the term *danshō* (cross-dressed male prostitute) featured in their title or subtitles along with 10 featuring *kagema* (Edo-period term for male cross-dressed prostitute), 54 featuring the term *okama* (effeminate homosexual/prostitute), 41 featuring *josō* (male-to-female cross-dressing) and 83 *dansō* (female-to-male cross-dressing), 25 featuring *danshoku* (traditional Edo-period term for male-male eroticism), and 76 featuring the general term *dōseiai* (Meiji-period translation of Western concept of "homosexuality"). Hence we can conclude that at least 378 articles directly concerned with male and female same-sex eroticism and transgenderism were published over this three-year period—a significant number given the reticence of the English-language press to report on these topics at the time. This list, of course, does not contain the many more articles that touch on these topics incidentally or expand on them at length but do not contain these key words in their titles.

Although *ryōki* interests encompassed a range of "perverse" (*hentai*) practices, these were not necessarily constructed as opposed to or outside of the marital relationship—what they were opposed to is what might be described as "ordinary sex." As discussed in Chapters 3, 4, and 5, in accordance with the psychological turn in postwar sexology and the new emphasis on the equality of the sexes, it was widely recognized that "sexual satisfaction" was an important aspect of the marital relationship. It was also recognized that the war had impacted upon both male and female psychology and resulted in a range of "abnormal predispositions" (*abunōmaru seikō*) that meant sexual satisfaction could not always be achieved in "normal" ways. This sentiment is well illustrated in Figure 6.1 below, a cartoon simply entitled "*Ryōki*" that appeared in the December 1947 edition of the *kasutori* magazine *Bishō* (smile). The wife, who is reading a book in the living room, turns around suddenly in surprise as her husband scales the neighboring fence and attempts to enter through the window. The text reads:

> Wife: What the…!?
> Husband: Don't you reckon that recently the spark's gone out? Hee hee.

Figure 6.1 Cartoon entitled "*Ryōki* (Curiosity hunting)" appearing in the December 1947 edition of the magazine *Bishō* (Smile)

Note: Original in the Gordon W. Prange Collection at the University of Maryland.

The import of the cartoon is that the husband wants to try something new (perhaps intruder role-play) to spice up their sex life and is an example of how "pulp magazines with their extolling of sexual, especially non-conventional, behavior . . . represented a break with the repressive strictures of prewar and wartime morality."[14]

What *ryōki* tales do have in common, irrespective of whether they have a homo- or heterosexual focus, or whether they include marital or extramarital relations, is their emphasis on the "strange" (*ki*). They are also mostly lacking in moralistic overtones. Protagonists who are inadvertently exposed to these strange sights do sometimes express shock and disgust, but as with stories from the prewar period, there is often fascination too. Many stories have ambivalent endings and we are left unsure as readers just how the protagonist will go about dealing with his or her newfound knowledge—or, rather, we are invited to speculate about their next *ryōki* adventure.

One typical example of this ambivalence was published in the May 1948 edition of *Ningen tankyū* (Human investigation)[15] with the title "A heavenly night while being spied on: a pan pan club tale."[16] This account, set at the close of the war, involved a Tokyo businessman who, feeling lonely because his wife had evacuated to the countryside, took up the invitation of his colleagues to visit a secret brothel. At the brothel he met and became infatuated with a young prostitute and continued to visit her regularly. One evening, as they were enjoying themselves, he heard a cry of pain from behind the wall. Upon investigating he discovered that the wall was fake and crouching behind it, with his crotch stained, was a man who had been peeping through a hole—a not unlikely scenario given that many of the "fake hotels" (*inchiki hoteru*) that catered to the pan pan trade were reported to offer opportunities for peeping at other customers as part of their service.[17]

More shocking than the discovery that his liaison was being observed, however, was the realization that the Peeping Tom was no other than the chief executive of the company where the man worked. Some days later the man was called to the executive's office and offered bribe money as well as a promotion to keep quiet about his boss's activity. The narrator closes the account wondering what the man will do with his extra cash, the insinuation being that he will spend it in pursuit of further sexual pleasure. Not only is the protagonist of this story rewarded for his infidelity but he receives an education, too, in *ryōki* pursuits.

As discussed in Chapter 2, top-down policies advanced by Occupation authorities and the Japanese government alike sought to integrate sexuality into their plans for the "peaceful reconstruction" of Japan in much the same way that the militarist government of the 1930s had intervened in the population's sex lives to support its nation-building program. In part then, the *ryōki* genre reemerged as a self-conscious ploy to subvert these attempts at domestication and normalization (note that the example just discussed was set at the most crucial point in the war effort). It is significant too that it was a magazine entitled *Ryōki* that, as we saw in Chapter 2, was the first to be prosecuted for obscenity in the postwar period. The police launching the prosecution were no doubt disapproving of the explicit rejection of the "nation building" rhetoric in the magazine's editorials. The disrespect shown toward the authorities on the part of *Ryōki* was certainly popular since its well-publicized prosecution led to a proliferation of the *ryōki* genre and the term *ryōki* itself became a site of resistance to state-sanctioned discourses of "correct" sexuality.

Marilyn Ivy has noted that in the immediate postwar years "the struggle for survival created an intensely fragmented, individualized sense of consciousness, that tended to preclude the formation of a 'mass' sensibility."[18] Instead she points to the presence of "a striking 'subjectivity' (*shutaisei*) present after the war," which she defines as "an autonomy and individualistic consciousness."[19] Certainly the *ryōki* paradigm, with its interest in purely personal pleasure and thrill seeking, fits this pattern. As discussed in Chapter 3, people's interest in *ryōki* matters can be seen as part of the turn toward the flesh—the body and its potentialities for both pain and pleasure. Unlike the "mass" ideology of nation building, the *ryōki* paradigm sought meaning in the purely personal realm of pleasure and experimentation. As Dower has pointed out, Japanese people's widespread "relief at the collapse of the authoritarian state" went alongside a "receptivity to, or at least a tolerance of, an immense variety of pleasures and activities."[20] He notes how "the most flamboyant early expression of the casting off of despair and the creation of new space was to be found at the margins of 'respectable society.'"[21] He identifies three main groups: the pan pan, the black market, and the "*kasutori* culture demimonde" and argues that "all three marginal worlds came to exemplify not merely the confusion and despair of the *kyodatsu* [collapsed] condition, but also the vital, visceral, even carnal transcending of it."[22] Importantly, he also notes how "the *kasutori* culture remained fundamentally indigenous . . . the conqueror's ideas had only negligible impact on this world."[23] Hence, the *ryōki* paradigm needs to be understood in relation to the celebration of the body and its appetites and pleasures that characterized *kasutori* culture in general. Unlike the Western-oriented erotic culture of the "new couple" discussed in Chapter 5, the *ryōki* subculture reflected understandings of sexuality and desire that referred more to Japanese tradition and practice than to Western sexology.

One prominent strand running through many *ryōki* narratives was the idea that the trauma of Japan's defeat had demasculinized Japanese men, leading to an increase in passive male homosexuality and a predisposition toward masochism,[24] most clearly exemplified in an upsurge in male cross-dressing prostitution. Homosexual behavior was also considered to have been prevalent in the armed forces, leading some men to try to reenact the close emotional and physical bonds they had established with other men during the war.[25] The vast majority of media reports referring to male homosexuality concerned *danshō*, a compound incorporating the characters for "man" 男 and "prostitute" 娼—the latter normally understood to be female due to the Chinese character's inclusion of the woman radical 女 in its makeup. These men were also sometimes referred to as *okama*,[26] literally a pot for cooking rice, but also a slang term for the buttocks and a sly reference to anal sex. *Okama* was often used to designate a cross-dressing male or a man who behaved in a highly feminine manner. However, due to the derogatory connotations of the term, cross-dressers themselves sometimes used the variant reading *okame* as a self designation. Some accounts suggest that Tokyoites were less tolerant of male cross-dressers on the streets than were people in Osaka who were more likely to refer to these men as *onēsan* (big sisters) than *okama* (faggots).[27]

An increase in male homosexuality was considered a symptom of defeated nations (*haisenkoku*), comparisons often being made with the situation pertaining in Weimar Germany that had also seen a sudden increase in the visibility of homosexual culture after Germany's defeat in the First World War. So numerous were reports about the sudden increase in this type of flamboyant male figure that we should add the *danshō* to Dower's list of characters who symbolized the confusion but also the vitality of the early postwar years. Many of the men who became *danshō* were thought to have first encountered male homosexuality while serving in the army, and there are multiple *ryōki* tales in which ex-soldiers tell of their experiences.[28] Needless to say, such open discussion of homosexual activities that had taken place in the US armed forces would not have been possible in the English-language press at that time—pointing to the comparative freedom with which minority sexualities could be dealt with in the Japanese press, including in mainstream outlets.[29]

Unlike the prewar treatment of male prostitution that presented it as a secretive and hidden aspect of urban life, postwar discussions of the topic assumed a familiarity with the *danshō* subculture. The censors clearly did not consider either homosexuality or male prostitution to be problematic per se since numerous accounts can be found in both the mainstream and *kasutori* press. An *Asahi gurafu* (Asahi graphic) photospread in June 1948, for instance, featuring "people of the night" showed a number of confronting images of homeless people living in and around Ueno Station. Highlighted among them was a cross-dressed prostitute[30] waiting for a customer at the entrance to Ueno Park (a key center for male prostitution). Tales about *danshō* became a staple of the *ryōki* genre after an incident in Ueno Park on November 22, 1948, when a group of male prostitutes fought back against a squadron of police officers who had been dispatched to arrest them. Press coverage of this scandalous event was widespread and served to disseminate information about Tokyo's cross-dressing prostitution subcultures based in areas such as Ueno, Shimbashi, Ginza, and Asakusa.

Male Prostitution as an Exemplar of *Ryōki*

Compared with the many thousands of pan pan girls who could be seen on the streets of Japan's major cities nightly, the number of *danshō* was never large. Tokyo and Osaka were the only two cities where *danshō* activity was reported in the postwar press. Although it was rumored that back in the early 1930s the *danshō* population of Osaka and the neighboring city of Kobe ran to as many as three hundred, in the early postwar years there were far fewer. One report mentions only small pockets of five or six *danshō* spread across Osaka.[31] This might seem at odds with the conviction in many reports that male prostitution had suddenly increased, but what had in fact increased was the visibility of unregulated street prostitution. While under the militarist regime prostitution had been confined to a few closely regulated areas, in the postwar chaos both male and female prostitutes solicited in an open and conspicuous manner. In Tokyo, the largest concentration of *danshō* was in Ueno where a group of about 30 cross-dressers rented rooms and plied their trade on Ueno Hill, a wooded area just inside Ueno Park. Other groups of ten or so could also be found in Shimbashi and Shinjuku.[32] They seem to have been accepted members of the working-class areas in which they lived due to the money they brought to local businesses such as hairdressers, sewing shops, and bars. Prostitution was also a surefire way to make sure the rent was paid on time during a period of high inflation when regular workers were often paid in arrears.

Despite these relatively small numbers, there was a conspicuous upsurge in media discussion of male prostitution after November 1948 when the spectacular punch-up between a group of "men of the night" and the police who had been sent to arrest them was widely reported in the press. The Ueno incident was described in the *Mainichi* newspaper on November 23 under the heading "Gang violence caused by 'men of the night.'" At around 7 pm on the previous evening, the superintendent of the Metropolitan Police had gone to inspect the effectiveness of the curfew that had been declared in Ueno Park to deter the lively prostitution scene that had developed there. At the back of the Shimizu-dō (a temple building), he, and his accompanying entourage of journalists, encountered a group of men dressed in women's attire. When the journalists and camera crew started taking pictures of the men using a flash, the cross-dressers started attacking them in an attempt to take the cameras. The superintendent and his men fled the scene in fear, but later returned to the Shimizu-dō with reinforcements, not only to discover that the cross-dressed men were still there but that their number had increased to more than ten. The cross-dressers once again demonstrated their "masculine nature" (*dansei no taisei*) and began to beat up the camera crew. Then, they started hitting the superintendent who once again fled. Although the cross-dressers were finally subdued and arrested when 15 reinforcement police arrived, all things considered, the police came off looking rather inept if not outright incompetent in their handling of the incident.[33]

As a result of this debacle humorous cartoons that depicted the different situations, sexual and otherwise, in which *danshō* might be mistaken for real women appeared in a range of newspapers and magazines.[34] One depicted a cross-dressed *female* robber hoping to target real women but continually running into cross-dressed *men*. Upon arrest she reveals herself to be a woman.[35] Other cartoons included a "woman" who removes her wig in the women's bath and turns out to be a man;[36] a "woman" who lifts her skirt to urinate while standing, revealing her hairy legs;[37] a man who, before agreeing to accompany a pan pan girl, insists on checking out her legs for hair because "last time I ended up with a man";[38] a young boy running after his dolled-up "sister" who shouts "hey big brother, you forgot your bag";[39] a "woman" entering a gynecology clinic only to be kicked out exclaiming "It turns out I'm a man!";[40] and a mugger who attacks what he thinks to be a woman, only to discover that his victim is in reality a cross-dressed man[41] (see fig. 6.2). These images sometimes featured the statue of Saigō Takamori, which was a notable feature of Ueno Park, in the background. Saigō, a samurai leader who had opposed the unequal terms upon which Japan was opened to the West, was a native of Kagoshima in Japan's southern island of Kyushu. In the Meiji period this area had a "reputation as a hot-bed of male-male sexual activity"[42] and Saigō himself was renowned for his interest in "beautiful boys." This image thus served as a shorthand reference to both Ueno Park's *danshō* community and Japan's longtime tradition of male-male love that would have been recognized by readers.

Ueno Park, the site of the fracas between the cross-dressed prostitutes and the police, was further established in the public imagination as the pre-eminent locale for the male prostitution scene due to the journalistic attention given to Sumi Tatsuya's eye-witness novel *Danshō no mori* (Grove of male prostitutes) published in 1949. However, Ueno, like its close neighbor Asakusa, had long been associated with the sex trade due to its proximity to Yoshiwara, the licensed pleasure quarters of the Tokugawa period. Both male and female sex workers frequented the unlit park at night time. In the dark and unpatrolled recesses of the park *danshō* even functioned as a kind of unofficial police force and the female sex workers would sometimes call upon their assistance when faced with unruly customers.[43] Ueno Station, next to the Park, was also the main rail terminal serving the north of Japan, and its vast underground network of connecting tunnels and

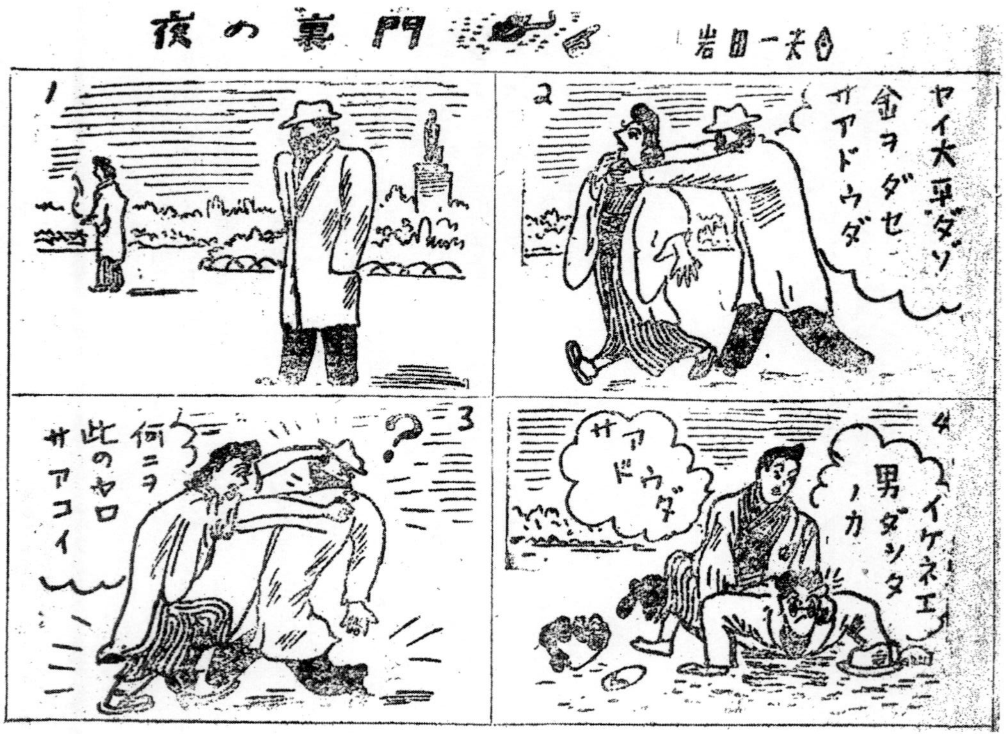

Figure 6.2 Cartoon of a mugger who attacks what he thinks to be a woman, only to discover that his victim is in reality a cross-dressed man from the February 1948 edition of *Tokudane zasshi* (Exclusive news magazine)

Note: Original in the Gordon W. Prange collection at the University of Maryland.

passageways had become home to many displaced people whose homes had been destroyed in the incendiary raids in the closing months of the war. Many repatriated soldiers, too, hung around the station, unsure when or if they should return to their hometowns. Ueno was also one of the departure points for the many thousands of city dwellers who travelled into the countryside daily in search of food to barter or purchase from local farmers. Ueno was, then, precisely the kind of chaotic and unregulated environment where one could pursue anonymous *ryōki* interests, and the reputation of the area as a sexual playground lived on into the 1970s.

According to press reports, Sumi had himself been homeless for a time and had lived among the displaced people in and around Ueno Station where he first encountered the *danshō*.[44] He had befriended one in particular, named Otomi, and she had provided him with an entrée into her tight-knit network of fellow male sex workers.[45] The real-life basis of the book generated much interest in the media. Numerous magazines featured discussions of the book, including some penned by the author and others featuring interviews with the prostitutes used as a base for its characters.[46] The liberal arts magazine *Bungei yomimono* (Literary reading matter), for instance, published a special report on the book in its February 1949 edition, complete with 15 photographs of actual *danshō* living in the area.[47] Sumi later rewrote some of the material from the book and staged it as a play featuring Otomi, whose life experience had been borrowed for the book, in the lead role. The play generated further controversy when Otomi went to the police, claiming that s/he had been defrauded of a share of the profits.[48]

Unlike female prostitution, which was regulated by a large number of local ordinances (*jōrei*), it was more difficult for the police to crack down on male-male sex work since the regulations "explicitly defined a sex worker as female."[49] If caught in a sex act while out in the open, *danshō* could be arrested for "public obscenity" but since male prostitution was not mentioned in the criminal code, simply being suspected of prostitution was not sufficient for an arrest. Unlike women suspected of prostitution whom police could detain and require to undergo compulsory examination for venereal diseases, *danshō* were simply cautioned by the police.[50] Also, whereas in the United States and elsewhere in the West at that time appearing in public while wearing clothes associated with the opposite sex was illegal,[51] there were no regulations concerning cross-dressing in Japan. Hence a "woman" who was detained at the ticket gate of Ueno Station for travelling on a rail pass issued under a man's name was later released by station staff when "she" removed the rubber insert from her bra and threw it at them.[52] There was little that the police could do with the *danshō*, then, other than encourage them to move on. The reports on *danshō* thus served to draw public attention to the cruising grounds where they could be located, enabling men (and even women) interested in this kind of partner to find them without exposing the *danshō* to fear of arrest.

The largely nonjudgmental attitude that the *kasutori* press took toward diverse sexual expression can be seen in the fact that members of otherwise stigmatized groups such as the pan pan were sometimes given a voice, especially in the *zadankai* or "roundtable" format where a journalist or editor guided discussion among a number of invited participants. At least four roundtables featuring *danshō* were published in 1949 alone. The choice of the *zadankai* format may have been expedient since it was an easy and cheap way of obtaining copy for one's publication. However, one advantage of this style of interviewing was the lack of journalistic input or overlay that maximized input from the participants. Although, as "chair" of the conversation, the house editor or journalist (who often went unnamed) had some control over the direction of the conversation, and the final copy was likely cut, edited, and rearranged to a certain extent, it was the opinions of the participants themselves that were highlighted. Thus, although these discussions might be framed in objectifying and pathologizing terms in the introductory matter or headlines, the course of the conversation does not necessarily fit these agendas.

For instance, the January 1949 edition of *Shakai tanbō* (Society stories) included an article with the title "A roundtable of *danshō* only: an analysis of perverse psychology and perverted desires."[53] However, very little analysis is forthcoming; instead the discussion offers a series of interesting and scurrilous vignettes as the various *danshō* participants discuss scenes from their lives. The conversation opens with eye-witness accounts of the previous year's police raid on the *danshō* community in Ueno Park. A *danshō* named Akiko demonstrates how she wrestled herself free from the detective who grabbed her wrist by hitting him with a handbag. To reinforce the comedy of this point, the incident is brought to life by a cartoon depicting the stunned detective falling onto his behind. The police come out of this account seeming rather foolish, like characters in a pantomime, and the reader cannot help but applaud this resistance to authority. Indeed, the police had been rather naive. Expecting to make easy arrests and be shown to be cleaning up the park, they had invited press photographers to accompany them. However the photos that were printed the following day showed the police being attacked by men dressed in kimono with handbags—hardly a dignified scene.

This motif of *danshō* triumph over police harassment was also repeated in another *zadankai*, this time published in a mainstream outlet *Gekkan yomiuru* (Monthly *yomiuri*) in October 1950, with the title "*Danshō* talk about their topsy-turvy lives."[54] In an attempt to stop the unlicensed prostitution that took place in Ueno Park after dark, the police had made Ueno Hill (a wooded area overlooking the Shinobazu Pond) off-limits at night.

However this did not stop the *danshō* from frequenting the area since unlike suspected female prostitutes who the police had the power to arrest and force to undergo a health inspection, there was little that could be done with the male cross-dressers. Late one night, about 3 am, a *danshō* called Machi-chan was walking down the pathway from the hilltop when she was accosted by a policeman who yanked her by the hair and demanded "What's a vermin like you doing here?" Without thinking, Machi, who had excelled at judo while in middle-school, simply grabbed the policeman and flipped him over onto his backside, ripping his uniform in the process. This disrespect toward the police, and the willingness of the press to present them in an unflattering light, is not surprising given the widespread corruption that existed among the force and the rude and often sanctimonious manner in which policemen lorded it over ordinary people who were, after all, just trying to make a living.[55]

A less upbeat account entitled "Confessions of a problem: a roundtable discussion with male prostitutes"[56] was published in the *kasutori* magazine *OK* in August 1949 and offers a fascinating glimpse of the conditions facing male sex workers in the Occupation period. The three male prostitutes, who today would probably identify as transgender or transsexual, all tell tales of sexual nonconformity, including homosexual liaisons, from an early age. With a lack of any marketable skills, prostitution became a way to support themselves in the chaotic postwar years. Interestingly, since they plied their trade while dressed in women's kimono, they revealed that many of their clients did not even realize that they were biological men. This was possible due to the fact that their customers were largely picked up and usually serviced at night in the shadow of the bushes in Ueno Park.

The *danshō* were reported to use a special sexual technique referred to as *renkon* that simulated vaginal sex. *Renkon* is literally a lotus root, a vegetable that contains numerous holes. The *renkon* technique involved making a hole shape with the fist of one hand, lubricating it with cold cream and then inserting it between the thighs. The use of this technique meant that both *danshō* and their customers could avoid the transmission of venereal disease and it is possible that some customers sought out *danshō* for this very reason. Anal sex, technically referred to as *keikan* or "sodomy" in sexological literature, was in *danshō* lingo referred to as *ura* or *ushiro*, "back" and "behind" but was usually avoided for health reasons.[57] Given that some *danshō* sought to pass as women, on occasions when they stayed over with clients, they were careful not to fall asleep in case their biological sex was discovered. Some even resorted to taking amphetamines, which were widely available as Japanese military stockpiles had been released onto the market.[58]

Despite their unconventional lifestyles, the participants reveal the extent to which romantic love ideology was important for them, and in this they have much in common with the pan pan girls who made similar comments in the roundtables discussed in Chapter 3. The *danshō* state: "our ideal is to live as a couple" with gender normative men in a normal husband-wife situation. Indeed they had all occasionally enjoyed this lifestyle with a "patron" for short periods of time although the relationships had never lasted. As one notes of her friend, "It is Otoki's dearest wish to get out of working for her livelihood, and into cooking and washing for a man she loves, and being taken care of by her husband." Although none of the participants is optimistic about the chance of finding true love and escaping a life of prostitution, and the discussion is certainly not upbeat about the challenges they face, the article itself is nonjudgmental, simply reporting the conversation between the sex workers and the journalist, and ending with a plea for understanding and compassion.

What emerges from these roundtables is a picture of the underdog in a determined and resilient attempt to survive against all the odds. Since readers were able to hear from the protagonists in their own words without critical comment or overlay, it is entirely possible that readers saw their own struggles for survival, including run-ins with petty authorities, reflected in the lives of the *danshō*. A common theme running through all these discussions is the search for romantic love, for the ideal "patron" whom the *danshō* can relate to as "husband" (*danna*) in a conventional marriage-like relationship. Hence, despite attempts by sexologists to pathologize the "perverse sexual desires" of the *danshō*, what these men say they are really looking for is not sexual stimulation, but love in a marriage-like relationship, and in this they have much in common with similar reports on the pan pan girls, or indeed people in general. As we have seen, the pursuit of romantic love was one of the key symbols of freedom in Japan's postwar "democratic" society. Through their endorsement of the ideal of romantic love and the gender binary implicit in the marital relationship, contemporary *danshō* were supporting rather than challenging contemporary mores, albeit they were expanding the notion of what it meant to be a "woman." Indeed most commentators and interviewers seem to have accepted the *danshō*'s female self-presentation and used the feminine pronoun *kanojo* or "she" to describe them, which, as one journalist noted, "seems more fitting."[59]

Thus, these personal accounts of survival, recounted with not a little joie de vivre and humor, although no doubt pandering to *ryōki* interests, do invite the reader to identify with the hardships faced by the *danshō*. Often accompanied by engaging photographs of the discussants, dressed in women's kimono, with nicely coiffed Western-style hairdos and accessories, these accounts could not be more different from contemporary sexological treatments that stressed the psychological abnormality and "perverse sexual desires" of the *danshō*.[60] It was however the roundtable accounts that reached the wider audience.

A further element within these popular accounts of male prostitution that works against the designation of the *danshō* as completely "other" to a normalized sexuality is the widespread assumption that some *danshō* at least were sexually responsive with women.[61] One amusing story rather similar in tone to the "erotic, grotesque nonsense" genre of the 1930s was published in *Kitan zasshi* (Colorful tales magazine) in June 1949.[62] Entitled "Varieties of Eros," the story concerned a man who was picked up by what he thought was a woman while strolling around Ueno Park one afternoon. The two retired to a coffee shop where he grabbed hold of one of her breasts, but was surprised to find it hard to the touch. Suddenly aware that he had been picked up by a *danshō,* the man hurried out in a fluster pursued by the *danshō.* In the struggle that followed a packet of condoms (a valuable commodity at the time) fell out of the man's pocket. The *danshō* asked that s/he be given one. "What are you talking about?" demanded the man. "These are for men!" In reply the *danshō* hitched up her skirt and grabbed her crotch saying "I am a man and I intend to buy a prostitute tonight!" The author was sent reeling at the sight of his/her hairy legs.

Danshō who took on both male and female clients were sometimes referred to as *donten*, an onomatopoeic term for "flip flop."[63] This idea was not surprising since, during the Tokugawa period, the *kagema* (an early term for male prostitute) were widely advertised as servicing both male and female clients. That some contemporary *danshō* were assumed to provide services for women is made clear in a number of accounts. One story published in *Shinsō jitsuwa* (True tales) in May 1947, purportedly contributed by a *danshō,* mentions that he was approached by a middle-aged woman who selected him because he resembled a Kabuki *onnagata* (female-role player) with whom she had been infatuated in her youth. He reported that her lovemaking that night had been "absolutely passionate."[64] Another story describes how a "sexually frustrated" wife, upon discovering that her husband was keeping a male lover, decided to share him with her husband.[65] Yet other reports mentioned that *danshō* were sometimes married to women.[66] That there was supposed to be a market for women who sought out the sexual services of men who themselves were acting as women is another factor pointing to the particularity of Japan's postwar sexual environment—and also the longevity of the Kabuki paradigm in which female-role players had been courted by both male and female patrons.[67]

Another category of male sex worker that was sometimes discussed alongside the *danshō* was the *kakusaku bōi* (cock-suck boy),[68] an adolescent youth who provided oral services to men.[69] Sources suggest that this behavior was not seen as deriving from "sexual perversity" as was sometimes suggested of *danshō,* but was more often a response to poverty. Likewise, the men seeking the cock-suck boys' services were not pathologized as the boys were represented as a substitute source of sexual pleasure when the pan pan girls (who the boys often pimped for) proved unavailable. Male sex work was not however motivated solely by extreme poverty, as more middle-class youths also engaged in prostitution in order to advance themselves. *Pan pan bōi* (pan pan boys) who were in their late teens often had day jobs or were university students and sought out liaisons with older men in order to supplement their income or seek help in their careers.[70] Unlike the *danshō* who could be found at the fringe of the city in Ueno Park, the *pan pan bōi* focused their attention on Hibiya Park, directly opposite GHQ, raising the question as to whether Occupation personnel, too, were in their sights.[71] Indeed, at least one post-Occupation account claimed that the park was the main cruising ground for Japanese youths who "chased after foreign ass."[72] The fact that in these accounts the male sex workers were presented as primarily motivated by the desire for money (or connections) also helped to normalize their activities in the context of postwar instability.

Given the stress in some previous scholarship on the conservative impact that the US Occupation had upon Japanese sex and gender mores, emphasizing the impact of Cold War containment policies, one might expect that this incitement to discourse about perverse or abnormal sexuality would be related to attempts to discipline and regulate sex and gender identities by delineating and policing the boundaries of the normal. However, the *ryōki* topos is more clearly related to existing Japanese understandings of sexuality than to the increasingly stark hetero/homo binary that was developing in the United States in response to Cold War anxieties. As Eve Sedgwick argues, the tendency in US culture since the beginning of the twentieth century has been to make an increasingly "paranoid" delineation between homosexual and heterosexual interests. She draws attention to "the paranoid insistence with which the definitional barriers between 'the homosexual' (minority) and 'the heterosexual' (majority) are fortified . . . by non-homosexuals, and especially by men against men."[73]

Scholarly work on homosexuality in the US context has shown how the potential for same-sex intimacies in the homosocial environment of the armed forces was a constant source of anxiety for both military and civilian authorities both at home and overseas. The US Occupation authorities in Japan, too, were aware of homosexual activity in the ranks, both male and female, and were proactively engaged in seeking out and dismissing anyone known to be engaging in homosexual activity. Anxieties about homosexuality only intensified as the Cold War took hold, as Koikari points out, at that time "any sexual transgression was immediately associated with political subversion and thus a cause for suspicion."[74] However we need to remember that in the Japanese context "homosexuality" had very different significations. Despite the fact that during the militarist period the authorities had intervened extensively in the regulation of the sex lives of the Japanese people, same-sex sexual acts, whether male or female, remained unregulated by law. This was at a time when virtually all the Allied and Axis nations were vigorously enforcing "sodomy" statutes that punished male homosexuality with prison sentences and a range of other social exclusionary measures. Indeed to talk of "homosexuality" (*dōseiai*) and "heterosexuality" (*iseiai*) in Japan at that time is problematic since same-sex sexual acts were hardly ever discussed in this binary framework, at least in the popular press.

In the early postwar context in Japan the "definitional barriers" polarizing sexual activity and identity were less insistent in that both male and female homosexual acts were represented as something that otherwise ordinary persons might fall into or indeed seek out due to their *ryōki* interests. Even "expert" medical opinions on the male-prostitution phenomenon, which offered much more stigmatizing descriptions of the *danshō* than those in the popular press, were, as Pflugfelder points out, "on the whole more self-satisfied than . . . hostile."[75] Significantly, the medical literature tends not to pathologize the customers of the *danshō*. For instance, a 1948 article in a journal dedicated to the study of psychoneuroses presented a rather damning description of typical *danshō*, stressing their effeminacy, low intelligence, and criminal orientation while at the same time pointing out that "their customers are not people who have sexual perversion."[76] Hence even in Japanese sexological writings we seldom see the totalizing denunciation of homosexuality that is more typical of the Western genre of sex research and that is replicated in official Cold War policies aimed at criminalizing and thereby expunging homosexuality from the body politic.

The *ryōki shumi otoko*

So far in our discussion of the *ryōki* phenomenon we have focused upon the "strange" characters and their "perverse" lifestyles that provided fodder for the stories so avidly consumed by readers. However there is another kind of character in these tales, referred to as the *ryōki shumi otoko*, or "man with curiosity hunting tastes," who occupies an ambivalent position.

Sedgwick reminds us that (speaking here of the US context)

> [i]t is a *rather amazing* fact that, of the very many dimensions along which the genital activity of one person can be differentiated from that of another . . . precisely one, the gender of object choice, emerged from the

> turn of the [twentieth] century, and has remained as the dimension denoted by the now ubiquitous category of "sexual orientation."[77]

Hence, in the United States popular opinion on homosexuality has tended to reflect the assumption that both partners in a homosexual liaison, whether "active" or "passive," gender normative or transgender, older or younger, paying or paid are equally contaminated by the "sexual perversion" label.[78] Yet, in Japan, on the contrary, the idea that men who sought out interactions with cross-dressing male prostitutes did not necessarily share a common perverse nature lived on well into the postwar period. For instance, writing in 1958, a decade after media exposure of *danshō* was at its height, popular sex journalist Kabiya Kazuhiko notes that "among the customers who buy *danshō*, there are more who are motivated by an interest in curiosity hunting (*ryōki shumi*) than those who are themselves homosexual."[79] As late as 1974, left-wing journalist and social reformer Kanzaki Kiyoshi, in his voluminous study of postwar prostitution, notes in a discussion of the male prostitution that took place in Ueno Park in the early postwar years that among visitors to the park were *ryōki shumi otoko*, that is, "men with curiosity hunting interests."[80] Kanzaki pointed out that the attraction of the park for those interested in *ryōki* was that it offered a range of "play" (*asobi*) and "thrills" (*suriru*) from different types of sex worker, including *danshō*.

Hence, although consorting with cross-dressed male prostitutes was certainly not considered a "normal" thing to do and was probably not a hobby that would have been included on a resume, transgressing the normal was the whole point of the *ryōki* paradigm, and it was precisely the thrill of transgression that many journalists and readers alike enjoyed in these accounts of "*abu rabu*" (that is, "abnormal love"). Writing in 1948, Tomita Eizō, a journalist and manga artist who was to become a chronicler of Japan's postwar "gay bar" scene,[81] was clearly more intrigued than repulsed by the glimpse of facial hair through heavy make-up he spied on a *danshō* he followed home one afternoon. After having interviewed her about her "outlandish" lifestyle he is left wondering "what kind of abnormal personality would find it amusing to play with *okama*, but then I wonder if it isn't the case that the fascination is in the thrill that comes with playing with someone other than a female partner?"[82] Obviously intrigued, he goes on to speculate that "being men themselves, they have complete knowledge of techniques to bring about ecstasy in a man." The implication seems to be, why wouldn't you give it a try?

The discourse stressing the nonpathological nature of the *danshō*'s customers was enabled by two main factors. First, the gender dimorphism that structured interactions between men and women was preserved in male customers' interactions with the cross-dressed *danshō*. The men who sought out sex with *danshō* were depicted as active and penetrative in much the same manner as in their relationships with female prostitutes. Indeed, drawing upon well-rehearsed arguments in support of the *onnagata* (female-role players) in the Kabuki theatre, it was argued that *danshō* were *more* feminine than actual women, especially in the postwar period where Occupation gender reforms were supposed to have resulted in more assertive and thus less conventionally feminine women. *Danshō* who were lucky enough to find a patron and to be supported by him as a "wife" were also described as making better wives since they were much more likely to take good care of their "husband" (*danna*) than an ordinary woman.[83] In one 1949 account of a visit to a *danshō* named Etsu-chan who roomed near Ueno Park, the male journalist is constantly amazed at the "woman-like" (*onnarashii*) mannerisms of his hostess. He notes that she was "even more woman-like" than two exquisite Japanese dolls on display in a case in her room. When Etsu served him a sliced apple, he caught a flash of her white undergarment inside the sleeve of her brightly colored kimono, commenting that the sight was "strangely erotic" (*hen ni iroppokute*).[84] Although this meeting does not end in a sexual encounter (at least that we know of), the journalist was certainly enchanted by the visit.

In the terms of the *ryōki* paradigm, then, interactions with male prostitutes actually reinforced the prevalent gender order. They might have been seen as evidence of an excessive or a poorly disciplined but hardly perverted libido. Second, male cross-dressing prostitution was not new to Japan. Indeed, it was recognized as a traditional part of Japan's sexual landscape, and as having provided the inspiration for much literary and theater culture of the Tokugawa period.[85] Thus, the treatment of homosexuality in popular discourse in Japan was rather different from that in the United States. As the 1950s progressed and the Cold War intensified, male homosexuality was frequently "othered" as a contaminating outside force in rhetoric deriving from the United States. Indeed homosexuals were signaled out as persons suffering from "psychopathic personalities" and denied immigration into the United States (and non-US citizens convicted of homosexual acts could be expelled from the country).[86] This maneuver was much more difficult to accomplish in Japan where cross-dressing prostitution, especially that associated with the Kabuki theater, was acknowledged as an indigenous practice with a long history. The upsurge in male homosexuality may well have been considered a postwar "problem" but it was a problem that had been part of the fabric of Japanese society for centuries.

That the *ryōki shumi otoko* represented a category not easily assimilated into the homo/hetero binary is illustrated by an article entitled "Ryōki yobanashi" (A night-tale of curiosity seeking) appearing in the October 1949 edition of *Bēze* (i.e., *baiser*—French for "kiss").[87] The article discusses the postwar phenomenon of male cross-dressed prostitution, offering tips to potential customers on how to distinguish cross-dressed male prostitutes from actual women. It might be supposed that this advice is aimed at reinforcing the definitional barriers between hetero- and homosexual customers. However, the article makes a distinction between *three* different types of customers on the basis of their object choice. These are: men who will only accept women; men who think "so long as [the prostitutes] entertain me in an interesting manner it doesn't matter;" and those who deliberately seek out *danshō* (only 5 out of every 100 men are identified as experiencing this "perverse desire"). It is the middle category, that of the *ryōki shumi otoko* who seek out "interesting" sexual scenarios irrespective of the sex or gender of object choice, that complicates the assertion that Cold War models of sexuality were exerting a structuring influence on Japanese modes of sexual identity and practice at that time.

Indeed it was common for articles to differentiate between *ryōki shumi* and those actions based on "perverse desire" suggesting that an interest in *ryōki* was not *in itself* considered perverse. An article on cross-dressing in both men and women in the May 1947 edition of the magazine *Ryōki*,[88] for instance, notes four motivations, which are, in order, *ryōki shisō* (curiosity-seeking mentality), *seiteki tōsaku* (sexual perversity), *hanzai riyō* (criminal purposes), and *bōkei shudan* (plot measure—for literary or stage characters). Cross-dressing undertaken out of "curiosity," then, seems to have been judged separately from a compulsion to cross-dress out of "perversity." The author is also at pains to establish cross-dressing as a practice with its roots in Japanese tradition, identifying examples of male cross-dressing for the purpose of "political plotting" in both the *Kōjiki* and *Nihon Shōki*, two classic Japanese historical texts of the eighth century.

Rather than fortify definitions of normalcy, the *ryōki* genre tended to stress the fluidity of identification and desire. For instance, a story entitled "Kagema yashiki" (A dwelling of male-prostitutes) in the July 1949 edition of *Bēze* begins with a man on the lookout for a regular encounter with a female prostitute.[89] However, after initially making contact with what he assumes is a willing woman, he comes to realize that s/he is in fact a male cross-dresser. Not perturbed, however, he follows her to the lodging she shares with other cross-dressers and they spend the night together. This sequence of events is not unusual in the *ryōki* literature. What renders this account so interesting is that the man fails to return home. Instead, he asks that he be allowed to stay on to train as a cross-dresser and entertain male customers of his own. Such accounts where protagonists clearly cross the boundary from being an observer of sexual curiosities to an active participant in them were not a postwar innovation. As Angles notes, even in narratives from the 1930s it was acknowledged that "people interested in *ryōki* might turn to gender-bending dress and perhaps even homoerotic encounters to satisfy their yearning for adventure."[90] Hence the early postwar *ryōki* paradigm carried over tendencies evident in the more liberal strand of prewar sexology identified by Mark Driscoll, who comments that "[p]eople were not profiled and policed as perverse, and erotic aspects were rarely linked to essentialized identities."[91] These *ryōki* stories and others like them point to the fact that official discourses of sexual propriety, whether those promulgated by Japan's old militarist regime or those of the new US-led Occupation, were never totalizing in their effects. Also they do not attest to a "paranoid insistence" on the definitional barriers between homo- and heterosexual but rather to the fluidity of these categories, at least when framed within the *ryōki* paradigm. Hence, to an extent, the *ryōki* paradigm comprised a "cultural scenario" that gave symbolic meaning to sexual acts and interests that were quite different from those on offer in the couple magazines examined in the previous chapter. Through engaging with *ryōki* accounts, readers were given the opportunity to style themselves as *ryōki shisō otoko* and to understand their "strange" tastes and desires as part of the search for new experiences and adventure and not as evidence of pathology or perversion.

On the whole *ryōki shumi* and *ryōki shisō* accounts concerning male prostitutes feature male protagonists—although there are descriptions of female clients, including four or five "widows' clubs," that enjoyed a range of services provided by *danshō*[92] and "beautiful young men." This is partly to do with the organization of public space in the immediate postwar years—the streets of Tokyo and other large cities were dangerous, especially so for women. Not only were unaccompanied women liable to receive unwanted attention from male passersby but they could also be accosted by the police who, if they suspected them of soliciting for sex, had the power to order them to undergo venereal examinations.[93]

To the extent that *ryōki* represented a kind of sexual tourism, it was mainly men who could traverse the city streets and parks at night in search of these thrills. However, it is important to note that the predisposition toward engaging in sexual thrill seeking was not imagined as an exclusively male prerogative as can be seen in the many early postwar accounts of female same-sex love. Although women's freedom of movement may have been more constrained, this does not discount the manner in which female readers may have been able to participate vicariously in the *ryōki* discourse through the many stories and accounts in the press featuring female protagonists. Indeed, there is some evidence that women could and did use these texts in fashioning their own sexual identities.

Female *ryōki* Characters

It was not only deviant male bodies and behaviors that were subject to *ryōki* interests. As Christine Marran points out, early postwar popular culture witnessed "the disintegration of the culturally and ideologically produced masculine ego" and the subsequent rise in representations of the "deviant female body."[94] Yet, if male cross-dressing prostitution was sometimes viewed with dismay as a symbol of postdefeat sexual instability, sexual irregularity on the part of women could be discussed more positively. Given their new status and rights as guaranteed by the constitution, women were thought to have discovered greater sexual agency and a predisposition toward female same-sex love and sadism.[95] In fact, cross-dressing by women, literally *dansō* or "male dressing," was as extensively reported upon as was cross-dressing by men. However, unlike the cross-dressed men who were largely associated with male prostitution, cross-dressed women appear in a wider range of circumstances, most often in association with crime.

A report in the November 21, 1946, edition of the *Asahi* newspaper for instance, described the arrest of four cross-dressed female truck drivers on suspicion of stealing iron scraps from the yard of a local dealer. Unfortunately we are not told the reason for the women's choice of men's attire but it is possible that they had to pass as men in order to gain this kind of employment. Other reports frequently mention cross-dressed women working as pickpockets, again potentially disguising as men so as to move about the city with greater freedom. A report in the December 19, 1947, edition of the *Yomiuri* newspaper, however, suggests that some cross-dressing women were recognized and respected in their male personae. This article concerns the cross-dressed women leaders of two rival crime gangs. One, known as "Elder Sister of the Mountain," controlled territory in Ueno whereas the other, known as "Elder Sister of the Underground,"[96] was based in Kanagawa. It was noted that between them they controlled gangs responsible for over 50 thefts totaling 10,000 yen. Another article mentions a woman arrested for embezzlement who had used the money to attire herself in "men's new look styles." She was reported to have had both male and female admirers who referred to her as "young master."[97] Another cross-dressed female thief confessed that she was motivated by the desire to "play around like a man." She used stolen money to buy expensive foreign suits and to hire female companions in Ginza cabarets and dance halls.[98] Yet other reports point to cross-dressing for potentially romantic or sexual reasons, especially in relation to cross-dressed suicide victims whose deaths were said to be due to "failed love affairs."[99]

Women's empowerment was sometimes expressed in sexual terms, women being considered free to give reign to their "sadistic" impulses.

These allegations of female sadism were however not new since sadism appears to have been commonly associated with nonconformist women even prior to the war's end. Miriam Silverberg,[100] for instance, notes that although to call certain representations of the 1920s' "modern girl" (*moga*) "sadistic," "might be extreme," there are many representations that suggest "she is self-centered and concerned only with sensual pleasures, and she is possessed of an extra touch of transgressive perversity," a picture not at all dissimilar to the postwar sadistic woman.

The sadistic woman par excellence was, of course, the murderer Abe Sada who in 1936, after strangling her lover to death—with his complicity—had cut off his penis and carried it about with her. Abe was released for good behavior in 1941 and after her return to Tokyo in 1945 became something of a media celebrity. This intense and torrid affair that took place at a time when the public at large was being precipitated into a state of "spiritual mobilization" was, in the immediate postwar period, reinterpreted as a symbol of resistance and a championing of individual autonomy. As Marran notes, "in this controversial time of restructuring social morality . . . the sexual, criminal woman [was] presented as an idealized component in the formation of a new democracy."[101]

Although the majority of publishers, editors, and writers involved in early postwar sex journalism were men, it should be acknowledged that women's sexual and emotional experiences were accorded a visibility not paralleled in the prewar period. As has been argued in previous chapters, the *kasutori* press was crucial in more widely disseminating knowledge about the mechanics of female sexual response that previously had only been available in medical and sexological publications. One of the most important innovations of early postwar sex journalism was the widespread acknowledgment that women did indeed experience sexual desire and that they had similar needs for "sexual satisfaction" (*sei manzoku*) as did men. As we saw in Chapter 5, women readers were specifically addressed in a number of general publications as well as in a variety of romance magazines that went into issues dealing with sex and courtship in great detail. Women also featured as authors and as participants in roundtable discussions concerning new trends in courtship and married life that were transcribed and published in the press. In fact, the need for "female perspectives" on a wide variety of topics, from "first experiences" of courtship and lovemaking to prostitution and the practice of bedroom arts, was recognized.

One such discussion entitled "The secrets of female students: a confessional roundtable"[102] published in the July 1949 edition of *Shinsō jitsuwa* (True tales) purportedly took place between a reporter and four schoolgirls aged between 17 and 19 in a café suitably named "Bohème." A wide range of topics were touched on in the 14-page article including contraception, thoughts about chastity, criticism of pan pan girls, favorite movies and actors, erotic literature, women's magazines, sex education, and the supposedly "flourishing" state of same-sex love among school girls. The journalist (whose name and sex are unspecified) mentions that he or she has heard that "S" (female same-sex love) relations are "all the rage" among schoolgirls[103] and wonders what the girls have to say on the matter. While noting that same-sex love "isn't exactly all the rage," one girl does admit to having recently received a "love letter" from M-chan, a girl in a junior class, who she thinks is "extremely cute." When asked to compare her feelings for her same-sex admirer with those toward the other sex (*isei*) she demurs, saying that she has not yet experienced any particularly deep feelings for the other sex. She has "no complaint" about receiving the letter, however, and would be happy to reciprocate M-chan's feelings with a hug.

One other girl volunteers a story of her own "lost love," this time toward an older girl. The relationship they enjoyed only came to an end when the older girl got married and had to follow her husband whose office posted him to a town in northern Japan. Had the discussion ended here it would have had much in common with prewar discussions of female same-sex love which, as we saw in Chapter 1, was often seen as a natural precursor to heterosexual romance and only problematic if it had "carnal" expressions. Indeed one of the girls compares same-sex love to the ephemeral pleasure experienced in relation to "fireworks" or "incense." However, not all agree, it being mentioned that same-sex love feelings can be stronger than those felt for the other sex (*isei yori sugoi*), sometimes strong enough to lead to "love suicides" (*shinjū*) where one or both partners kill themselves unable to live without the other. As we saw earlier, the tradition of love suicide was usually interpreted as the pathological outcome of same-sex love so it is significant to see in the postwar context it being invoked as a sign of authenticity. Japan's long tradition of "boys' love" (*bishōnen shūmi*) is also mentioned as is its popularity overseas "made famous" by the likes of Oscar Wilde. These comments, which close discussion on this topic, are thus more open-ended than might have been expected in prewar accounts.

The *True Tales* discussion was framed in terms of "same-sex love," a phrase that, because of its emphasis upon sentiment over sexuality, did not cause particular consternation. However, women's "perverse" experiences and desires were also well described in the *ryōki* genre. As mentioned earlier, Marran has made use of contemporary sources stressing female sexual agency in her discussion of the early postwar celebrity murderer Abe Sada. Marran uses these accounts to demonstrate how Abe was "portrayed as a transgressive heroine for those espousing postwar liberation and freedom from . . . totalitarian nationalism."[104] The widespread media interest in

Abe, her history, psychology, and motivations was but part of a wider interest in women's newly "discovered" sexual agency, an interest that also encompassed a range of same-sex identifications and desires.

The manner in which these accounts could be potentially used as catalysts for self-realization on the part of some women is exemplified in a story by fiction writer Ikeda Michiko[105] that appeared in the liberal arts magazine *Bungei* (Literary arts) in 1953.[106] The story describes Mitsue, an "athletic young woman," who experiences two failed marriages. Mitsue had been a regular masturbator since her school days and on account of this experience was aware of her own sexual responsiveness; however, her first husband simply "used her as a tool to satisfy his own desire." This fact, in addition to domestic violence, resulted in her leaving her husband and training as a mathematics teacher in order to support herself. Yet, despite being financially self-sufficient, Mitsue married again in her mid-30s, mainly out of anxiety about being alone in her postretirement years. However, her new more "mild mannered" husband also failed to satisfy her, and the couple drifted apart.

During her marriages, Mitsue had put her inability to satisfy or be satisfied by either husband down to her own "disability" (*fugu*) but after reading widely in the postwar "sex magazines" (*sei zasshi*)[107] she came to realize that she was "a woman with no attraction toward men," thus underlining the importance of the popular sex press in disseminating new sexual ideas. After divorcing her second husband, Mitsue sets up her own household and takes in a female lodger, a waitress named Yoshiko. Since Yoshiko entertains a number of gentlemen, Mitsue finds herself becoming jealous of their attentions. Mitsue finally realizes that she has come to love Yoshiko and after she confesses her love, the two spend the night together in the same futon "lost to shame in ecstasy." After that night they begin to live together "as a couple."

Although published in a prestigious literary journal, Ikeda's story shares many elements with the *ryōki* genre and acknowledges a debt to the postwar "sex press." It describes a woman who, dissatisfied with her "normal" sex life is led through a series of chance encounters toward the acknowledgment and expression of sexual desire toward another woman. The kind of accounts of women's same-sex love (*joshi no dōseiai*) that Ikeda probably had in mind when drafting her story were very common in the early postwar press. Although many stories were aimed at titillating a male audience, less graphic accounts were likely to appear in magazines directed at women. For instance, one nostalgic account of female same-sex love in a women's teachers' college appeared in the magazine *Bara* (Rose) amidst other articles largely about female fashion.[108] The plots of these stories could be remarkably inventive—such as a story involving the "secret frolics" between a cross-dressing stage actress and her three lovers: a rich widow, a widowed doctor, and a youth, that appeared in the magazine *Shin fūfu* (New couple) in 1949.[109] That such a story could appear in a magazine directed at "new couples" points toward the variety of sexual scripts on offer in the popular press.

A typical discussion of female same-sex love appeared in the July and August 1948 editions of the *kasutori* magazine *Bēze* (Kiss). Significantly, these articles were placed in a section entitled "gynecology classroom," suggesting that the topic was considered relevant to women in general, not just a perverse minority. The first article, subtitled a "study of Tribades,"[110] uses a relationship between a male-dressing woman and her feminine partner as an excuse to speculate on the origin and nature of Tribades (*toribādo*) and Sapphists (*Safuisto*) whom it describes in terms of an active/passive binary. "Tribades" were considered to possess "male looks, posture and passion" and to be the "active" agents in female same-sex relations and were considered to have an "innate propensity from birth" toward same-sex love. The follow-up article on "Sapphists,"[111] however, explains that these women are not particularly averse to men nor do they display masculine characteristics. They tend to encounter same-sex love "by chance" in the context of school or factory dormitories and consequently such romances are "not permanent."

In many of these accounts, female same-sex attraction is portrayed as relatively easy to provoke, one article comparing the rapid spread of female same-sex love in women-only environments to "a fever or the measles," pointing out that "women cannot help radiating their emotions to the same sex."[112] Same-sex love feelings were also thought to occur among young women "when drunk," for example, or as a result of "seduction by a Tribade," or as a response to "bad treatment by men."[113] This last point was often rehearsed, men being warned that in the new climate of sexual liberation, women who had been poorly treated by men were prone to seek satisfaction in the arms of other women. This idea was dramatically emphasized in the accompanying illustration to a story entitled "The strange story of a girl and a woman who was cast aside" that showed the spurned young girl in question locked in a passionate kiss with her older female lover (see fig. 6.3).[114]

This mode of categorization is at once both minoritizing in the case of the Tribades but universalizing in the case of the Sapphists. The latter category is significant in that it suggests that although women in general might not have had the same freedom as men to actively seek out unusual sexual experiences, they were considered capable of falling into these situations when circumstances presented themselves. The popular assumption that given the opportunity women in general might fall into same-sex love

Figure 6.3 Illustration of a female same-sex love affair from the June 1946 edition of *Kibatsu zasshi* (Eccentric magazine)

Source: Original held in the Gordon W. Prange Collection at the University of Maryland.

relationships is further evidence that there was not at that time a clear-cut definitional barrier between homosexual and heterosexual identities, at least at the level of popular discourse. Just like the male clients of cross-dressing prostitutes whose "active" role reinforced accepted gender patterns, women who played the "female" (or "passive") role in relationships with other more masculine women were not considered to be perverse, at least in a congenital sense. Like the *ryōki shumi otoko* who was driven to experiment with same-sex sexuality out of "curiosity," in the case of the Sapphists, homosexual experience per se was not sufficient to brand a woman as perverse—other factors were necessary, such as the gender inversion that identified the Tribade as "innately" different.

Space has not allowed for a detailed description of all facets of the early postwar *ryōki* boom, however, even a cursory review of popular sex journalism published during the Occupation period suggests that various policies deriving from US "containment politics" and Japanese government concerns to establish correct sexual behavior as a basis of national renewal were not entirely successful in overriding Japanese constructions of sexuality at the popular level, at least in terms of representation. In particular the following points stand out. Despite the fact there was some paranoia at the level of government policy concerning sexual confusion among the masses, bottom-up, street-level accounts on the whole stress the fluidity of categories and encourage (or are at least nonjudgmental of) experimentation. Rather than being deployed as homilies to underline the distinction between proper and perverse sexual interests, *ryōki* accounts use terms such as *shumi* (interest), *suriru* (thrill), *omoshiroi* (interesting), and *asobi* (play) to downplay the moral seriousness of these acts and restrict them to the purely personal realm of exploration and fantasy. Although there is a growing awareness of hetero and homosexual polarization, and a proliferation of sexual "types" in the early postwar sex press, *ryōki* stories endorsed a middle ground of experimentation for both men and women. In many of these accounts, traditional paradigms of female passivity and male activity, rather than being reinforced, are contested. Thus, the accounts of women-like men and men-like women (as well as their many admirers) who populated both the streets and the texts of early postwar Japan do much to complicate our understanding of how sex and gender ideologies played out in the daily lives, and particularly imaginations, of ordinary people.

Having reviewed the postwar *ryōki* genre, we can conclude that at precisely the same time as official directives from above were stressing the need to return to domesticated forms of (especially female) sexuality, there were representations within popular culture pointing out the "instability" of sex and gender roles, going in a contrary direction. Rather than being suppressed, or at least regulated by the censorship regime instigated by the Americans, *ryōki* accounts of sexually deviant figures were ignored by the Occupation authorities, and also largely overlooked by the Japanese police.

It is important to note that *ryōki* accounts flourished in the enabling context established by press reports on the two Kinsey surveys, particularly the 1948 volume on the male. Although the reports' translators had explicitly stated that their motivation was to advance "scientific understanding" of sex, and not to pander to *ryōki* interests, the fact that Kinsey, an "American scientist," had himself uncovered a wide range of sexual activities among American men and women, including premarital sex, infidelity, masturbation, and homosexual behavior, added to the legitimacy of the *ryōki* genre. Reports that offered an "analysis" of "strange behavior," whatever the real motivation of their authors, were able to make claims to furthering the "scientific understanding of sex." This was a tactic explicitly deployed by Takahashi Tetsu[115] in his early 1950s' magazines *Ningen tankyū* (Human investigation) and *Amatoria* that proclaimed themselves to be "sexual science magazines for cultured persons" on the covers. These magazines pioneered what was to become an entire publishing genre dedicated to the exploration of "perverse sexuality" that continued on into the late 1960s and was to prove an important resource for Japan's developing sexual minority subcultures.[116] This genre was characterized by many essays showing progressive attitudes toward so-called perverse sexuality[117] by authors such as Ōta Tenrei, Kabiya Kazuhiko, and Ōgiya Afu[118] and could not have developed as quickly as it did were it not for the interest in nonstandard forms of sexual expression generated by early postwar *ryōki* accounts.

Afterword: Postwar Legacies

> Although it is said that after the war sexuality has been liberated, we are still a "closed country." Even if it can be said that knowledge about sexuality is overflowing, this process is not yet complete and more and more knowledge needs to flood out. As long as words such as bollocks, cock, cunt, and pussy are still only able to appear in print as XX, we can't say that sex has been liberated.
>
> Takahashi Tetsu[1]

Takahashi Tetsu, among the most progressive of the early postwar commentators on sexuality, was exceptionally well-read and was almost certainly aware of the historical restrictions on the expression of sexuality, particularly "perverse" sexuality, in the European and American context. Hence his claim that Japan was still a "closed country" (*sakoku*),[2] isolated from the rest of the world regarding the free expression of sex, was clearly rhetorical. Like many reform-minded Japanese of the period, he is here gesturing toward the more advanced, democratic, and scientific state of knowledge that supposedly existed in the United States in order to criticize the backward, feudal, and moralistic attitudes that he believed still pertained among leaders in Japan.

As we have seen, the most powerful weapons in any early postwar sex reformer's arsenal were the Kinsey reports. The fact that a highly respected American scientist, based at a well-regarded university, had received public funding to reveal, among other things, the masturbatory practices of people's grandparents, was, for Japanese like Takahashi, a stunning sign of democratic freedom and proof of the power that "science" wielded over dogma in the minds of many Americans. Campaigners for sex reform used both the American and the scientific pedigree of the Kinsey reports to open up sexual discussion and exploration in the Japanese press of the late 40s and early 50s to a degree not previously possible. Yet, as we have seen, Takahashi's use of Western science was always tactical. There were many aspects of Western sexology that Takahashi and his followers distanced themselves from, particularly the highly pathologizing treatment of homosexuality characteristic of the Cold War period. Takahashi's early 1950s journals *Ningen tankyū* (Human investigation) and *Amatoria* provided valuable space for recording the rapid reconfigurations of male same-sex desiring subcultures that were taking place in Tokyo at that time. As an amateur ethnologist, Takahashi also did much to recover Japan's "lost" tradition of sexual knowledge through his exposition of ancient and Tokugawa-period erotic art and culture as well as rural folk practices in an attempt to foster culturally appropriate expressions of Japanese sexuality. Takahashi, along with other reform-minded sexologists such as Ōta Tenrei,[3] who in 1957 was to publish the first detailed sociological study of postwar male homosexuality,[4] were important figures who tried to maintain a discourse of Japanese sexuality that included, rather than repudiated, same-sex sexuality.

For reformers like Takahashi, the postwar liberation of the body (particularly the sexual body) was intimately conjoined with the liberation of thought and seen as a positive and welcome aspect of postwar democratization. Certainly there is a libidinal pleasure apparent in many of the early postwar accounts we have surveyed—a pleasure that is still able to shock and delight readers today. However, as Foucault warns us, "We must not think that by saying yes to sex, one says no to power."[5] The postwar rhetoric of sexual liberation, albeit preferable in many ways to the highly eugenic paradigm characteristic of the wartime period, did not enable the liberation of a previously repressed sexuality so much as insist on the creation of a new, "modern" sexual sensibility. This sensibility required the implementation of a whole new regime of sexual scrutiny and management that was anything but spontaneous or free. The sexual liberation on offer was also highly asymmetrical: it was men who were granted greater access to the bodies of women whether on stage, in print, or on the streets. Despite the fact that women were now afforded some agency to negotiate this "democratic" process of exploration, the freedoms offered to men and women remained highly gendered, thus carrying over attitudes and behaviors characteristic of the wartime regime.

Wartime propaganda had pitted disciplined and chaste Japanese in a fight to the death against self-indulgent and libidinous Westerners. However the Japanese were now being told that they were "weak in sexual love" and encouraged to develop greater sexual stamina as well as explore new frontiers in sexual pleasure. A new set of discourses now placed "sex for pleasure" at the very centre of married people's lives and refigured male-female relationships, from the first date onwards, in terms of the search for sexual satisfaction. Yet these discourses structuring postwar sexuality were just as concerned with differentiating "correct" from "incorrect" sexual practices as were prewar models. The need to be properly informed about sex, to discover just the right position that worked for you and your partner, to be able to sketch the difference between onset and duration of a male and a female orgasm, discuss the pros and cons of a range of contraceptive practices, and take steps to ensure one's "potency" suddenly became important responsibilities. As Sabine Fruhstuck observes, in the postwar era "the intimacy of sexuality—perhaps always imagined—has been turned into a long list of criteria against which one can measure oneself and others."[6] Indeed, as the volume of information about sexuality proliferated, exhortations to apply this sexual knowledge to one's own sex life became ever more insistent and invasive.

One of the consequences of the boom in sexological surveys that followed in the wake of the Kinsey reports was an increasing and ever more detailed interrogation of Japanese people's sex lives. When did you first start to have sex? How many times a week do you have sex? How long does the sex act last? How much time do you devote to foreplay? How do you regulate your orgasms? What is your sexual type? Are you sexually satisfied? This new emphasis on sexual satisfaction as the foundation of the marital relationship placed undue pressure on many couples to interrogate and rate their performance against league tables published in the press that purported to outline "normal" patterns. It is perhaps fitting that three years before his death in 1971, Takahashi appeared as himself in Ōshima Nagisa's 1968 movie *Shinjuku no dorobō* (Diary of a Shinjuku thief). The plot involves a young couple who seek advice from a number of real-life experts in pursuit of the ultimate orgasm, suggesting that even in the more liberated sexual atmosphere of the late 60s, "sexual satisfaction" was still an elusive goal.

Furthermore, despite the ubiquity of his writings, in terms of public policy debate sexual reformers such as Takahashi remained marginal. As early as 1947 the Ministry of Education was developing its policy of "purity education" (*junketsu kyōiku*) that stressed the need for abstinence before marriage, particularly on the part of women.[7] From that point on, government agencies tended to support policies that reinforced the connection between sex and procreation within a marital context, thus maintaining via the education system attitudes characteristic of the wartime regime. In particular, the government-sponsored "New Life Movement" of the 1950s introduced a range of educational programs aimed at "rationalizing" Japanese households, including regulating reproduction.[8] As Sonia Ryang points out, in official sex education discourse, appropriate standards of sexual behavior "were not to be set randomly by individual men and women, but by the state."[9] Yet, for those whose reading habits were not exclusively guided by the Education Ministry, there were plenty of other sources of information as a range of sex-related textbooks continued to flood into the market throughout the 1950s.[10] These included the reissue of previously suppressed Edo-period and Chinese erotic classics, as well as more Western-oriented titles.[11] It is difficult, then, to point to one single set of restrictions or guidelines concerning the "correct" expression of sexuality that held sway in the 1950s.

All the above, of course, beg the question as to how the exuberant explosion of discourse about "new" or "modern" dating practices and forms of heterosexual coupledom related to actual lived experience on Japan's streets and in parks, movie houses, and bedrooms. To a large extent, the popular press reports on which this book has been based are similar to those comprising the mid-50s media controversy over the role of the Japanese housewife analyzed by Jan Bardsley, who comments that these debates "do not draw from surveys or demographic reports but are wholly based on personal experience, anecdote, random observation and conjecture."[12] Bardsley also points to "a vested interest in believing in the newness of the postwar era," arguing that the "new" roles for women being discussed in the mid-1950s had clear prewar analogues that had been obscured by postwar cultural amnesia.[13] Hence the late 1940s' "sex press" can be seen as characteristic of what Carol Gluck has termed Japan's "mythistoric postwar"[14] in which the postwar present is constructed as an inverse "anti-past" wherein a largely rhetorical enthusiasm for the new obscures the continuity of the old. Indeed, even in the 1960s, Japanese visiting overseas were *still* being shocked by the level of intimacy expressed between the sexes at social events. Well-known psychologist Doi Takeo, for instance, upon arriving at an American university and attending a faculty gathering expressed surprise at "the emphasis laid in America, unlike traditional custom in Japan, upon contact between the sexes not only after marriage but before it."[15] We must therefore be cautious when reading media discourse as indicative of actual shifts in practice.

Were there, then, no changes in sexual attitudes and behaviors in the early postwar period? The limited scope of research published into generational shifts in Japanese sexual practices makes this a difficult question to answer with certainty, but as we have seen, there do exist research data and narrative accounts published soon after the war and in later decades that suggest the immediate postwar years were pivotal in bringing about a reconsideration of male-female relationships not simply in terms of the "cultural scenarios" that gave symbolic meaning to sexual acts but also in the lived experience of the everyday.[16] For a variety of reasons that have been outlined earlier, various Occupation initiatives enabled a new set of "cultural scenarios" that encouraged Japanese men and women to rethink the conjugal relationship and the place of sexual intimacy in it. During the Occupation, young couples were also inducted into a whole new range of "techniques of the body," actions such as hand-holding and even kissing in public that would have seemed unremarkable to Americans, but which occasioned furious debate in the Japanese press. These various techniques of the body needed to be practiced and assembled into wider techniques of the self that produced the "modern couple," which can still be seen on the streets and in the restaurants and movie houses of Japan today.

Hence the popular culture of the Occupation period is clearly crucial for understanding later changes in Japan's sexual customs. The presence of the Americans and the prestige of American culture established an enabling environment for the development of a new range of ideas and lifestyle choices. Yet, this hardly amounted to "liberation" of the body. It can, after all, be argued that the postwar enthusiasm for "sexual liberation" was really nothing more than the freedom of a male-dominated entertainment industry to commodify the bodies of women in general. The freedom that the newly conspicuous dating couples wielded was the freedom to bring their relationships into line with an ever expanding US-led economy of identity, consumption, and desire. As Anthony Giddens reminds us, "Modernity opens up the project of the self, but under conditions strongly influenced by the standardizing effects of commodity capitalism."[17] The postwar "new couple" was, after all, following a script devised in Hollywood on a stage furnished with American consumer goods. Yet this is not the entire picture. There was much else going on in late 1940s Japan that challenged and subverted American ways of living. Takahashi, sensing the challenge that the one-size-fits-all approach of Western "science" posed to local Japanese culture, was keen to reclaim the lost sexual knowledge of Japan's past. The progressive tradition of "sexual customs research" that he did so much to foster in the postwar period resolutely refused to be drawn into the Cold War paranoia about sexual perversion. For Japanese people "curiosity hunting" in sexual matters never did take on the same moral and political overtones typical of concern over "sexual deviants" in the United States during the 1950s.

Also, a look at recent media panics about sex in Japan shows that Japanese anxieties have not always been paralleled in the West. The 1980s, for instance, witnessed an explosion of media concern about Japan's declining birth-rate and the growing number of "sexless couples" too tired to procreate. At the same time, the media went wild over claims that Japanese high-school girls were engaging in "compensated dating" with older men, exchanging sexual favors for cash and luxury goods. More recently, in the 90s the press was full of reports on "parasite singles," young women who eschewed the responsibilities of marriage and motherhood in pursuit of their own individualistic lifestyles. The 2000s, too, witnessed a new media panic, this time about "herbivorous" young men who were too shy and enervated to take much of an interest in the opposite sex. Anxieties about sex—particularly the peculiarly modern notion that we are not getting enough of it—have clearly not gone away.

Notes

Introduction

1. The members' only Fūzoku Shiryōkan (not very helpfully translated into English on their website as Perverts Museum) is an initiative set up by Takakura Ichiji, a former editor of postwar sexology magazine *Fūzoku kitan* (Strange tales of moral customs), and houses a large collection of postwar sexology magazines and erotica. For more on Takakura, see Nagae, "Adaruto-kei shuppansha no rūtsu," 12.
2. The description refers to Shioda, "Kimi shiru."
3. See their website: http://www.lib.umd.edu/prange/index.jsp. Accessed May 4, 2011.
4. Shimokawa, "Gaitō no ero shasshin uri," 32.
5. Mauss, "Techniques of the Body," 75.
6. Bourdieu, "Belief and the Body," 88.
7. Mauss, "Techniques of the Body," 74–75.
8. Bourdieu, "Belief and the Body," 87.
9. Mead, *The American Troops and the British Community.*
10. On the development of courtship practices in America, see Bailey, *From Front Porch.*
11. Simon and Gagnon, "Sexual Scripts," 491–97, 492.
12. Gagnon and Simon, *Sexual Conduct,* 105.
13. Ibid.
14. Ibid.
15. Foucault, *History of Sexuality*, 127.
16. Martin, *Situating Sexualities,* 251.
17. Gagnon and Simon, *Sexual Conduct*, 106.
18. Ibid., 111.
19. Ibid.
20. See in particular Kelsky, *Women on the Verge*, 55–84; Koikari, *Pedagogy of Democracy*; Shibusawa, *America's Geisha Ally*; Tanaka, *Japan's Comfort Women*, 111–66.
21. Yonezawa refers to this corpus as "mass entertainment magazines," *Sengo ero manga shi,* 11, but I am not using the Japanese term *taishū bunka* (mass culture) here because of its class connotations. The *kasutori* genre has been regarded as "low-brow" but it was not consistently so. As will be discussed in

subsequent chapters a range of writers, some well established, contributed to the *kasutori* press and in many cases the range of cultural references made supposed an educated audience. For a discussion of the difficulty of giving fixed meaning to terms such as "popular" or "mass" culture in Japan, see Bardsley, "Purchasing Power."

Chapter 1

1. Smith, "Making Village Women," 74.
2. Johnston, *Geisha, Harlot, Strangler,* 33–34.
3. Fruhstuck, *Colonizing Sex*, 120.
4. Ogino, "Kindai Nihon no sekushuariti," 82.
5. Smith, "Making Village Women," 79.
6. Walthall, "Masturbation and Discourse on Female Sexual Practices," 3–4.
7. Plugfelder, *Cartographies of Desire.*
8. Walthall, "Masturbation and Discourse on Female Sexual Practices," 8.
9. Ibid., 16.
10. See the discussion of Takahashi's pioneering work in Chapter 5 of this volume.
11. Leupp, *Interracial Intimacy*, 197.
12. Steiner, "The Revision of the Civil Code," 289.
13. Garon, "State and Family in Modern Japan," 318.
14. Smith, "Making Village Women," 78.
15. Johnston, *Geisha, Harlot, Strangler,* 30.
16. Steiner, "The Revision of the Civil Code," 291.
17. Wagatsuma and de Vos, "Attitudes toward Arranged Marriage," 187.
18. It was possible, however, in the absence of a male heir, for a woman to assume the responsibilities of a family head but these responsibilities would default to her husband were she to (re)marry.
19. Fujitani, *Splendid Monarchy,* 185.
20. Ibid., 188.
21. Ibid., 189.
22. Ibid.
23. Smith, "Making Village Women," 77.
24. Fujitani, *Splendid Monarchy,* 190–91.
25. Iga, "Sociocultural Factors in Japanese Prostitution," 129.
26. Dore, *City Life in Japan,* 159.
27. Uno, "Death of Good Wife," 294.
28. Mitsuishi, "Otome," 72.
29. Shibuya, "*Dōtei,*" 65.
30. Fruhstuck, *Colonizing Sex*, 69.
31. Johnston, *Geisha, Harlot, Strangler*, 32–33.
32. Kuno, "Life in Japan," 193.
33. Yokota-Murakami, *Don Juan East-West.*
34. Ibid., 36.

35. As seen in the phrase *danson johi* or "respect men, despise women."
36. Morton, "The Concept of Romantic Love," 82.
37. Yokota-Murakami, *Don Juan East-West*, 42.
38. Leupp, *Interracial Intimacy*, 166–67.
39. Yokota-Murakami, *Don Juan East-West*, 41.
40. Kamei, "The Kiss and Japanese Culture," 114.
41. Blood, *Love Match*, 129.
42. Hastings, "Dinner Party," 123.
43. Dore, *City Life in Japan*, 161.
44. Morton, "The Concept of Romantic Love," 93.
45. Ibid., 82.
46. Suzuki, *Becoming Modern Women*, 9.
47. Kuno, "Life in Japan," 195.
48. Kawamura and Takeda, "Kindai Nihon no sekkusu," 235.
49. Suzuki, *Becoming Modern Women*, 66.
50. Kuno, "Life in Japan," 193.
51. Morton, "The Concept of Romantic Love," 84.
52. Reichert, *In the Company of Men*, 227.
53. Watanabe and Iwata, *Love of the Samurai*.
54. *Vocabularia Erotica et Amoris*, 67.
55. Reichert, *In the Company of Men*, 71.
56. Ibid., 28.
57. Karlin, "The Gender of Nationalism," 64.
58. Dore, *City Life in Japan*, 159.
59. Angles, *Writing the Love of Boys*, 22–24.
60. Fruhstuck, *Colonizing Sex*, 75.
61. Suzuki, *Becoming Modern Women*, 9.
62. Curran and Welker, "From the Well of Loneliness," 69–70.
63. S stood for "sister" or sometimes "*shōjo*" (girl).
64. The term "homosexuality" was itself a recent construct, first appearing in English in the 1890s. The term first appeared in German slightly earlier, in an anonymous pamphlet published in 1869. See Spencer, *Homosexuality*, 10.
65. Suzuki, *Becoming Modern Women*, 24.
66. Ibid., 26.
67. Murata, "Dōsei no koi."
68. This point was also made in an early postwar roundtable discussion where the commentators note that sexual desire "used not to be a problem" for unmarried women in the prewar period since "women from good families" were protected from sexual stimulation before marriage. However, both masturbation and homosexuality were considered rife among lower-class women who worked in factories and shared communal dormitories; see *Josei raifu*, "Zadankai," 18–19.
69. Robertson, "Dying to Tell."
70. Suzuki, *Becoming Modern Women*, 66.
71. Ibid.
72. Wagatsuma and de Vos, "Attitudes toward Arranged Marriage," 188.

73. Hayashi, "Shin ren'ai no michi," 36.
74. Blood, *Love Match*, 6.
75. Ibid., 7.
76. Kamei, "The Kiss and Japanese Culture," 114.
77. Ōtsuka, "Dualism of Love and 'Wago.'"
78. Ibid., 43 (emphasis in the original).
79. Ibid., 45.
80. Kuno, "Life in Japan," 196.
81. Steiner, "The Revision of the Civil Code," 292.
82. Suzuki, *Becoming Modern Women*, 67.
83. Ibid., 75.
84. Silverberg, *Erotic Grotesque Nonsense*, 112–13.
85. The edition referred to in this volume is the 1930 Covici Friede version published out of New York. The title of the original Japanese translation was *Kanzen naru fūfu,* which is rendered more accurately as "perfect conjugal couple."
86. Akita, *Sei no ryōki modan*, 186. For a discussion of the popularity of Van de Velde's text throughout Europe and America in the prewar period, see Bullough, *Science in the Bedroom*, 140–41.
87. Van de Velde, *Ideal Marriage*, 159.
88. Ibid., 224.
89. Driscoll, *Absolute Erotic, Absolute Grotesque*, 183.
90. Yamamoto, *Kasutori zasshi kenkyū*, 44.
91. Akita, *Sei no ryōki modan*, 186–87.
92. Yamamoto, *Kasutori zasshi kenkyū,* 54.
93. Yokota-Murakami, *Don Juan East-West*, notes that "it seems to have been the compound *sei-yoku* that first conveyed the meaning of sexuality in the modern sense" and that it first appeared in dictionaries in 1907 after which "it was soon widely used," 133. See also Kawamura and Takeda, "Kindai Nihon no sekkusu," 234.
94. Fruhstuck, *Colonizing Sex*, 110–15.
95. Driscoll, *Absolute Erotic, Absolute Grotesque*, 153.
96. Ogino, "Kindai Nihon no sekushuariti," 85.
97. Pflugfelder, *Cartographies of Desire*, 287.
98. Driscoll, *Absolute Erotic, Absolute Grotesque*, 153.
99. See Freedman, *Tokyo in Transit*, for a discussion of how expanding public transport in Tokyo provided increased opportunity for recreation and distraction for the city's bourgeois.
100. Angles, "Seeking the Strange," 131.
101. Silverberg, "Constructing a New Cultural History," 123.
102. For a discussion of the contents of some of these magazines and their trouble with the censors, see Umehara, "Zasshi 'Gurotesuku.'"
103. Domenig, "History of Sex Education Films in Japan," Part 1.
104. Angles, *Writing the Love of Boys*, 21.
105. Angles, "Seeking the Strange," 102.
106. Pflugfelder, *Cartographies of Desire*, 320.

107. As detailed in Chapter 6, male cross-dressing prostitution in particular had a long history in Japan and was historically associated with the Kabuki theater. Robertson argues that, inspired by memories of Kabuki, "frontline soldiers staged shows in which some of them performed as women." She notes that in one recorded instance, the cross-dressed soldier "was the biggest attraction" and was hugged, kissed, and had "her" dress lifted by other men, *Takarazuka*, 102.
108. See Giles, "The Denial of Homosexuality"; Micheler, "Homophobic Propaganda"; Spencer, *Homosexuality*, 347.
109. Ibid., 347–51.
110. See McLelland, *Queer Japan*, 42–54.
111. *Gekkan yomiuri*, "Danshō wa kataru."
112. Pflugfelder, *Cartographies of Desire*, 327.
113. Sakai, *Nihon kanrakukyō annai.*
114. In a 1937 article from *Shufu no tomo* cited by Silberberg, *Erotic Grotesque Nonsense*, 158.
115. Freedman, *Tokyo in Transit*, 145.
116. Sato notes that in 1921 only 10 percent of the Japanese population fit the definition of middle class and that middle-class consumer culture was "conspicuously urban centered" with large parts of the country relatively unaffected by these modernizing forces; Sato, "Contesting Consumerisms," 264.
117. Kuno, "Life in Japan," 200.
118. Kitamura, *Screening Enlightenment*, 1.
119. Freedman, *Tokyo in Transit*, 178.
120. Kuryu, "Gendai no ren'ai," 66.
121. Ōya, "Ero guro nansensu jidai," 68.
122. Sato, "Contesting Consumerisms."
123. Fujiki, "Gakubuchi no shō," 38.
124. Cited in Abel, "The *Ero-Puro* Sense," 344.
125. Ibid.
126. Ibid., 345.
127. Pratt, "Arts of the Contact Zone," 4.
128. Drea, *In the Service of the Emperor*, 79.
129. Ibid., 80.
130. Ibid., 77.
131. Ryang, *Love in Modern Japan*, 52.
132. Timm, "Sex with a Purpose," 224.
133. Suzuki, "Senso ni okeru dansei sekushuariti."
134. Ibid.
135. Shin and Cho, "Characteristics and Special Nature," 53.
136. Suzuki, "Senso ni okeru dansei sekushuariti," 103.
137. Matsumoto, *Contemporary Japan*, 24.
138. Ono, *Angura Shōwashi*, 69.
139. Nakamura, *Kindai teikoku Nihon*, 262.
140. *Bōzu* refers to the bald head of Buddhist monks.
141. Ryang, *Love in Modern Japan*, 53.

142. Fruhstuck, *Colonizing Sex*, 90.
143. Dai ni ji shin seikatsu kenkyūkai, "Nihonjin no 'hatsutaiken.'"
144. Ibid., 30.
145. Low, "Emperor's Sons."
146. Abe, Kiyohara, and Nakajima, "Sport and Physical Education."
147. Igarashi, *Narratives of War*, 48.
148. Yamamoto, "Kasutori zasshi," 244.
149. Igarashi, *Narratives of War*, 48.
150. Blacker, "Japan's Population Problem," 32.
151. Yamamoto, *Kasutori zasshi kenkyū*, 44.
152. That is, penetration without foreplay.
153. As discussed in Yamamoto and Ozawa, "Kisu o suru koto," 86; and Yamamoto, "Kasutori zasshi," 244.
154. Ogino, "Kindai Nihon no sekushuariti," 74.
155. For example in 2007 Yanagisawa Hakuo, then Minister for Health, Labor and Welfare, drew criticism for describing Japanese women as "child-bearing machines" and encouraging families to have more than two children to address Japan's falling birth rate. See *Japan Times*, "Yanagisawa Apologizes Anew."
156. Silverberg, *Erotic, Grotesque, Nonsense*, 162.
157. Havens, *Valley of Darkness*.
158. Silverberg, *Erotic, Grotesque, Nonsense*, 162.
159. Garon, "State and Family in Modern Japan," 327.
160. Ike, "Birth Control in Japan," 272.
161. Homei, "Giving Birth to a Rich Nation," 17.
162. Ike, "Birth Control in Japan," 272.
163. Abe, Kiyohara, and Nakajima, "Sport and Physical Education."
164. Gordon, "Managing the Japanese Household," 249.
165. Uno, "The Death of 'Good Wife,'" 300.
166. Igarashi, *Narratives of War*, 50; Fruhstuck, *Colonizing Sex*, 167; Robertson, "Blood Talks," 199.
167. Timm, "Sex with a Purpose," 223.
168. Uno, "The Death of 'Good Wife,'" 300.
169. Havens, *Valley of Darkness*, 916.
170. Garon, *Molding Japanese Minds*, 144.
171. Robertson, "Japan's First Cyborg?" 26.
172. Adams, *The Best War Ever*.
173. Haste, *Rules of Desire*; Costello, *Virtue under Fire*; Berube, *Coming Out under Fire*.
174. Haste, *Rules of Desire*, 122.
175. Ibid.
176. Costello, *Virtue under Fire*, 236.
177. Takemae, *Allied Occupation*, 384.
178. Kushner, *Thought War*, 108.
179. Ibid., 96.
180. Morris, *Phoenix Cup*, 134.
181. Ibid.

182. Atkins "The War on Jazz," 378.
183. Ibid., 351.
184. Ibid., 353.
185. Ibid., 354.
186. Schattschneider, "The Bloodstained Doll," 333.
187. Ibid., 337.
188. These highly erotic figures were also considered to have talismanic properties, see Westbrook, "I Want a Girl."
189. Standish, *Myth and Masculinity in the Japanese Cinema,* 51.
190. For a discussion of the repression of eroticism in Japanese film during the war years, see Matsuura, *Senchū, senryōka no masukomi,* 160–61.
191. Standish, *Myth and Masculinity in the Japanese Cinema,* 51.
192. Ibid., 63.
193. Westbrook, "I Want a Girl," 595.
194. Bae, "Girl Meets Boy Meets Girl," 347.
195. Kushner, *Thought War,* 61.
196. Ibid., 62.
197. Dollase, "Girls on the Homefront," 335.
198. Ibid., 336.

Chapter 2

1. Shimokawa, *Nihon ero shashinshi,* 32.
2. He refers to the "wild parties" that were staged in some neighbourhoods after news of the defeat; *Narratives of War,* 48.
3. Tanaka, *Japan's Comfort Women,* 160. Haste, *Rules of Desire,* also notes that the spread of VD among US troops stationed in the UK tended to be blamed on British "good time" girls, not the troops themselves, 134.
4. Koikari, *Pedagogy of Democracy;* Shibusawa, *America's Geisha Ally;* Tanaka, *Japan's Comfort Women.*
5. Morris, *Phoenix Cup,* 18.
6. Ibid., 20.
7. Igarashi, *Narratives of War,* 53.
8. Mishima, *Broader Way,* 90.
9. About 20 percent of youth were estimated to have lost or left their families by the war's end. Many of these ended up working in the black market or the sex trade. Police round-ups of sex workers sometimes brought in girls as young as ten. See Shimokawa, *Sei fūzoku nenpyō,* 28.
10. Mishima, *Broader Way,* 96.
11. Ibid., 183.
12. On the black market, see Dower, *Embracing Defeat,* 139–48.
13. Shimokawa, *Sei fūzoku nenpyō,* 15.
14. Morris, *Phoenix Cup,* 21.
15. Other areas in Japan, such as the prefectures surrounding Hiroshima, were under the supervision of other Allied powers, particularly the British

Commonwealth forces. However, it was American culture that had the most impact on Occupation mores.

16. The term is Benedict Anderson's; see Anderson, *Imagined Communities.*
17. Pratt, "Arts of the Contact Zone," 4. For a detailed description of how this mentality was achieved, see Ohnuki-Tierney, *Kamikaze*, especially Chapter 4.
18. Pratt, "Arts of the Contact Zone," 4.
19. Koikare, "Rethinking Gender and Power," 314.
20. Cited in Pharr, "Politics of Women's Rights," 224–45.
21. Ibid., 231.
22. Ibid.
23. Ibid., 241.
24. Tanaka, *Japan's Comfort Women*, 112–16.
25. Shimokawa, *Sei fūzoku nenpyō,* 14.
26. Igarashi, *Narratives of War*, 35.
27. Takemae, *Allied Occupation*, 41; Tanaka, *Japan's Comfort Women*, 116–25.
28. Tanaka, *Japan's Comfort Women*, 13.
29. On the foundation and eventual demise of the RAA, see Tanaka, *Japan's Comfort Women*, 141–50.
30. Cohen, *Remaking Japan,* 125.
31. Tanaka, *Japan's Comfort Women,* 146.
32. Ibid., 136.
33. Cohen, *Remaking Japan,* 126. See also Tanaka, *Japan's Comfort Women,* 153–54.
34. Shimokawa, *Sei fūzoku nenpyō,* 15.
35. Tanaka, *Japan's Comfort Women*, 155.
36. An ex-service member, who was a newly qualified doctor serving with the Occupation at the time, told me of an incident involving an army chaplain outside of Sugamo jail (used to house accused war criminals prior to the Tokyo Trials). The street in front of the main entrance to the jail was crowded with makeshift shacks that were used for prostitution services for the many Occupation personnel working in the jail. One chaplain was famous for patrolling these shacks, even going to the extent of dragging army personnel out and shaming them in the street. One afternoon he was shot in the back and killed. Apparently "nobody saw anything" since it was neither in the interests of the women working as pan pan, nor their American customers, to cooperate with the investigation.
37. Kovner, *Prostitution in Postwar Japan,* 29.
38. Ibid., 30.
39. Ibid., 26–27.
40. Tanaka, *Japan's Comfort Women*, 160–61.
41. Cohen, *Remaking Japan,* 131.
42. *Yomiuri* newspaper, morning edition, May 31, 1947, p. 2.
43. *Asahi* newspaper May 31, 1947, p. 4.
44. Cohen, *Remaking Japan,* 128.
45. Koikare, *Pedagogy of Democracy,* 166.
46. Ibid., 166.

47. Ibid., 169.
48. Tsubaki, *Seppun nendai ki,* 166.
49. Yamamoto, "Kasutori zasshi," 244.
50. Beer, *Freedom of Expression in Japan,* 282.
51. Cited in Rubin, "Impact of the Occupation on Literature," 169.
52. Luther and Boyd, "American Occupation Control over Broadcasting," 43.
53. Etō, "One Aspect of the Allied Occupation."
54. Ibid., 17.
55. See Appendix B: 2a reproduced in Report of Government Section Supreme Commander for the Allied Powers, 460.
56. The CCD was based in Tokyo with branch offices in Osaka and Fukuoka. At its height it consisted of 66 officers, 63 enlisted men, 244 civilians, and 149 other non-Japanese foreign nationals in addition to a Japanese staff of 5,658. See Etō, "One Aspect of the Allied Occupation," 21.
57. Ibid., 17.
58. Ochi, "What Did She Read?" 363.
59. Nishi, *Unconditional Democracy,* 101, gives a summary of 15 categories of articles commonly suppressed by the CCD, none pertaining to morals; Journalist William Coughlin in *Conquered Press* does not mention obscenity at all in his discussion of CCD grounds for censorship.
60. Etō, "One Aspect of the Allied Occupation."
61. Rubin, "Impact of the Occupation on Literature," 167–74.
62. Memo contained in *Momo iro raifu* microfiche in Gordon W. Prange Collection.
63. Hasegawa, *Waisetsu shuppan no rekishi,* 36.
64. Sherif, *Japan's Cold War,* 227n31.
65. Yamamoto, in *Kasutori zasshi kenkyū,* 42–43, suggests three possible reasons for the designation *kasutori.* First, *kasutori shōchū* was a poor quality alcoholic drink made from a mixture of fermented rice and potatoes that, like the bad journalism of the *kasutori* press, was best avoided. Second, a *kasutori* drinker was only able to survive three cups before entering into a dangerous state, similarly *kasutori* magazines were unlikely to survive past their third issue. Finally, it was suggested that *kasutori* was a term applied to the poor quality paper used to print the magazines, as opposed to the deleterious nature of their contents.
66. Shamoon, "Misora Hibari and the Girl Star," 135.
67. See Yamamoto, *Kasutori zasshi kenkyū*; Matsuzawa, "Kasutori zasshi to 'Garo' no Nagai-san"; Shimokawa, *Shōwa seisō shi: sengohen.*
68. *Ningen tankyū,* "Zadankai: Onna gakusei no seitai," 76.
69. Marran, *Poison Woman,* 138. See also Kōno, "Hihyō to jitsuzon," 44–51, 46, who also argues that the Japanese authorities used pulp culture as a kind of "camouflage." Another list of "three S's" popular in the *pre*war period comprised "speed, sport and screen."
70. Front cover of *Esu,* June 1948.
71. Chapman, "Japan: Propaganda to Pornography," 8.
72. Ibid.

73. Dower, *Embracing Defeat,* 150.
74. Ishikawa, "Kanzen naru kekkon kara," 113.
75. Keene, *Dawn to the West,* 967.
76. Censorship notes following on from the galley proofs of the May 1946 edition of the magazine *Toppu* microfiche in the Prange collection.
77. Document preserved in Gordon W. Prange Collection, JP/TOK/PPB/c/356.
78. Luther and Boyd, "American Occupation Control over Broadcasting," 46.
79. Mayo, "Literary Reorientation in Occupied Japan," 143–44.
80. In reference to the April 1948 edition of the magazine *Jigoku* (also entitled *L'enfer*, i.e., hell) on *Jigoku* microfiche in Gordon W. Prange Collection.
81. Luther and Boyd, "American Occupation Control over Broadcasting," 49n6.
82. Censorship document signed by S. Nagoshi following on from April 1949 edition of *Momo iro raifu* on microfiche in the Gordon W. Prange Collection.
83. Friman, "The Impact of the Occupation on Crime," 98.
84. Shikita and Tsuchiya, *Crime and Criminal Policy in Japan,* 81.
85. Hasegawa, *Waisetsu shuppan no rekishi,* 31–32.
86. Kitagawa, "H taisa fūjin."
87. Miyanaga, "Ōchō kōshoku kokkei tan."
88. Hasegawa, *Waisetsu shuppan no rekishi,* 31–32.
89. Dower, *Embracing Defeat,* 149.
90. Cather, *Great Censorship Trials of Literature,* 23, notes that the widespread discussion of sexual irregularities in the popular press was introduced by the defense in the 1951 obscenity trial of the publisher and translator of *Lady Chatterley's Lover* in an attempt to show that graphic depictions of sex were consistent with community standards. It was however the *adulterous* nature of the sex described in *Chatterley,* as in "Mrs. Captain H," that rendered these descriptions problematic, as Cather notes, "the prosecution was attempting to stop adultery in reality via a ban in representation," 32.
91. Hasegawa, *Waisetsu shuppan no rekishi,* 34.
92. Kushner, *Thought War,* 67.
93. Ibid., 185.
94. McLelland, "Short History of *Hentai*." Another potential derivation I did not know about at the time is that "H" is the letter that comes between G and I—a reference to the lecherous nature of some of the GIs serving with the Occupation. See Inoue, "Ecchi to esuemu."
95. Hasegawa, *Waisetsu shuppan no rekishi,* 34.
96. Mayo, "Literary Reorientation in Occupied Japan," 143.
97. Hasegawa, *Waisetsu shuppan no rekishi,* 34.
98. Driscoll, *Absolute Erotic, Absolute Grotesque,* 183.
99. Hasegawa, *Waisetsu shuppan no rekishi,* 34.
100. Yamamoto, "Kasutori zasshi," 246–47.
101. Ibid., 246.
102. Sherif, *Japan's Cold War,* 74. That there was disagreement about the nature of obscenity between Japanese and Occupation authorities is also suggested by the fact that in 1952 the Japanese police prosecuted a cinema owner for showing a "birth-control film" that had been developed in the late 1940s and

passed CIE inspection; see Domenig, "History of Sex Education Films in Japan," Part 2.

103. Cather, *Great Censorship Trials,* 67. The *Lady Chatterley* obscenity case has much in common with the prosecution of *Ryōki.* As Cather notes, the Chatterley trial "was an attempt by the government to assert their authority in the realm of representation to deflect attention from their lack of effective control in the realm of reality," 33.
104. Hasegawa, *Waisetsu shuppan no rekishi,* 36.

Chapter 3

1. Dore, *Embracing Defeat,* 162.
2. Rubin, "From Wholesomeness to Decadence," 80.
3. Dower, *Embracing Defeat,* 148.
4. Igarashi, *Narratives of War,* 48.
5. Dower, *Embracing Defeat,* 133.
6. Mishima, *Broader Way,* 100.
7. Ibid., 102.
8. Narumigi, "Sekkusu kaihō no ayumi," 40.
9. Matsumoto, *Contemporary Japan,* 24.
10. In a 1949 survey 70 percent of those surveyed, both male and female, considered licensed prostitution houses to be necessary. However, only 20 percent felt that street walkers were necessary. See Matsumoto, *Contemporary Japan,* 25.
11. Wildes, *Typhoon in Tokyo,* 168.
12. Shimokawa, *Sei fūzoku nenpyō,* 24.
13. See Kovner, "Base cultures."
14. Mishima, *Broader Way,* 162.
15. Kamei, "The Kiss and Japanese Culture," 115.
16. Morris, *Phoenix Cup,* 45.
17. Whiting, *Tokyo Underworld,* 14.
18. Tsurumi, *Cultural History of Postwar Japan,* 11.
19. Muto, "Democracy and Chastity," 30.
20. Sanders, *Prostitution in Postwar Japan,* 83–87.
21. Account given in CCD records pertaining to August 1946 issue of *Van* on microfiche in the Prange collection.
22. Fukuoka, *Sei no atarashii ninshiki,* 211–15; Koshiro, *Trans-Pacific Racisms,* 86.
23. Tsurumi, *Cultural History of Postwar Japan,* 11.
24. Koschmann, *Revolution and Subjectivity,* 57–58.
25. Igarashi, *Narratives of War,* 47.
26. Rubin, "Impact of the Occupation on Literature," 169.
27. Yonezawa, *Sengo ero manga shi,* 11.
28. Dower, *Embracing Defeat,* 148.
29. Yamamoto, *Kasutori zasshi kenkyū,* 20.

30. In contemporary China, for instance, pornographers may face the death penalty. For an overview of different censorship regimes, see Procida and Simon, *Global Perspectives on Social Issues.*
31. Kamei, "The Kiss and Japanese Culture," 120–21.
32. Igarashi, *Narratives of War*, 58.
33. Ibid.
34. A Home Ministry survey conducted in 1947 found that there were over 80,000 women working in red-light districts and over 150,000 women altogether working in the *fūzoku*, that is, the sex and entertainment trades. See Shimokawa, *Sei fūzoku nenpyō*, 30.
35. See Tanaka, *Japan's Comfort Women*, Chapters 5 and 6.
36. Narumigi, "Sekkusu kaihō," 48.
37. Shibusawa describes the vulnerable legal as well as emotional and financial position these women found themselves in. Since US personnel in Japan had legal immunity, it was not possible for Japanese women to serve paternity writs on the men who had made them pregnant. See, *America's Geisha Ally.*
38. Shimokawa, *Nihon ero shashinshi*, 32.
39. Matsuzawa, "Kasutori zasshi to 'Garo' no Nagai-san," 28.
40. Yonezawa, *Sengo ero manga shi*, 11.
41. Cited in Nagae, "Adaruto-kei shuppansha no rūtsu," 15.
42. Ibid., 18.
43. Matsuzawa, "Kasutori zasshi to 'Garo' no Nagai-san," 30.
44. According to the respective microfiche records for each title preserved in the Prange collection.
45. Yamamoto, *Kasutori zasshi kenkyū*, 50.
46. Narumigi, "Sekkusu kaihō no ayumi," 41.
47. Yamamoto, *Kasutori zasshi kenkyū*, 22–23.
48. Matsuzawa, "Kasutori zasshi to 'Garo' no Nagai-san," 28.
49. Yamamoto and Ozawa, "Kisu o suru koto," 84.
50. Yamamoto, *Kasutori zasshi kenkyū*, 24.
51. Ibid., 32–33.
52. Yonezawa, *Sengo ero manga shi*, 15.
53. Ibid., 17.
54. Fruhstuck, *Colonizing Sex*, 180.
55. Takahashi Tetsu was a ubiquitous presence in early postwar sex journalism in both high-brow and popular contexts and even appeared as himself in Ōshima Nagisa's 1968 "youth culture" movie *Shinjuku dorobō nikki* (Diary of a Shinjuku thief). He was involved in the rewriting of school textbooks to reflect new perspectives in sexual education but bemoaned the interference of the education department in such matters, pointing out that unlike American sex-education texts that (he seemed to think) were unabashed at representing "pleasure" as a key purpose of the sex act, Japanese authorities still required him to speak only of the role of sex in human reproduction. For more biographical details, see *Erochika's* 1972 special edition on Takahashi: *Takahashi Tetsu tokushū.*
56. For a discussion of early 50s sexology magazines, see McLelland, *Queer Japan*, Chapter 2; and Ishida, McLelland, and Murakami, "Origins of 'Queer Studies.'"

57. Yamamoto, *Kasutori zasshi kenkyū*, 48.
58. Ibid., 130.
59. This point is also reinforced by medical doctor Miyata Shigeo who believed that unlike women in foreign countries where "the environment is different," before the war unmarried women in Japan were "mostly untroubled by feelings of sexual desire." He notes that this all changed in the postwar period when young women were suddenly exposed to all kinds of sexual stimuli. *Josei raifu*, "Zadankai," 18.
60. *Shinsō shinbun*, "Onna bakari."
61. See for example *Ai*, "Panpan zadankai."
62. Domenig, "History of Sex Education Films in Japan," Part 3.
63. See for example, *Seishun romansu*, "Kekkon hatsu yoru." This discussion included three women out of a panel of six.
64. Other examples of women's participation in popular sexual discourse are the medical doctors Itō Chizuko, who sometimes spoke alongside Takahashi and other male experts to offer a "woman's perspective" on sexual issues, and Tsuneyasu Tazeko who, alongside "sex education" tracts, also published fiction; see Itō, "Seikan hattatsu" and Tsuneyasu, *Wakaki joi kiroku.*
65. Pharr, "The Politics of Women's Rights," 246.
66. *Ai*, "Panpan zadankai."
67. Ibid., 36.
68. *OK*, "Danshō zadankai." An English translation can be found in *Queer Voices from Japan*, ed. McLelland, Suganuma, and Welker, 69–79.
69. Chauncey, *Gay New York*, 66–76.
70. Streitmatter, *Unspeakable.*
71. Angles, "Seeking the Strange."
72. See McLelland, "From Sailor-Suits to Sadists." So far researchers have only discussed the impact of Japan's defeat upon *heterosexual* relations, particularly the crisis of heterosexual male identity. However, researchers working on early postwar literature, particularly the work of Ōe Kenzaburō, have noticed his deployment of homosexual male characters to signify a defeated Japanese masculinity; see for instance, Hillenbrand, "Doppelgangers, Misogyny, and the San Francisco System"; and Iwamoto, "Ōe Kenzaburō's *Warera no jidai.*"
73. See Koikari, *Pedagogy of Democracy*, who considers the Occupation period sexual dynamics to be symptomatic of Cold War containment politics but without attending to the early postwar boom in "queer" (*hentai*) sexual networks and discourse and the large impact that gay US servicemen had upon nascent indigenous homosexual identities at that time. Shibusawa, *America's Geisha Ally,* reinforces this heterosexist bent when she focuses solely upon the importance of US-Japanese heterosexual relations in "reimagining the Japanese enemy." However, American gay men too, as lovers, scholars, and translators, played an important role in this process of revisioning from the earliest days of the Occupation. Shibusawa does note however (p. 131), that in the American journalistic imagination at least, Japanese men were sometimes represented as effeminate and tending toward homosexuality, but it is important to stress that the Japanese press at the time was also making these observations, particularly in regard to the upsurge in male cross-dressing prostitution

(discussed in Chapter 6). For an alternative account stressing the relative plasticity and openness of that period from a sexual-minority perspective, see Ishida, McLelland, and Murakami, "The Origins of 'Queer Studies'"; and McLelland, *Queer Japan*, Chapters 2 and 3. For a discussion of the influence gay American men have had upon Western perceptions of Japanese culture as effeminate, see Johnson, *The Japanese through American Eyes*, 89; and Treat, *Great Mirrors Shattered.*

74. Shimokawa, *Sei fūzoku nenpyō*, 31. Akita mentions that the book sold a total of half a million copies but gives no source for that figure; Akita, *Sei no ryōki modan*, 188.
75. Kawamura and Takeda, "Kindai Nihon no sekkusu," 236.
76. Fukuoka was influenced by Kinsey's empirical approach to sex research and in 1954 published an analysis of the implications of Kinsey's book on the sex lives of American women for Japanese women; see Fukuoka, *Kinzei hōkoku.*
77. Fukuoka, *Sei to atarashii ninshiki,* 14.
78. Ibid., 17–18.
79. Tatsumi, "Sei ai no gikō."
80. See for example, *Fūfu seikatsu*. "Tsuma ga otto ni kōshite hoshii seiai."
81. Ōtsuka, "Dualism of Love and 'Wago.'"
82. Marran, *Poison Woman*, 136.
83. Dower, *Embracing Defeat*, 164.
84. See for instance, the articles in the "romantic-love marriage system" special edition of the August 1948 edition of the magazine *Hanashi* (Talk).
85. *Shin fūfu,* "Sei ai kyōshitsu."
86. In these comparative surveys of the supposed sexual differences between races, the Japanese were commonly described as less passionate and sexually adept than other races (even the English!). See for example, Iwabuchi, "Sekai junbō meguri."
87. Ōya, "Fūfu seiai tokuhon."
88. Yarita, "Ikoku seppun kō."
89. Igarashi, *Narratives of War*, 53.
90. Ibid., 55.
91. Ike, "Birth Control in Japan," 273.
92. See for instance an advert for "birth control jelly" (a kind of pessary) in the July 1949 edition of *Ōru ryōki*, unpaginated back page. A box of five tubes cost 100 yen. Shimokawa, *Sei fūzoku nenpyō*, 47, notes that the June 1949 edition of *Fūjin kai* (Woman's world) came with a coupon that could be exchanged for "contraceptive medicine."
93. Majima Kan, a medical doctor, had long campaigned for poor women's access to birth control and was briefly imprisoned in 1935 for performing an illegal abortion.
94. Majima, cited in Ike, "Birth Control in Japan," 273.
95. Domenig, "History of Sex Education Films in Japan," Part 2.
96. Matsumoto, *Contemporary Japan,* 20.
97. Shimokawa, *Sei fūzoku nenpyō,* 47, notes that the June 1949 edition of *Fūjin kai* (Woman's world) came with a coupon that could be exchanged for "contraceptive medicine."

98. Fukushima, "To the Rhythm of Jazz," 335.
99. Luther and Boyd, "American Occupation Control over Broadcasting," 47.
100. Morris, *Phoenix Cup*, 134.
101. Taxi dancers were women hired by the dance halls. Male customers would purchase a booklet of ten coupons upon entry to the dance hall and exchange a coupon for each dance with the women working in the club.
102. Kovner, "Base Cultures," 782.
103. Mishima, *Broader Way*, 170.
104. Ibid., 156.
105. Idditie, *When Two Cultures Meet*, 118.
106. Akurosu, *Sutoriito Fasshon*, 16.
107. Mishima, *Broader Way*, 167.
108. Idditie, *When Two Cultures Meet*, 136.
109. Fujiki, "Gakubuchi shō," 37.
110. Domenig, "History of Sex Education Films in Japan," Part 2.
111. Ibid., 42.
112. Scott, *The Flower and Willow World*, 160.
113. Dower, *Embracing Defeat*, 136–37.
114. Ibid., 138.
115. Ochi, "What Did She Read?" 363.
116. *Asahi gurafu*, "Kōzen taru hikyō."
117. For instance, Mochizuki notes how "even among Americans, this predisposition stands out strongly," Mochizuki, "Sengo ni okeru sei seikatsu."
118. For a discussion of the reception of the Kinsey report in the United States, see Markell Morantz, "The Scientist as Sex Crusader."
119. Fruhstuck, *Colonizing Sex*, 180.
120. For more on Shinozaki's career, see ibid., 179.
121. This skepticism was also reflected in the wake of the 1953 publication of Kinsey's report on the human female. In a roundtable discussion of the report, critic Ishigaki Ayako commented that it would be pointless to try to replicate the study in Japan since "isn't it the case that [Japanese women] know absolutely nothing about sex?" See Tsuge, Ishigaki, Yasugi, Abe, and Minami, "Kinzei hōkoku joseihan."
122. Little is known about Kabiya's biography. However he was one of the most prolific and progressive of early postwar sex journalists who specialized in research into male homosexuality. For an English translation of one of his ethnographic forays into Tokyo's developing "gay bars" in the early 50s, see *Queer Voices from Japan*, ed. McLelland, Suganuma, and Welker, 105–38.
123. Ōta was one of the most influential sexologists in the postwar period, well known for his liberal views on contraception, abortion, premarital sex, and sexual minorities. He had been briefly imprisoned before the war due to his suspected Communist sympathies. After the war he was elected to Parliament as a member of the Socialist Party where he sponsored legislation recognizing the rights of women to control their own reproductive decisions. In 1957 he published *Dai san no sei* (The third sex), the first book in Japan about male

homosexuality to be produced with the cooperation of homosexual men themselves.

124. Ōta and Kabiya, "Pettingu wa ryūkō suru."

Chapter 4

1. Mead, *The American Troops and the British Community.*
2. Ibid., 10.
3. Ibid.
4. Ibid., 11.
5. See Mauss, "Techniques of the Body."
6. My understanding of this term is derived from Mauss via Bourdieu who defines it as a conglomeration of acquired "dispositions" that structure a person's perceptions, thoughts, and actions. See Bourdieu, *Outline of a Theory of Practice.*
7. For more on American courtship customs, see Bailey, *From the Front Porch.*
8. Blood, *Love Match*, 53.
9. See for instance, Burkman, *The Occupation of Japan: Arts and Culture*; Mayo, Rimer, and Kerkham, *War, Occupation, and Creativity*; Dower, *Embracing Defeat*; Hirano, *Mr. Smith Goes to Tokyo*; Molasky, *The American Occupation of Japan*; Ward and Sakamoto, *Democratizing Japan.*
10. Hirano, *Tennō to seppun*, also points to the important role that the *kasutori* press played in spreading the idea that kissing was an "anti-feudal" act, 253–54.
11. This idea was most closely associated with sexologist Takahashi Tetsu; see Yamamoto and Ōzawa, "Kisu o suru koto," 83.
12. For an outline of the dimensions of the debate, see Yamamoto, *Kasutori zasshi kenkyū,* 54–77.
13. *Nihon seiteki fūzoku jiten*, 23. Fukuoka argues that this practice wasn't really related to kissing but more akin to "tongue sucking," *Sei no atarashii ninshiki*, 154–55.
14. Ōba, *Seppun*, 99.
15. Kuno, "Life in Japan," 193.
16. Richie, "The Japanese Kiss"; Ōba, *Seppun*, 102.
17. Korekushon modan toshi bunka, *Manga*, 143.
18. Nakano, "Seppun tsuya goroku."
19. Habuto, "Seppun to baidoku."
20. Bennett, *Doing Photography and Social Research.*
21. Hashimoto, "Japanese Tea Party."
22. Dalby, *Geisha*, 55.
23. Nakano, "Seppun tsuya goroku"; see also, *Nihon seiteki fūzoku jiten,* 27. Silverberg, in *Erotic, Grotesque Nonsense,* notes that euphemisms were employed to avoid referring to the tongue directly as in, "the teahouse woman who looks like she will only engage in raw fish," 111.
24. Richie, "The Japanese Kiss," 220. The psychological impact of the first kiss is well described in Mishima Yukio's 1949 novel *Kamen no kokuhaku*

(Confessions of a mask) where the kiss the protagonist finally gives to the young lady he has been courting is the (anti-) climax of the novel. Earlier in the novel, after sharing his first kiss with an older and experienced distant relative, the narrator is overcome by the sensation that he is now a "man who knows kisses"; Mishima, *Confessions of a Mask*, 187.

25. Iryo, "'Seppun' go-shi," 51.
26. Nakano, "Seppun tsuya goroku."
27. Shimura, "Dai ni no seppun," 107.
28. Ibid., 109.
29. Bonbon, "Seppun no rekishi," 103.
30. Maruki, "Seppun."
31. Yamamoto, *Kasutori zasshi kenkyū,* 56.
32. Takahashi, *Kinsei kindai 150 nen sei fūzoku,* 273.
33. Mishima, *Broader Way*, 68.
34. Ibid., 72.
35. Cohen, in *Remaking Japan,* 121, recalls two US soldiers riding on a trolley car that had been brought to a halt by an overturned fruit cart. To the amazement of the Japanese passengers the two GIs immediately jumped down and helped the elderly owner of the cart pick up the fruit so as to speed the trolley on its way.
36. Mauss, "Techniques of the Body."
37. Ibid., 124.
38. Such instruction may well have been necessary as research done in Osaka in 1948 among female students between the ages of 18 and 22 discovered that only 25 percent had experience of kissing; see Shimokawa, *Sei fūzoku nenpyō,* 43.
39. Kamei, "The Kiss and Japanese Culture," 116.
40. Yamamoto and Ozawa, "Kisu o suru koto," 83; Yamamoto, *Kasutori zasshi kenkyū,* 48.
41. Takahashi, "Nihon fūzokushi ni okeru seppun." Nakano Eizō agreed with Takahashi that "tongue sucking" had indeed long been part of Japan's erotic culture but that until the Meiji period there had not existed a word that covered the full extent of the English term "kiss." See Nakano, "Seppun tsuya goroku."
42. *Aka to kuro*, "Ketsu to suna."
43. Yarita, "Ikoku seppun kō."
44. Wani, "Kuchi ni jō ge no hedate." It was not unusual for cunnilingus and fellatio to be discussed in these accounts of kissing. Indeed, the "lower mouth" mentioned in Wani's article refers to the vagina.
45. Yamamoto, *Kasutori zasshi kenkyū*, 62.
46. Ibid., 51.
47. Seidensticker, *Tokyo Rising*, 179, notes that the first kiss that took place in the "legitimate theater" was in 1946, but he does not mention in what context.
48. Leiter, "Performing the Emperor's New Clothes," 129.
49. Leiter, "From Bombs to Booms," 16.
50. Beech, "Tokyo Audience Cheers 'Mikado.'"

51. Bennett, *Doing Photography and Social Research.*
52. Hayashi, "Kissu arabesuku"; Matsuba, "Amerika no eiga no janru."
53. Shimizu, *Sensō to eiga*, 180.
54. Hirano, *Mr. Smith Goes to Tokyo,* 154. See also Hirano, *Tennō to seppun*, 242–43.
55. Standish, *Myth and Masculinity.*
56. Tosaka, "Discourse of Anti-Americanism," 64.
57. Ibid., 65.
58. Shimizu, *Sensō to eiga*, 181.
59. Morris, *Phoenix Cup*, 105.
60. The Occupation forces had their own opportunities to see movies screened at the Ernie Pyle Theater in Hibiya, Tokyo. However, Japanese not connected with the Occupation administration were not normally allowed in the venue.
61. Smulyan, "Using Hollywood Films," 57.
62. Ibid., 59.
63. See for instance the 1921 report in *The Chicago Defender* noting 120,000 feet of US film stock had been edited out of the Japanese versions; *Chicago Defender*, "Japan Bans Movie Kissing."
64. Kamei, "The Kiss and Japanese Culture," 171. When I asked my older sister's Japanese husband's mother if she had seen any "kissing movies" after the war, she recalled having gone to see this Deanna Durbin movie with a high-school girlfriend at an open-air showing in Yokohama, probably in 1946.
65. Kitamura, *Screening Enlightenment,* 21.
66. Hayashi, "Kissu arabesuku."
67. See for example the photograph of a young Japanese couple gazing at a large billboard depicting the lips of Montgomery Clift and Jennifer Jones locked together outside a cinema screening the 1953 film *Terminal Station* in *Sandē Mainichi*, "Nihonjin no sei kōdō."
68. Kitamura, *Screening Enlightenment,* 118.
69. Bae, "Girl Meets Boy Meets Girl," 359n11.
70. Izbicki, *Scorched Cityscapes and Silver Screens,* 136.
71. Tachiki, *Seppun no hakubutsu shi,* 175.
72. Mauss, "Techniques of the Body," 74–75.
73. See for example, Tanaka, "Ren'ai no hyōgen gikō."
74. See for example, *Fūfu seikatsu,* "Tokushū: Eiga ni arawareta fūfu no aijō."
75. Cited in Shibusawa, *America's Geisha Ally*, 25.
76. Crockett, *Popcorn on the Ginza*, 204.
77. Ibid., 205.
78. Idditie, *When Two Cultures Meet,* 143.
79. Hirano, *Mr. Smith Goes to Tokyo*, 162.
80. Kitamura, *Screening Enlightenment*, 36.
81. Takemae, *Allied Occupation*, 398.
82. The phrase is "*bisho nure ni natta futari no seppun*" (the kiss of a couple who had become soaking wet), which could just as easily have occurred in a pornographic narrative. This point is made by Yamamoto, *Kasutori zasshi kenkyū,* 57.
83. Hirano, *Mr. Smith Goes to Tokyo*, 155; Hirano, *Tennō to seppun*, 243.

84. Hirano, *Mr. Smith Goes to Tokyo*, 156; Kamei, "The Kiss and Japanese Culture," 117; Ōba, *Seppun*, 102. A report in the July 21, 1946, edition of the *Yomiuri* newspaper mentioned that it was gauze the actress placed on her lips.
85. Cited in Kamei, "The Kiss and Japanese Culture," 117.
86. Cited in ibid., 118.
87. Ibid., 119.
88. Both *Aru yoru no seppun* and *Hatachi no seishun* were advertised in the *Yomiuri* newspaper in May 1946.
89. Cited in Hirano, *Mr. Smith Goes to Tokyo*, 157.
90. Franklyn, "Sexual Freedom in Japanese Cinema," 57.
91. Hirano, *Tennō to seppun*, 249.
92. Hoberecht, "Yank Tutors Jap Actress."
93. Cited in Yamamoto, *Kasutori zasshi kenkyū*, 62.
94. The hermeneutic function of movie magazines was not a postwar innovation. Silverberg, in *Erotic Grotesque Nonsense*, notes that even in the 1930s, *Eiga no tomo* contained articles on "how modern sexualized gestures in foreign movies could be read in modern Japan," 110.
95. Kitamura, *Screening Enlightenment*, 157.
96. Ibid., 156.
97. Ibid., 158.
98. Ibid., 170.
99. *Yomiuri* newspaper April 22, 1951.
100. Kitamura, *Screening Enlightenment*, 153.
101. Yamamoto, "Kasutori zasshi," 244.
102. Cited in Hirano, *Mr. Smith Goes to Tokyo*, 157.
103. Ibid.
104. Fukuoka, "Eigakan ni okeru abekku."
105. Ibid., 165.
106. *Jitsuwa to shinsō*, April (1949): unpaginated.
107. Yamamoto, *Kasutori zasshi kenkyū*, 248, uses the term "infantile."
108. Ibid., 64.
109. Tsubaki, *Seppun nendai ki*, 167.
110. Tajima, *Senetsushitsu noyami ni tsubuyaku*, 332.
111. *Josei raifu*, "Zadankai," 18–19.
112. The "solution" was, of course, marriage (albeit both sports and masturbation were lightheartedly offered as interim measures); see ibid., 22.
113. Ibid., 19.
114. Hirano, *Tennō to seppun*, 246–47.
115. Cited in ibid., 247.
116. *Pacific Stars & Stripes*, "Delinquency Group Attempts Kissing Ban."
117. Emerson Wilde, *Typhoon in Tokyo*, 168.
118. There were, in fact, a number of "kiss robberies" reported where young women would allow a man to insert his tongue between their lips and then they would bite down hard. As the man reeled in pain, the young woman would make off with his bag or wallet; see Shimokawa, *Sei fūzoku nenpyō*, 38.

119. *Yomiuri* newspaper April 22, 1951.
120. Tsubaki, *Seppun nendai ki,* 168.
121. Hayashi, "Kissu arabesuku," 64.
122. Nanbu, "Sutā no seishun."
123. Fukuoka, *Sei no atarashii ninshiki*, 27, also argued that Japanese people needed to stop thinking about sex in terms of obscenity (*waisetsu*) and instead recognize it as a "beautiful" part of married life.
124. For a detailed discussion of these films, see Domenig, "A History of Sex Education Films in Japan," Part 3.
125. This idea was apparently widespread; see Yamamoto, *Kasutori zasshi kenkyū*, 55–56, and Fukuoka, *Sei no atarashii ninshiki*, 150.
126. *Ningen tankyū,* "Zadankai: Onna gakusei," 67.
127. A 1966 article explaining the relevant "time, place and occasion" for different types of kissing, repeated the claim that "[t]he Japanese are poor kissers," pointing toward ongoing anxieties about the role that kissing played in courtship behavior in Japan. *Heibon panchi*, "kissu ni wa 12 tōri," 16.
128. *Sandē Mainichi,* "Sei no tōsaku dai san."
129. Tsuge, Ishigaki, Yasugi, Abe, and Minami, "Kinzei hōkoku," 117.
130. Hirano, *Mr. Smith Goes to Tokyo*, 161.
131. Yamamoto, "Kasutori zasshi," 242–43.
132. Kiwa, "Rabu shiin manwa."
133. Yoshimi, "'America' as Desire and Violence," 438.
134. Ibid., 439.
135. Hirano, *Tennō to seppun*, 253.
136. Ibid.
137. Takahashi, *Kinsei kindai 150 nen sei fūzoku*, 273.

Chapter 5

1. Kushner, *Thought War*, 172.
2. Mishima, *Broader Way*, 166.
3. Ibid., 166.
4. Koshiro, *Trans-Pacific Racisms,* 65.
5. Cited in Koshiro, *Trans-Pacific Racisms,* 66.
6. Hulse, "Effects of the War," 41.
7. Tsurumi, *Cultural History of Postwar Japan*, 11.
8. Hasegawa and Takagi, "Senzen sengo ero sesō," 160.
9. Sanders, *Prostitution in Postwar Japan,* 89.
10. Dore, *City Life in Japan*, 159.
11. On the disciplining of male-female interaction, see Ambarass, "Juvenile Delinquency and the National Defense State."
12. Dore, *City Life in Japan*, 159.
13. Ibid.
14. Atkins, "The War on Jazz," 353.
15. Mishima, *Broader Way*, 162.

16. Dower, *Embracing Defeat*, 163.
17. Simon and Gagnon, "Sexual Scripts."
18. Shibuya, *Nihon no dōtei*, 139–40.
19. Goda, "Seikōi to shakaiaku."
20. Mishima, *Broader Way*, 152.
21. Ibid., 155.
22. Kovner, *Prostitution in Postwar Japan*, 57.
23. Takemae, *Allied Occupation*, 364.
24. Ibid., 366.
25. Dore, *City Life in Japan*, 170.
26. Finn, "Reform and Japanese Higher Education," 204.
27. Dore, *City Life in Japan*, 170.
28. Bae, "Girl Meets Boy Meets Girl," 352.
29. Ibid., 350.
30. Ibid.
31. *Fujin Asahi*, "Kono goro no gakusei."
32. Ibid., 85.
33. Ibid., 84.
34. Narumigi, "Sekkusu kaihō no ayumi," 42.
35. This service was offered by the magazine *Raburii*, among others. See the December 1947 edition, p. 34.
36. Narumigi, "Sekkusu kaihō no ayumi," 48.
37. Matsumoto, *Contemporary Japan*, 17.
38. Ibid.
39. *Fujin Asahi*, "Kono goro no gakusei," 89.
40. Furuzawa, "Sengo no shingo," 55.
41. Saitō, "Abekku wa kappuru?"
42. Idditie, *When Two Cultures Meet*, 138.
43. Saitō, "Abekku wa kappuru?" 178.
44. *Asahi* newspaper September 9, 1950.
45. *Ningen tankyū*, "Abekku kenkyū."
46. Ibid., 77.
47. *Asahi* newspaper, June 1, 1948.
48. *Asahi* newspaper December 6, 1948.
49. *Asahi* newspaper, September 3, 1950.
50. *Asahi* newspaper June 3, 1950.
51. Yoshida, "Gaitō abekku sanpuru."
52. Mauss, "Techniques of the Body."
53. Ōnishi, "Ren'aigaku kōza."
54. Yamamoto, *Kasutori zasshi kenkyū*, 64.
55. Luther and Boyd, "American Occupation Control over Broadcasting," 48.
56. Manchester, *American Caesar*, 511.
57. Onnasuki, "Ren'ai gakkōshitsu."
58. *Randebū* from the French "rendezvous" was a common term for a date and, like the borrowing of the French term "*avec*" for a dating couple, underlines the foreignness of both concepts.

59. Akita, *Sei no ryōki modan*, 188; Yamamoto, *Kasutori zasshi kenkyū*, 32.
60. Akita, *Sei no ryōki modan*, 187.
61. Akita, *Sei no ryōki modan*, 190–91; Shūkan shinchō, "Kanzen naru kekkon," 32; Osaki, "Sei no shisō senkakusha."
62. Takahashi, *Arusu Amatoria*. Takahashi offered 84 suggestions for the establishment of the right mood.
63. See for instance, his advice on these issues in Takahashi, "Dokushinsha no nayami," and "Kekkon ai gijutsu mondō."
64. *Erochika*, "Takahashi Tetsu tokushū," 260.
65. Takahashi, *Kekkon ai kaiwa jiten*.
66. Ibid., 27–28.
67. Ibid., 3.
68. See for example, Walthall, "Masturbation and Discourse on Female Sexual Practices." For a discussion of classic Japanese texts discussing male-male love, see Watanabe and Iwata, *Love of the Samurai*.
69. *Shūkan shinchō*, "Kanzen naru kekkon," 32; Takahashi often included illustrations and discussions concerning Edo erotic art and texts in his journal *Amatoria*, published throughout the early 50s. The May 1951 edition of *Amatoria* was dedicated to the study of Edo-period erotic classics and contained an essay penned by Takahashi himself, entitled "Edo erotic book research"; See Takahashi, "Edo enpon kenkyū." Takahashi also stressed that much could be learned from non-Western erotic classics from China and India.
70. *Miyata*, "Atarashii sei seikatsu kōza."
71. *Shūkan Asahi*, "Ibu no subete."
72. *Yomiuri* newspaper, November 26, 1954.
73. *Fujin Asahi*, "Kinzei hakase no shinsho."
74. *Shūkan Asahi*, "Ibu no subete," 17.
75. Shinozaki, *Nihonjin no sei seikatsu*.
76. Tsuge, "Kinzei hōkoku joseihan zadankai," 117.
77. *Yomiuri* newspaper, August 21, 1953.
78. See for example, *Fūfu seikatsu*, "Tokushū: sei no waka gaeri."
79. Shimokawa, *Sei fūzoku nenpyō*, 47, states that it sold out its print run of 770,000 on the first day.
80. Silverberg, *Erotic Grotesque Nonsense*, 162.
81. Hoshino, "Apartment Life in Japan," 314.
82. Mishima, *Broader Way*, 134.
83. Ibid., 185.
84. Beardsley, Hall, and Ward, *Village Japan*.
85. Ibid., 78.
86. See for instance, *Fūfu seikatsu*, "Semai ie taizuru fūfu."
87. Vogel, *Japan's New Middle Class*, 279.
88. That the "home" was very much imagined as an idealized "Western" space was also indicated by the occasional non-sex-related feature that introduced American "dream items" such as fridges, vacuum cleaners, and electric washing machines. See for instance, Furuda, "Bijin o umi dasu denki."
89. Kiwa, "Rabu shiin manwa."

90. Beardsley, Hall, and Ward, *Village Japan*, 76.
91. Furukawa, "Ero hoteru," 77.
92. Shimokawa, *Sei fūzoku nenpyō*, 36.
93. Ishinaka, "Shinkon nikki no tsukekata."
94. Tanabe, "Hatsu yoru," 11.
95. Ibid., 19.
96. Yonezawa, *Sengo ero manga shi,* 19.
97. Dore, *City Life in Japan,* 178.
98. Ibid.
99. In this they had much in common with the *ero-guro* representations of the "modern girl" in the prewar period. As Silverberg points out in *Erotic Grotesque Nonsense*, p. 111, the male body was hardly ever presented as an object for dissection and evaluation in these magazines.
100. Dore, *City Life in Japan,* 178, notes that this kind of "erotic magazine" was often read by men on their commute home and then discarded.
101. From 1951, however, the style changed and only women were represented on the covers.
102. Furusawa, "Donna nyūbō ga risō?"
103. Sakurai, "Kōshite nyūbō wa utsukushiku."
104. Sakurai and Kurosaka, "Danna sama ga kapuri tsuku." For a discussion of the introduction of silicone and other breast enhancement procedures into Japan, see Miller, *Beauty Up*, 82–84.
105. *Fūfu seikatsu,* "Tsuma ga otto ni kōshite hoshii seiai gikō."
106. *Fūfu seikatsu,* "Otto to tsuma ga tagai ni ikō," 207.
107. See for example, an article in the September 1952 edition, written by a female medical doctor who explained the anxieties that women had about the first night of marriage from physiological and psychological perspectives; Nomura, "Hana hiraku hatsu yoru."
108. Cather, *Great Censorship Trials of Literature,* 23, notes that the kind of detailed sexual instruction that could be found in popular magazines such as *Fūfu seikatsu* was introduced by the defense in the 1951 obscenity trial of the publisher and translator of *Lady Chatterley's Lover,* in an attempt to show that graphic depictions of sex were consistent with community standards. However the existence of this kind of "pulp" literature was judged irrelevant since it was the "high" artistic nature of works of literature that afforded them more impact. It was however the *adulterous* nature of the sex described in *Chatterley* that rendered the description problematic, as Cather notes, "the prosecution was attempting to stop adultery in reality via a ban in representation," 32.
109. Yonezawa, *Sengo ero manga shi,* 19.
110. Ibid.
111. *Modan fūfu tokuhon,* "Shigekitekina sei ai gikō," 69.
112. Ibid., 67.
113. Ibid., 72, 78–79.
114. Ibid., 68.
115. Shimokawa, *Sei fūzoku nenpyō,* 38.
116. *Modan fūfu tokuhon,* "Shigekitekina sei ai gikō," 70.

117. Driscoll, *Absolute Erotic, Absolute Grotesque*, 183.
118. Takeda, "Mai asa shukkin mae."
119. Isehara, "Hito ke mo matowanu."
120. Uno, "The Death of 'Good Wife'?" 304.
121. Igarashi, *Narratives of War*, 57.
122. *Fūfu seikatsu,* "Tokushū: sei no waka gaeri," 10.
123. *Fūfu seikatsu,* "Tokushū: fūfu no nenrei to sei seikatsu."
124. Ōtsuka,"Dualism of Love and 'Wago,'" 43.
125. Nakajima, "Nenrei sa no tadashii fūfu," 23.
126. Ibid., 59.
127. Ibid., 60.
128. Ibid.
129. *Josei raifu,* "Zadankai," 19–20.
130. Miyata, "Atarashii sei seikatsu kōza," 29.
131. See, for instance, the July 1950 edition of *Fūfu seikatsu*, p. 64–70, where the advice was dished out by no less that Ernest Hoberecht, the "gallant Yank" who had instructed actress Mimura Hideko in the art of kissing (see Chapter 4). *Bēze* also ran regular "*jinsei*" (life) and "*seishun*" (youth) advice columns addressing such matters as kissing, masturbation, and same-sex love. Takahashi Tetsu's two magazines launched in 1951, *Ningen tankyū* (Human research) and *Amatoria,* were notable for the giving of sex advice. *Ningen tankyū* even offered American sex advice columns translated from the English; see *Ningen tankyū,* "Amerika no seiai sōdan." The mainstream press also offered advice, see for example, the discussion in the July 21, 1948, edition of the *Yomiuri* newspaper about adolescent masturbation, in a column titled "health advice."
132. *Shūkan shinchō,* "Kanzen naru kekkon," 32.
133. Gagnon and Simon, *Sexual Conduct,* 105.
134. Shimokawa, *Sei fūzoku nenpyō,* 47, notes that the June 1949 edition of *Fūjin kai* (Woman's world) came with a coupon that could be exchanged for "contraceptive medicine."
135. Gordon, "Managing the Japanese Household," 253.
136. Norgren, *Abortion before Birth Control,* 83.
137. Tanabe, "Hatsu yoru no kanzen seikō," 10. For a wife who makes a similar inference in the prewar period, see Fruhstuck, *Colonizing Sex,* 116.
138. Norgren, *Abortion before Birth Control,* 84. Norgren notes that the official and popular understandings of contraception were quite different, but in her analysis she notes that popular understandings tended to focus on the economic benefits of family planning.
139. *Miyata,* "Atarashii sei seikatsu kōza," 30.
140. Takahashi, "kekkon ai gijutsu," 52.

Chapter 6

1. Ryang, *Love in Modern Japan,* 67.
2. Koikari, *Pedagogy of Democracy.*

3. Igarashi, *Narratives of War*, 48.
4. Dower, *Embracing Defeat*, 132.
5. For example, Shibusawa, *America's Geisha Ally.*
6. Luther and Boyd, "American Occupation Control over Broadcasting," 47.
7. Koikari, *Pedagogy of Democracy*, 161.
8. Angles, "Seeking the Strange," 112.
9. Ibid., 134.
10. Omori, *Detecting Japanese Vernacular Modernism*, 94.
11. Angles, *Writing the Love of Boys*, 113.
12. Angles, "Seeking the Strange," 104.
13. Matsuzawa, "Kasutori zasshi to 'Garo' no Nagai-san," 27.
14. Marran, "*From Pathography to Pulp*," 56.
15. This was a *kasutori* title and is not to be confused with the more serious sexology magazine with the same title published by Takahashi Tetsu from 1950.
16. Aoki, "Nokozareta yoru."
17. Furukawa, "Ero hoteru," 81.
18. Ivy, "Formations of Mass Culture," 245.
19. Ibid.
20. Dower, *Embracing Defeat*, 122.
21. Ibid.
22. Ibid., 122–23.
23. Ibid., 154.
24. See for example, Akasaka, "Senso to mazo"; Asakura, "Sensen ni okeru dōseiai."
25. See Takahashi, *Abu rabu*, 213. Also, Takahashi believed that the physical punishment meted out on the buttocks of soldiers and sailors had awoken awareness of the backside as an "erogenous zone" leading some men to seek out anal stimulation, see Takahashi, "Tengoku ka?" 75. For a purportedly first-person account of a male homosexual affair in the army, see Morihara, "Waga guntai jidai," and the English translation of this account in *Queer Voices from Japan*, ed. McLelland, Suganuma, and Welker, 51–57.
26. Kurumada, "Tōkyō okama."
27. Ōwada, "Danshō o hadaka ni suru," 74. Some reports also suggest that *danshō* in Osaka were more aggressive in recruiting customers, perhaps because of this greater tolerance; see Nanri, "Danshō o tsuku."
28. See for example, Hirano, "Gunpuku no danshō-tachi"; for some accounts that have been translated into English, see *Queer Voices from Japan*, ed. McLelland, Suganuma, and Welker.
29. See for example, *Gekkan Yomiuri*, "Danshō wa kataru."
30. The caption describing the photo concerned a "reverse male-dressing beauty" (*gyaku dansō no reijin*). This is a reference to the "trouser role" stars of women's theater troupes popular in the prewar period; see Robertson, *Takarazuka.*
31. Nanri, "Danshō o tsuku."
32. Tomita, "Josō otoko-tachi."
33. The account given here is based on that appearing in the *Mainichi* newspaper, November 23, 1948.

34. There were even humorous poems in the traditional *senryū* style published in the newspapers such as one printed in the *Yomiuri* newspaper on August 5, 1950.
35. *Omoshiroi kōdan* (Interesting tales), August (1948): 131.
36. Ibid., 130.
37. *Jitsuwa to shōsetsu* (Truth and fiction), April (1949): unpaginated.
38. *Gekkan Niigata* (Monthly Niigata), "Karā sekushon," date illegible, unpaginated.
39. *OK*, August (1949): 37.
40. *Yomikiri kōdan sekai* (World of non-serialized stories), July (1949): 114.
41. *Tokudane zasshi* (Exclusive news magazine), February (1948): 32. The title of the cartoon, "Yoru no ura mon (Back gate of the night)," is probably also a sexual reference.
42. Pflugfelder, *Cartographies of Desire*, 210.
43. Sumi, "Danshō no mori."
44. Ibid.
45. Ekkusu, "Danshō geki jiken."
46. See for example, Sumi, "Danshō no mori" and Danshō no sekai"; Higuma, "Danshō no mori."
47. Moriya, "Danshō no seitai."
48. Ekkusu, "Danshō geki jiken."
49. Kovner, *Prostitution in Postwar Japan,* 142.
50. Kurumada, "Tōkyō okama," 38.
51. Achilles, "The Development of the Homosexual Bar."
52. *Yomiuri* newspaper, January 20, 1951.
53. *Shakai tanbō,* "Danshō bakari no zadankai."
54. *Gekkan yomiuru,* "Danshō wa kataru."
55. Frederick Hulse who, as part of the Civilian Morale Division, was trusted with gathering local opinions about the progress of the Occupation, noted that there still existed "considerable dread of the police" and that "the average Japanese was just plain scared of them, and wanted nothing to do with them." See Hulse, "Some Effects of the War," 40.
56. *OK*, "Danshō zadankai." For an English translation, see *Queer Voices from Japan*, ed. McLelland, Suganuma, and Welker, 69–79.
57. See, Kurumada, "Tōkyō okama," 36.
58. Friman, "The Impact of the Occupation on Crime," 95.
59. Tomita, "Josō otoko-tachi," 34.
60. See for example, Minami Takao's objectifying treatment of two *danshō* who had been hospitalized in his psychiatric facility. His article, published in *Clinical Medical Digest* in July 1948, contained two full-frontal naked photographs of the patients alongside a detailed description of their many "abnormalities." See Minami, "Danshō ni kan suru."
61. Misushu, "Onna ni haru wo utta otoko."
62. *Kitan zasshi,* "Kōshoku no buaraieti."
63. Kogure, "Onna demo otoko de mo nai."
64. Hirano, "Gunpuku no danshō-tachi."

65. *Fūfu no sei seikatsu*, "Danshō no mon."
66. Hirano, "Gunpuku no danshō-tachi"; Honshi Chōsabu, "Danshō no ijō seiai chōsa."
67. Indeed as late as 1963 Ichikawa Kon directed the movie *Yukinojo henge* (The revenge of Yukinojo) featuring one-time *onnagata* Hasegawa Kazuo (who also starred in the 1935 original). In the movie, Hasegawa played the role of an *onnagata* who used his (her?) erotic allure to seduce and bring destruction to the wives and daughters of his enemies. Women's erotic interest in the male-role players of all-female theater troupes such as the Takarazuka shōjo kagekidan was also widely acknowledged; see Robertson, *Takarazuka*.
68. The loanword "cock-suck boy" begs the question whether it was not the Occupation forces that came up with this designation, the term "cock sucker" being a common insult used to denigrate homosexual men. Contemporary sources could not, due to censorship, mention Allied personnel in this regard. However, it is interesting to note that prior to the Occupation male homosexuality in Japan was almost exclusively associated with anal sex. Fellatio (along with kissing) was later spoken of as an *American* innovation introduced during the Occupation to Japanese homosexual circles (see McLelland, *Queer Japan,* 77). Shimokawa, *Sei fūzoku nenpyō,* 34, states that the partners of the cock-suck boys were indeed American, and the going rate was 100 yen (at the time a bowl of noodles cost 30 yen), but he does not cite his source.
69. *Hanzai yomimono,* "Hentai chōsho."
70. Murata, "Nami o oyogu pan pan bōi."
71. Shimokawa, *Sei fūzoku nenpyō,* 42, states that they were but frustratingly doesn't provide any references. He notes that the cruising spot for Japanese youths seeking foreign partners was in front of the Imperial Hotel, opposite Hibiya Park.
72. Oka, "Ryōsei dōbutsu," 100.
73. Sedgwick, *Epistemology,* 55.
74. Koikari, *Pedagogy of Democracy,* 24.
75. Pflugfelder, *Cartographies of Desire,* 332.
76. Minami, "Danshō ni kan suru," 23.
77. Sedgwick, *Epistemology of the Closet,* 8; italics in the original.
78. This had not always been the case. As Chauncey, *Gay New York*, 358, points out, in the early twentieth century effeminate homosexual men known as "fairies" had sought out sexual liaisons with straight men known as "trade." These interactions supported the existing gender hierarchy and the trade partner was able to maintain his masculine identity. By the late 1940s, however, Cold War anxieties about a generalised "homosexual menace" had rendered these differences moot, at least in the eyes of the authorities; see Berube, *Coming Out under Fire.*
79. Kabiya, *Yoru no itansha*, 62.
80. Kanzaki, *Kanzaki repōto baishun,* 71.
81. Tomita was the author of the 1958 book *Gei* (Gay) about Tokyo's emerging homosexual bar scene. For a discussion of this book, see McLelland, *Queer Japan*, 104–05.

82. Tomita, "Josō otokotachi," 34.
83. Mon, "Ryōki yobanashi."
84. Ōwada, "Danshō o hadaka ni suru," 77.
85. See for example, Tomioka "Hensō to dōseiai"; Hamakawa, "Danshō no rekishi"; Kurumada, "Tōkyō okama."
86. Canaday, "'Who Is a Homosexual?"
87. Mon, "Ryōki yobanashi."
88. Tomioka, "Hensō to dōseiai."
89. Horii, "Kagema yashiki."
90. Angles, "Writing the Love of Boys," 116.
91. Driscoll, *Absolute Erotic, Absolute Grotesque*, 149.
92. *Shin jiyū*, "Danshō no kokuhaku."
93. Wildes, *Typhoon in Tokyo,* 287.
94. Marran, *Poison Woman,* 142.
95. For a discussion of the masochist/sadist typology in early postwar sexological literature, see Ishida and Murakami, "Process of Divergence."
96. *Yama no anego* and *Chikadō no anego,* respectively.
97. *Yomiuri* newspaper, June 23, 1950.
98. *Yomiuri* newspaper, May 14, 1950.
99. See for example, the report in the December 23, 1952, edition of the *Asahi* newspaper, where what appeared to be a young man threw himself in front of a train at Yoyogi, but later turned out to be a woman dressed in a man's suit. The suicide note apparently pointed to disappointment in love as the reason for her death but the gender of the lost lover is not specified.
100. Silverberg, *Erotic Grotesque Nonsense,* 163.
101. Marran, *Poison Woman,* 140.
102. *Shinsō jitsuwa,* "Onna gakusei no himitsu."
103. Ibid., 47.
104. Marran, *Poison Woman,* 140.
105. Ikeda's novel *Shanghai* was a candidate for the eleventh Akutagawa Prize in 1940. She became well-known after the war for her novels that focused on sexual exploration.
106. Ikeda, "Dai san no sei."
107. Ikeda herself also wrote for the postwar sex press, see for example, her short story "Tsuma no taion" in *Fūfu seikatsu.*
108. Koito, "Dōseiai monogatari."
109. Yamagami, "Hisokana geki."
110. Hirakawa, "Joshi dōseiai toribādo."
111. Hirakawa, "Joshi dōseiai saffuisuto."
112. Koito, "Dōseiai monogatari."
113. Hirakawa, "Joshi dōseiai saffuisuto."
114. Hayakawa, "Shōjo kibun."
115. Takahashi's own response to "sexual perversion" was heavily influenced by Freud. A review of advice to readers expressing anxiety over a range of "abnormal" sexual desires shows that he generally stressed the ubiquity of these feelings—especially homosexual feelings—which he said were

experienced by most people (including himself) at some stage in their lives. However, good Freudian that he was, he did encourage readers to move out of their homosexual "phase" and try to make a heterosexual adjustment; see for instance, Takahashi, "Kekkon ai gijutsu," 51. He was also pragmatic, suggesting to one man with strong homosexual feelings that his "mission" in life might be to practice "both sex love" (*ryōseiai*) by marrying a "proper wife" but also having male lovers; see Takahashi "Tengoku ka?" 79.

116. See McLelland, *Queer Japan,* Chapter 2.
117. For example, the *zadankai* "round table" format that allowed members of sexual minority groups to speak in their own voices was continued in these publications. See, for instance, Takahashi, "Tengoku ka?"
118. Ōgiya Afu collaborated with Ōta and Kabiya on *Dai san no sei* (The third sex), the 1957 book based on research into Japan's burgeoning male homosexual subculture. Unlike Ōta and Kabiya who tended to keep an academic distance in their writings, Ōgiya's own journalistic work on male homosexuality in the early 50s came very close to advocacy; see McLelland, *Queer Japan,* 131, for a discussion.

Afterword

1. Quoted in Takenaka, "Takahashi Tetsu sensei ni tsuite."
2. A reference to the Tokugawa-period policy of national seclusion.
3. For more on Ōta, who refused to condemn premarital sex, see Fruhstuck, *Colonizing Sex,* 181.
4. Ōta, *Dai san no sei.* This was one of the first nonpathologizing treatments of male homosexuality to be conducted with the cooperation of same-sex desiring men themselves in any language. It also contains a brief discussion of female same-sex love (*resubosu*) but this is based on secondary sources and not engagement with an actual community of women. For a discussion see McLelland, *Queer Japan,* 105–06.
5. Foucault, *History of Sexuality,* 157.
6. Fruhstuck, *Colonizing Sex,* 197.
7. Ibid., 180.
8. Gordon, "Managing the Japanese Household."
9. Ryang, *Love in Modern Japan,* 68. Ryang in her discussion lays great emphasis on the influence of government-sponsored purity literature, but as I have detailed in this book, there were a plethora of other, contrary views easily available in the popular media that countered this approach.
10. See for example, the 1959 review article "In Van de Velde's footsteps" that surveys the "sex books" (*sei shō*) published in the 13-year period since the release of *Kanzen naru kekkon; Shūkan shinchō,* "Ban de Berudo kara no shinpō."
11. Ibid., 33–34.
12. Bardsley, "Discourse on Women in Postwar Japan," 4.
13. Bardsley, "What Women Want," 11.
14. Gluck, "The 'End' of the Postwar," 4.

15. Doi, *Amae no kōzō*, 135.
16. The generational shifts identified by Dai ni ji shin seikatsu kenkyūkai in the 1980s, for instance, largely support the arguments made in Ōta and Kabiya, "Petting wa ryūkō suru;" Hasegawa and Takagi, "Senzen sengo ero sesō ōdan"; and Fukuoka, *Sei no atarashii ninshiki*. The numerous works by Yamamoto Akira (who was a middle-school student at the close of the war and who draws on incidents from his own autobiography in his many writings) also suggest that the juxtaposition of democracy and "sexual liberation" was not simply rhetorical but a lived reality for many.
17. Giddens, *Modernity and Self Identity*, 196.

Bibliography

Abe Ikuo, Kiyohara Yasuharu, and Nakajima Ken. "Sport and Physical Education under Fascistization in Japan." *International Journal of the History of Sport* 9, no. 1 (1992): 1–28.

Abel, Jonathan. "The *Ero-Puro* Sense: Declassifying Censored Literature from Prewar Japan." *Japan Forum* 19, no. 3 (2007): 341–67.

Achilles, Nancy. "The Development of the Homosexual Bar as an Institution." In *Sexual Deviance*, edited by John Gagnon and William Simon. New York: Harper and Row, (1967): 228–244.

Adams, Michael. *The Best War Ever: America and World War II*. Baltimore: Johns Hopkins University Press, 1994.

Ai. "Panpan zadankai: waga mune no soko niwa (Prostitutes' roundtable: at the bottom of our hearts)." April (1948): 36–41.

Aka to kuro. "Ketsu to suna (Blood and sand)." October (1946): 25.

Akasaka Tsuyoshi. "Senso to mazo (War and masochism)." *Kitan kurabu*, June (1952): 69.

Akita Masami. *Sei no ryōki modan* (Modern curiosity hunting sexuality). Tokyo: Seikyūsha.

Akurosu henshū shitsu. *Sutoriito Fasshon: Wakamono sutairu 50 nen shi* (Street fashion: a 50-year history of young people's style). Tokyo: PARCO, 1995.

Ambarass, David. "Juvenile Delinquency and the National Defense State: Policing Young Workers in Wartime Japan, 1937–1945." *Journal of Asian Studies* 63, no. 1 (2004): 31–60.

Anderson, Benedict. *Imagined Communities: Reflections on the Origins and Spread of Nationalism*. London: Verso, 1983.

Angles, Jeffrey. "Seeking the Strange: *Ryōki* and the Navigation of Normality in Interwar Japan." *Monumenta Nipponica* 63, no. 1 (2008): 101–41.

———. *Writing the Love of Boys: Origins of Bishōnen Culture in Modernist Japanese Literature*. Minneapolis: University of Minnesota Press, 2011.

Aoki Shigeru. "Nokozareta yoru no tengoku: aru pan pan kurabu no jitsuwa (A heavenly night of being spied on: a true pan pan club tale)." *Ningen tankyū*, May (1948): 21–33.

Arai Kaku. *Kindai meishoku* (Contemporary bright colors). Tokyo: Chūō kōronsha, 1929.

Asahi gurafu. "Kōzen taru hikyō (Opening up unexplored regions)." December 17 (1947): 10–11.

Asakura Shirō. "Sensen ni okeru dōseiai (Homosexuality on the battle front)." *Kitan kurabu*, June (1952): 137.

Asayama Shin'ichi. "Sexual Behavior in Japanese Students: Comparisons for 1974, 1960 and 1952." *Archives of Sexual Behavior* 5, no. 5 (1976): 371–90.

Atkins, E. Taylor. "The War on Jazz or Jazz Goes to War: Toward a New Cultural Order in Wartime Japan." *Positions* 6, no. 2 (1998): 345–92.

Baber, Ray. *Youth Looks at Marriage and the Family: A Study of Changing Japanese Attitudes.* Tokyo: International Christian University, 1958.

Bae, Catherine. "Girl Meets Boy Meets Girl: Heterosocial Relations, Wholesome Youth, and Democracy in Postwar Japan." *Asian Studies Review* 32, no. 3 (2008): 341–60.

Bailey, Beth. *From Front Porch to Back Seat: Courtship in Twentieth Century America.* Baltimore: Johns Hopkins University Press, 1989.

Bardsley, Jan. "Discourse on Women in Postwar Japan: The Housewife Debate of 1955." *US-Japan Women's Journal English Supplement* no. 16 (1999): 3–47.

———. "Purchasing Power in Japanese Popular Culture." *Journal of Popular Culture* 31, no. 2 (1997): 1–22.

———. "What Women Want: *Fujin Kōron* Tells All in 1956." *US-Japan Women's Journal English Supplement* no. 19 (2000): 7–48.

Baskett, Michael. "Dying for a Laugh: Post 1945 Japanese Service Comedies." *Historical Journal of Film, Radio and Television Studies* 23, no. 4 (2003): 291–310.

Beardsley, Richard, John Hall, and Robert Ward. *Village Japan.* Chicago: University of Chicago Press, 1959.

Beech, Keyes. "Tokyo Audience Cheers 'Mikado.'" *Los Angeles Times*, January 30 (1948): 6.

Beer, Lawrence. *Freedom of Expression in Japan: A Study in Comparative Law, Politics, and Society.* Tokyo: Kodansha International, 1984.

Bennett, John. *Doing Photography and Social Research in the Allied Occupation of Japan 1945–52: A Personal and Professional Memoir.* Ohio State University Library. Online, accessed May 14, 2011: http://library.osu.edu/projects/bennett-in-japan/about.html.

Berube, Alan. *Coming Out under Fire: The History of Gay Men and Women in WWII.* New York: Free Press, 1990.

Blacker, C. P. "Japan's Population Problem." *The Eugenics Review* 48, no. 1 (1956): 31–39.

Blood, Robert. *Love Match and Arranged Marriage.* New York: The Free Press, 1967.

Bonbon Shigeo. "Seppun no rekishi shōzen (The history of kissing continued)." *Hentai shiryō*, November (1927): 84–106.

Bourdieu, Pierre. "Belief and the Body." In *The Body: A Reader*, edited by Mariam Fraser and Monica Greco. London: Routledge (2006): 87–91.

———. *Outline of a Theory of Practice.* Cambridge: Cambridge University Press, 1977.

Bullough, Vern. *Science in the Bedroom: A History of Sex Research.* New York: Basic Books, 1994.

Burkman, Thomas, ed. *The Occupation of Japan: Arts and Culture*. Norfolk, VA: General Douglas MacArthur Foundation, 1988.

Canaday, Margot. "'Who Is a Homosexual?' The Consolidation of Sexual Identities in Mid-Twentieth Century American Immigration Law." *Law and Social Inquiry* 28, no. 2 (2003): 351–86.

Cather, Kirsten. *The Great Censorship Trials of Literature and Film in Postwar Japan, 1950–1983*. PhD Thesis, University of California, Berkeley, 2004.

Chapman, Ralph. "Japan: Propaganda to Pornography." *Saturday Review of Literature*, no. 31, July 31 (1948): 8–9, 34.

Chauncey, George. *Gay New York: Gender, Urban Culture, and the Making of the Gay Male World, 1890–1940*. New York: Basic Books, 1995.

Chicago Defender (The). "Japan Bans Movie Kissing: 120,000 Feet of American Films Edited Out by Censor." September 3 (1921): 6.

Cohen, Theodore. *Remaking Japan: The American Deal as New Deal*. New York: The Free Press, 1987.

Coox, Alvin. "The Japanese Army Experience." In *New Dimensions in Military History*, edited by Russell Weighley. San Rafael: Presidio Press (1975): 125–51.

Costello, John. *Virtue under Fire: How WWII Changed Our Social and Sexual Attitudes*. Boston: Little, Brown and Company, 1985.

Coughlin, William. *Conquered Press: The MacArthur Era in Japanese Journalism*. Palo Alto: Pacific Books, 1952.

Coutts, Angela. "*Meshi* by Hayashi Fumiko: Using the Domestic to Explore Gendered Concepts of National Identity." *National Identities* 7, no. 2, (2005): 133–49.

Crockett, Lucy Herndon. *Popcorn on the Ginza: An Informal Portrait of Postwar Japan*. London: Victor Gollancz, 1949.

Curran, Beverly, and James Welker. "From the *Well of Loneliness* to the *Akarui Rezubian*: Western Translations and Japanese Lesbian Identities." In *Genders, Transgenders and Sexualities in Japan*, edited by Mark McLelland and Romit Dasgupta. London: Routledge (2005): 65–80.

Dai ni ji shin seikatsu kenkyūkai hensanbu hen. "Nihonjin no 'hatsutaiken' ni kan suru sedai betsu ankēto chōsa (Questionnaire research concerning generational differences in Japanese people's 'first sexual experiences')." *Sei seikatsu hōkoku*, August (1982): 28–42.

Dalby, Liza. *Geisha*. Berkeley: University of California Press, 1998.

Doi Takeo. *Amae no kōzō* (Anatomy of dependence), 2nd edition. Tokyo: Kōbundō, 1985.

Dollase, Hiromi. "Girls on the Homefront: The Examination of *Shōjo no tomo* 1938–1945." *Asian Studies Review* 32, no. 4 (2008): 323–99.

Domenig, Roland. "A History of Sex Education Films in Japan, Part 1: The Pre-War Years." *Midnight Eye*, December 2006. Online accessed February 17, 2011: http://www.midnighteye.com/features/a-history-of-sex-education-films-in-japan-part-1.shtml.

———. "A History of Sex Education Films in Japan, Part 2: The Post-War Years and *Basukon Eiga*." *Midnight Eye*, March 2007. Online accessed February 17, 2011: http://www.midnighteye.com/features/a-history-of-sex-education-films-in-japan-part-2.shtml.

———. "A History of Sex Education Films in Japan, Part 3: The Seiten Films." *Midnight Eye*, August 2009. Online accessed February 17, 2011: http://www.midnighteye.com/features/a-history-of-sex-education-films-in-japan-part-3.shtml.

Dore, Ronald. *City Life in Japan: A Study of a Tokyo Ward*. Richmond, UK: Japan Library, 1999, [1958].

Dower, John. *Embracing Defeat: Japan in the Wake of World War II*. New York: W. W. Norton, 1999.

Drea, Edward. "In the Army Barracks of Imperial Japan." *Armed Forces and Society* 15, no. 3 (1989): 329–48.

———. *In the Service of the Emperor: Essays on the Imperial Japanese Army*. Lincoln: University of Nebraska Press, 1998.

Driscoll, Mark. *Absolute Erotic, Absolute Grotesque: The Living, Dead, and Undead in Japan's Imperialism 1895–1945*. Durham: Duke University Press, 2010.

Ekkusu. "Danshō geki jiken no shinsō (The truth about the male-prostitution play incident)." June (1949): 7.

Erochika. "Takahashi Tetsu tokushū (Takahashi Tetsu special edition)." Tokyo: Mitsuzaki shobō, June 1972.

Etō Jun. "One Aspect of the Allied Occupation of Japan: The Censorship Operation and Post-War Japanese Literature." *Occasional Paper, East Asia Program*, The Wilson Center, Washington, D.C., 1980.

Finn, Dallas. "Reform and Japanese Higher Education." *Far Eastern Survey* 20, no. 20 (1951): 201–06.

Foucault, Michel. *History of Sexuality*, vol. 1. New York: Vintage, 1976.

Franklyn, Frederic. "Sexual Freedom in Japanese Cinema." *Transition* 34 (1968): 55–62.

Freedman, Alisa. *Tokyo in Transit: Japanese Culture on the Rails and Road*. Stanford: Stanford University Press, 2011.

Friman, Richard. "The Impact of the Occupation on Crime in Japan." In *Democracy in Occupied Japan: The U.S. Occupation and Japanese Politics and Society*, edited by Mark Caprio and Yoneyuki Sugita. London: Routledge, 2007.

Fruhstuck, Sabine. "Male Anxieties: Nerve Force, Nation and the Power of Knowledge." *Journal of the Royal Asiatic Society* 15, no. 1 (2005): 71–85.

Fruhstuck, Sabine. *Colonizing Sex: Sexology and Social Control in Modern Japan*. Berkeley: University of California Press, 2003.

Fūfu no sei seikatsu. "Danshō no mon (Gateway to male prostitutes)." August (1949): 44–47.

Fūfu seikatsu. "Otto to tsuma ga tagai ni ikō (Things husbands and wives can do together)." January (1952): 204–14.

———. "Semai ie taizuru fūfu no sei seikatsu dō shitari ii ka? (What to do about the sex lives of couples staying in small homes?)" October (1949): 80–85.

———. "Tokushū: Eiga ni arawareta fūfu no aijō to tekkuniku (Special feature: conjugal couples' love techniques as expressed in the movies)." June (1954): 86–102.

———. "Tokushū: fūfu no nenrei to sei seikatsu (Special edition: age and the sex lives of couples)." December (1949): 11–21.

———. "Tokushū: sei no waka kaeri (Special edition: rejuvenating sex)." October (1949): 9–17.

———. "Tsuma ga otto ni kōshite hoshii seiai gikō 25 (25 sexual love techniques that wives want their husbands to do)." September (1952): 20–44.

Fujiki Tadashi. "Gakubuchi no shō (Picture frame shows)." *Sei media 50 nen.* Tokyo: Takarajimasha (1995): 37–47.

Fujin asahi. "Kinzei hakase no shinsho: onna no sei seikatsu no juyōten (Dr. Kinsey's new book: the main points concerning women's sex lives)." October (1953): 34–40.

———. "Kono goro no gakusei ren'ai to kekkon (Love and marriage among today's students)." July (1953): 84–89.

Fujitani Takashi. *Splendid Monarchy: Power and Pageantry in Modern Japan.* Berkeley: University of California Press, 1996.

Fujitani, T., Geoffrey White, and Lisa Yoneyama, eds. *Perilous Memories: The Asia-Pacific War(s).* Durham: Duke University Press, 2001.

Fukuoka Takeo. "Eigakan ni okeru abekku no seitai (Lifestyles of couples in the movie theater)." *Chūō kōron*, December (1950): 162–67.

———. *Kinzei hōkoku to Nihon josei no sei kōdo* (The Kinsey report and the sex lives of Japanese women). Tokyo: Shunyōdō shoten, 1954.

———. *Sei no atarashii ninshiki to rinri* (New consciousness and morals of sex). Tokyo: Kasei kyōiku kyōkai, 1949.

———. *Sei no atarashii ninshiki to ronri: sei seikatsu tokuhon* (New sex consciousness and theory: a sexual lifestyle reader). Tokyo: Nihon shuppan haikyū kabushikigaisha, 1949.

Fukushima Jūrō. *Sengo zasshi no shuhen* (The environment of postwar magazines). Tokyo: Tsukuma shobō, 1987.

Fukushima Yoshiko. "To the Rhythm of Jazz: Enoken's Postwar Musical Comedies." In *Rising from the Flames: The Rebirth of Theater in Occupied Japan*, edited by Samuel Leiter. Lanham: Lexington Books (2009): 335–60.

Furuda Hisamitsu. "Bijin o umidasu denki no naryoku (The power of electricity that can give rise to a beautiful woman)." *Fūfu seikatsu*, July (1950): 86–90.

Furuda Kenkichi. "Gaitō abekku sanpuru (Street couple sample)." *Raburii*, May (1948): 29–30.

Furukawa Sumio. "Ero hoteru no naimaku o nozoku (Peeping inside love hotels)." *Shinsō jitsuwa*, June (1949): 74–81.

Furuzawa Nobuō. "Donna nyūbō ga risōteki ka? (What kind of breasts are ideal?)." *Fūfu seikatsu*, July (1950): 124–26.

Gagnon, John, and William Simon. *Sexual Conduct: The Social Sources of Human Sexuality.* London: Hutchinson, 1973.

Garon, Sheldon. *Molding Japanese Minds: The State in Everyday Life.* Princeton, NJ: Princeton University Press, 1997.

———. "State and Family in Modern Japan: A Historical Perspective." *Economy and Society* 39, no. 3 (2010): 317–36.

Gekkan Yomiuri. "Danshō wa kataru: saka sama jinsei zadankai (Male prostitutes talking: a roundtable about upside-down lives)." October (1950): 53–57.

Giddens, Anthony. *Modernity and Self Identity: Self and Society in the Late Modern Age.* Cambridge: Polity Press, 1991.

Giles, Geoffrey. "The Denial of Homosexuality: Same-Sex Incidents in Himmler's SS and Police." *Journal of the History of Sexuality* 11, nos. 1/2 (2002): 256–90.

Gluck, Carol. "The 'End' of the Postwar: Japan at the Turn of the Millennium." *Public Culture* 10, no. 1 (1997): 1–23.

Goda Tadashi. "Seikōi to shakaiaku: seikō wa akugyō de wa nai (The sexual act and social evil: sexual acts are not wicked)." *Sūing,* December (1947): 11.

Gordon, Andrew. "Managing the Japanese Household: The New Life Movement in Postwar Japan." *Social Politics* 4, no. 2 (1997): 245–83.

Habuto Eiji. "Seppun to baidoku (Kissing and syphilis)." *Hentai shiryō*, August (1927): 2–12.

Hamakawa Takashi. "Danshō no rekishi (A history of male prostitution)." *Jitsuwa no izumi*, September (1949): 40–41.

Hanzai yomimono. "Hentai chōsho kakusakubōi no maki satsu no miryoku (Perverse notes: the cock-suck boy and the attraction of money)." October (1947): 20–21.

Hasegawa Ryū, and Takagi Takeo. "Senzen sengo ero sesō ōdan (Cross-section of pre- and postwar erotic conditions." *Amatoria* (1953): 159–63.

Hasegawa Takuya. *Waisetsu shuppan no rekishi* (History of obscene publications). Tokyo: Sanichi shobō, 1978.

Hashimoto Yorimitsu. "Japanese Tea Party: Representations of Victorian Paradise and Playground in *The Geisha.*" In *Histories of Tourism: Representation, Identity and Conflict*, edited by John Walton. Clevedon, UK: Channelview Publications (2005): 104–24.

Haste, Kate. *Rules of Desire: Sex in Britain: World War 1 to the Present.* London: Chatto & Windus, 1992.

Hastings, Sally. "A Dinner Party Is Not a Revolution: Space, Gender and Hierarchy in Meiji Japan." *US-Japan Women's Journal English Supplement*, no. 18 (2000): 107–32.

Havens, Thomas. *Valley of Darkness: The Japanese People and WWII.* Lanham: University Press of America, 1986.

Hayakawa Tetsuo. "Shōjo kibun nagetobasu onna (The strange story of a girl and a woman who was cast aside)." *Kibatsu zasshi*, June (1949): 18–22.

Hayashi Fusao. "Shin 'ren'ai no michi' Korontai fūjin no ren'ai kan (The new 'way of love,' Alexandra Kollontai's perspective). *Chūō kōron*, July (1928): 25–40.

Hayashi Fuyuko. "Kissu arabesuku (Kiss arabesque)." *Amatoria*, November (1952): 62–64.

Heibon panchi, "TPO ga aru: kissu ni wa 12 tōri (Time, place and occasion: 12 ways of kissing)." August 8 (1966): 16–22.

Hicks, George. "The 'Comfort Women.'" In *The Japanese Wartime Empire 1931–1945*, edited by Peter Duus. Princeton, NJ: Princeton University Press, 1996.

High, Peter. "The Dawn of Cinema in Japan." *Journal of Contemporary History* 19, no. 1 (1984): 23–57.

———. *The Imperial Screen: Japanese Film Culture in the Fifteen Years' War.* Madison, WI: University of Wisconsin Press, 2003.

Higuma Kan. "Danshō no mori (Grove of male prostitutes). *Jitsuwa to shōsetsu*, April (1949): 4.

Hillenbrand, Margaret. "Doppelgangers, Misogyny, and the San Francisco System: The Occupation Narratives of Ōe Kenzaburō." *Journal of Japanese Studies* 33, no. 2 (2007): 383–414.

Hirakawa Jun. "Joshi dōseiai saffuisuto no kenkyū (Female same-sex love research: a study of sapphists)." *Bēze*, August (1948): 12–13.

———. "Joshi dōseiai toribādo no kenkyū (Female same-sex love research: a study of tribades)." *Bēze*, July (1948): 16–17.

Hirano Kyōko. *Mr. Smith Goes to Tokyo: Japanese Cinema under the American Occupation, 1945–1952*. Washington, D.C.: Smithsonian Institution Press, 1992.

———. *Tennō to seppun* (The emperor and the kiss). Tokyo: Sōshisha, 1998.

Hirano Toshi. "Gunpuku no danshō-tachi (Male prostitutes in military uniform)." *Shinsō jitsuwa*, May (1949): 114–17.

Hoberecht, Ernest. "Yank Tutors Jap Actress in Kissing." *The Washington Post*, March 30 (1946): 9.

Homei Aya. "Giving Birth to a Rich Nation and Strong Soldiers: Midwives and Nation Building in Japan between the Meiji Period and the 1940s." A paper for the *Joint Princeton-Columbia Graduate Student Workshop* (National Identity and Public Policy in Comparative Perspective) Princeton, September 29–October 1, 2000.

Honshi Chōsabu. "Danshō no ijō seiai chōsa (Research into the abnormal sexual love of male prostitutes)." *Kitan kurabu*, May (1954): 92–98.

Horii Shōgo. "Kagema yashiki (Male prostitute dwelling)." *Bēze*, July (1947): 40–44.

Hoshino Ikumi. "Apartment Life in Japan." *Journal of Marriage and the Family* 26, (1964): 312–17.

Hulse, Frederick. "Some Effects of the War on Japanese Society." *The Far Eastern Quarterly* 7, no. 1 (1947): 22–42.

Idditie Junesay. *When Two Cultures Meet: Sketches of Postwar Japan, 1945–1955*. Tokyo: Kenkyusha, 1955.

Iga Mamoru. "Sociocultural Factors in Japanese Prostitution and the 'Prostitution Prevention Law.'" *The Journal of Sex Research* 4, no. 2 (1968): 127–46.

Igarashi Yoshikuni. *Narratives of War in Postwar Japanese Culture, 1945–1970*. Princeton, NJ: Princeton University Press, 2000.

Ike Nobutaka. "Birth Control in Japan." *Far Eastern Survey* 17, no. 23 (1948): 271–74.

Ikeda Michiko. "Dai san no sei (The third sex)." *Bungei*, November (1953): 50–65.

———. "Tsuma no taion (A wife's body temperature)." *Fūfu seikatsu*, December (1949): 192–202.

Inoue Shōichi. "Ecchi to esuemu (H and SM)." In *Sei no yōgo shū*, edited by Inoue Shōichi and Kansai Seiyoku Kenkyū Kai. Tokyo: Kōdansha gendai shinshō (2004): 37–44.

Iritani Toshio. *Group Psychology of the Japanese in Wartime*. London and New York: Kegan Paul International, 1991.

Iryo Sakiko. "'Seppun' go-shi: Kirisuto-kyō yōgo no shiten kara no zai kōchiku (History of the word 'kiss': reconstruction from the perspective of Christian usage)." *Kokubungaku Kai Bulletin Paper*. Kyushu University Institutional Repository, 2007.

Isehara Jirō. "Hito ke mo matowanu: watashi tachi no yoru no tengoku (Our heavenly nights spent without a stitch on)." *Fūfu seikatsu*, October (1949): 76.

Ishida Hitoshi, Mark McLelland, and Takanori Murakami. "The Origins of 'Queer Studies' in Japan." In *Genders, Transgenders and Sexualites in Japan*, edited by Mark McLelland and Romit Dasgupta. London: Routledge (2005): 33–48.

Ishida Hitoshi and Takanori Murakami. "The Process of Divergence between 'Men who Love Men' and 'Feminised Men' in Postwar Japanese Media." *Intersections: Gender and Sexuality in the Asia Pacific* 12, 2006, online accessed May 14, 2011: http://intersections.anu.edu.au/issue12_contents.html.

Ishikawa Hiroshi, ed. *Nihon fūzoku jiten: Amerikan karuchā* vol. 1 (Dictionary of Japanese customs: American culture, vol. 1). Tokyo: Sanseidō, 1981.

Ishikawa Hiroyoshi. "*Kanzen naru kekkon* kara *HOW TO SEX* e no sengo shi (A postwar history from *Perfect Marriage* to *How to Sex*)." *Kurowassan*, July (1977): 113–15.

Ishikawa Jun. "Ren'ai ni tsuite (On romantic love)." In *Shōwa hihyō taikei* vol. 3, edited by Endō Sasuke. Tokyo: Banmachi Shobō, 1968 [1951]: 277–87.

Ishinaka Masafumi. "Shinkon nikki no tsukekata (How to write a newlywed diary)." *Kōdan hiwa*, November (1952): 63–68.

Itō Chizuko. "Seikan hattatsu kō (Thoughts on the progress of sexual feelings)." *Amatoria*, October (1952): 28–44.

Ivy, Marilyn. "Formations of Mass Culture." In *Postwar Japan as History*, edited by Andrew Gordon. Berkeley: University of California Press (1993): 239–58.

Iwabuchi Akitaka. "Sekai junbō meguri (A tour of the world's bedchambers)." *Fūzoku kagaku*, December (1954): 30–37.

Iwamoto Yoshio. "Ōe Kenzaburō's *Warera no jidai* (Our Generation): Sex, Power and the Other in Occupied Japan." *World Literature Today* 76, no. 1 (2002): 43–51.

Izbicki, Joanne. *Scorched Cityscapes and Silver Screens: Negotiating Defeat and Democracy through Cinema in Occupied Japan*. PhD Thesis, Cornell University, 1997.

Japan Times. "Yanagisawa Apologizes Anew." February 8 (2007), online accessed May 11, 2011: http://search.japantimes.co.jp/cgi-bin/nn20070208a2.html/.

Johnson, Sheila. *The Japanese through American Eyes*. Stanford: Stanford University Press, 1991.

Johnston, William. *Geisha, Harlot, Strangler, Star: A Woman, Sex, and Morality in Modern Japan*. New York: Columbia University Press, 2005.

Josei raifu. "Zadankai: Kekkon nan to sei ai (Roundtable: marital problems and sexual love." January (1949): 18–23.

Kabiya Kazuhiko. *Yoru no itansha* (Heretics of the night). Tokyo: Nanōsha.

Kamei Shunsuke. "The Kiss and Japanese Culture after World War II." *Comparative Literature Studies* 18, no. 2 (1981): 114–24.

Kanzaki Kiyoshi. *Ketteihan: Kanzaki repōto baishun* (The Kanzaki report on prostitution). Tokyo: Gendaishi shuppankai, 1974.

Karlin, Jason. "The Gender of Nationalism: Competing Masculinities in Meiji Japan." *Journal of Japanese Studies* 28, no. 1 (2002): 41–77.

Kasza, Gregory. *The State and the Mass Media in Japan, 1918–1945*. Berkeley: University of California Press, 1988.

Kawamura Kunimitsu, and Takeda Shōgo. "Kindai Nippon no sekusu zō ikani umaretaka (When did Modern Japan's image of sex arise?)." *Sei media 50 nen*. Tokyo: Takarajimasha (1995): 233–41.

Kawashima Takeyoshi. *Kekkon* (Marriage). Tokyo: Iwanami shōten, 1954.

Kawashima Takeyoshi, ed. *Gendai kazoku kōza*, vol. 1, *atarashii kazoku* (Contemporary marriage lectures, vol. 1, the new family). Tokyo: Kawade shobō, 1956.

———. *Gendai kazoku kōza*, vol. 2, *kekkon e no michi* (Contemporary marriage lectures, vol. 2, the road to marriage). Tokyo: Kawade shobō, 1956.

Keene, Donald. *Dawn to the West: Japanese Literature in the Modern Era*. New York: Henry Holt, 1984.

Kelsky, Karen. *Women on the Verge: Japanese Women, Western Dreams*. Durham: Duke University Press.

Kitagawa Chiyomi. "H taisa fūjin (Mrs. Captain H)." *Ryōki*, December (1946): 40–49.

Kitamura Hiroshi. *Screening Enlightenment: Hollywood and the Cultural Reconstruction of Defeated Japan*. Ithaca, NY: Cornell University Press, 2010.

Kiwa Kōtarō. "Rabu shiin manwa (Discussing love scenes)." *Eiga yomimono* 2, no. 5 (1948): 18–20.

Kogure Kenji. "Onna demo otoko demo nai danshō dekameron (Neither women nor men: a male prostitute *Decameron*)." *Kibatsu kenkyū*, August (1952): 22–30.

Koikari Mire. *Pedagogy of Democracy: Feminism and the Cold War in the US Occupation of Japan*. Philadelphia: Temple University Press, 2008.

———. "Rethinking Gender and Power in the US Occupation of Japan 1945–1952." *Gender and History* 11, no. 2 (1999): 313–35.

Koito Nobu. "Dōseiai monogatari (A homosexual love story)." *Bara*, August (1948): 20–21.

Kokugo kitan zasshi. "Tokushū sono ni kōshoku no buaraieti kidanza hatsunatsu kōgyō (Special edition part 2: an early summer special of colorful stories about the varieties of love)." June (1949): 13–16.

Kōno Kensuke. "Hihyō to jitsuzon: sengo hihyō ni okeru sekushuariti (Criticism and existence: postwar criticism and sexuality)." *Kokubungaku kaishaku to kyōzai no kenkyū* 40, no. 8 (1995): 44–51.

Korekushon modan toshi bunka. *Manga*, vol. 39, Tokyo: Yumanishobō, 2008.

Koschman, Victor. "Intellectuals and Politics." In *Postwar Japan as History*, edited by Andrew Gordon. Berkeley: University of California Press (1993): 395–423.

———. *Revolution and Subjectivity in Postwar Japan*, Chicago: University of Chicago Press, 1996.

Koshiro Yukiko. *Trans-Pacific Racisms and the U.S. Occupation of Japan*. New York: Columbia University Press, 1999.

Kovner, Sarah. "Base Cultures: Sex Workers and Servicemen in Occupied Japan." *Journal of Asian Studies* 68, no. 3 (2009): 777–804.

———. *Prostitution in Postwar Japan: Sex Workers, Servicemen, and Social Activists, 1945–1956*. PhD Thesis, Columbia University, 2004.

Kuno Yoshi. "Life in Japan." *The Journal of Race Development* 6, no. 2 (1915): 192–202.

Kurumada Kingo. "Tōkyō okama (danshō) kumiai tanbōki (A journalistic investigation of Tokyo faggots (male prostitutes)." *Bakuro*, July (1949): 35–38.

Kuryu Takeo. "Gendai no ren'ai (Contemporary romantic love)." *Chūō kōron*, November (1935): 50–66.

Kushner, Barak. *The Thought War: Japanese Imperial Propaganda*. Honolulu: University of Hawaii Press.

Leiter, Samuel. "From Bombs to Booms: When the Occupation Met Kabuki." In *Rising from the Flames: The Rebirth of Theater in Occupied Japan, 1945–1952*, edited by Samuel Leiter. Lanham: Lexington Press (2009): 11–74.

———. "Performing the Emperor's New Clothes: *The Mikado, The Tale of Genji* and Lese Majeste on the Japanese Stage." In *Rising from the Flames: The Rebirth of Theater in Occupied Japan, 1945–1952*, edited by Samuel Leiter. Lanham: Lexington Press (2009): 125–74.

Leupp, Gary. *Interracial Intimacy in Japan: Western Men and Japanese Women 1543–1900*. New York: Continuum, 2003.

Low, Morris. "The Emperor's Sons Go to War: Competing Masculinities in Modern Japan." In *Asian Masculinities: The Meaning and Practice of Manhood in China and Japan*, edited by Kam Louie and Morris Low. London: RoutledgeCurzon (2003): 81–99.

Luther, Catherine, and Douglas Boyd. "American Occupation Control over Broadcasting in Japan 1945–52." *Journal of Communication* 47 (1997): 39–59.

McLelland, Mark. "A Short History of *Hentai*." *Intersections: Gender and Sexuality in Asia and the Pacific* no. 12, 2006. Online accessed February 11, 2011: http://intersections.anu.edu.au/issue12_contents.html.

———. "From Sailor-Suits to Sadists: Lesbos Love as Reflected in Japan's Postwar 'Perverse Press.'" *U.S.-Japan Women's Journal* 27 (2004): 27–50.

———. *Queer Japan from the Pacific War to the Internet Age*. Lanham: Rowman and Littlefield, 2005.

McLelland, Mark, Katsuhiko Suganuma, and James Welker, eds. *Queer Voices from Japan: First-Person Narratives from Japan's Sexual Minorities*. Lanham: Lexington, 2007.

McLelland, Mark, and Romit Dasgupta, eds. *Genders, Transgenders and Sexualites in Japan*. London: Routledge, 2005.

Mainichi shimbun. "'Yoru no otoko' no shūdan bōkō: keishi sōkan nagurareru (Group violence by 'men of the night': police superintendent is struck)." November 23, 1948.

Mainichi shimbunsha, ed. *Shōwa mangashi* (Shōwa manga history). Tokyo: Mainichi shimbunsha, 1977.

Manchester, William. *American Caesar: Douglas MacArthur 1880–1964*. Melbourne: Huchinson, 1978.

Markell Morantz, Regina. "The Scientist as Sex Crusader: Alfred C. Kinsey and American Culture." *American Quarterly* 29, no. 5 (1977): 563–89.

Marran, Christine. "*From Pathography to Pulp: Popular Expressions of Female Deviancy, 1930–1950*." In *A Century of Popular Culture in Japan*, edited by Douglas Slaymaker. New York: Mellen Press (2000): 45–69.

———. *Poison Woman: Figuring Female Transgression in Modern Japanese Culture*. Minneapolis: University of Minnesota Press, 2007.

Martin, Fran. *Situating Sexualities: Queer Representations in Taiwanese Fiction, Film and Public Culture*. Hong Kong: Hong Kong University Press, 2003.

Maruki Sado. "Seppun (Kissing)." *Chūō kōron*, January (1929): 179–95.

Matsuba Jūsaburō. "Amerika no eiga no janru (American movie genres)." *Shinema gurafikku*, 3 (1947): 7.

Matsumoto, Yoshiharu Scott. *Contemporary Japan: The Individual and the Group*. Philadelphia: The American Philosophical Society, 1960.

Matsuura Sōzō. *Matsuura Sōzō no shigoto*, vol. 2, *senchū, senryōka no masukomi* (Matsuura Sōzō's works, vol. 2, mass communications during wartime and the occupation). Tokyo: Ōtsukishoten, 1984.

———. "Minshuteki eigajin to hōsōjin e no danatsu (Repression of democratic film and broadcast personnel)." In *Senryōka no genron danatsu*, Matsuura Sōzō. Tokyo: Gendai jyānarizumu shuppansha (1969): 157–253.

———. *Senchū, senryōka no masukomi* (Mass communications during the war and Occupation). Tokyo: Ōtsukisha, 1984.

Matsuzawa Kureichi. "Kasutori zasshi to 'Garo' no Nagai-san (The kasutori press and 'Garo's' Mr Nagai)." *Sei media 50 nen*. Tokyo: Takarajimasha (1995): 23–31.

Mauss, Marcel. "Techniques of the Body." In *The Body: A Reader*, edited by Mariam Fraser and Monica Greco. London: Routledge (2006): 73–77.

Mayo, Marlene. "Literary Reorientation in Occupied Japan: Incidents of Civil Censorship." In *Legacies and Ambiguities: Postwar Fiction and Culture in West Germany and Japan*, edited by Ernestine Schlant and J. Thomas Rimer. Washington, D.C.: Woodrow Wilson Center Press (1991): 135–62.

Mayo, Marlene J., Thomas Rimer, and H. Eleanor Kerkham, eds. *War, Occupation, and Creativity: Japan and East Asia 1920–1960*. Honolulu: University of Hawaii Press, 2001.

Mead, Margaret. *The American Troops and the British Community: An Examination of the Relationship between the American Troops and the British*. St. Albans: Fisher, Knight & Co., 1944.

Micheler, Stefan. "Homophobic Propaganda and the Denunciation of Same-Sex Desiring Men under National Socialism." *Journal of the History of Sexuality* 11, nos. 1/2 (2002): 95–130.

Miller, Laura. *Beauty Up: Exploring Contemporary Japanese Body Aesthetics*. Berkeley: University of California Press, 2006.

Mitchell, Richard. *Censorship in Imperial Japan*. Princeton, NJ: Princeton University Press, 1983.

———. *Thought Control in Prewar Japan*. Ithaca, NY: Cornell University Press, 1976.

Minami Takao. "Danshō ni kan suru no ni san seishin igaku teki kōsatsu (A consideration of male prostitutes from two or three perspectives of medical psychology)." *Shinsatsu daijesuto*, July (1948): 18–24.

Mishima Sumie Seo. *The Broader Way: A Woman's Life in the New Japan*. New York: John Day Co., 1953.

Mishima Yukio. *Confessions of a Mask*. Translated by Meredith Weatherby. Tokyo: Charles Tuttle Inc., 1970.

Misushu Akira. "Onna ni haru o utta otoko (Men who sell sex to women)." *Ningen tankyū*, October (1951): 46–49.

Mitsuhashi Junko. "Okama." In *Sei no yōgo shū* edited by Inoue Shōichi and Kansai Seiyoku Kenkyū Kai. Tokyo: Kōdansha gendai shinshō (2004): 111–18.

Mitsuishi Ayumi. "Otome." In *Sei no yōgo shū* edited by Inoue Shōichi and Kansai Seiyoku Kenkyū Kai. Tokyo: Kōdansha gendai shinshō (2004): 72–82.

Miyanaga Shizuo. "Ōchō kōshoku kokkei tan (Humorous tales of dynastic lust)." *Ryōki*, December (1946): 24–27.

Miyata Shigeo. "Atarashii sei seikatsu kōza: fūfukan no seiteki fuman o dō suru? (New sex life seminar: what to do about sexual dissatisfaction between couples?)" *Fujo kai*, September (1949): 28–30.

Mochizuki Mamoru. "Sengo ni okeru sei seikatsu no tenbō (Observing postwar sex lives)." *Sandē mainichi*, June 26 (1949): 3.

Modan fūfu tokuhon. "Tokushō: Shigekitekina sei ai gikō (Special edition: stimulating sexual love techniques)." June (1952): 65–79.

Molasky, Michael S. *The American Occupation of Japan and Okinawa: Literature and Memory*. New York: Routledge, 2001.

Mon Kōtarō. "Ryōki yobanashi: danshō (A night tale of curiosity hunting: male prostitutes)." *Bēze*, October (1949): 22–23.

Morihara Taichi. "Waga guntai jidai no kaiko: dansei nūdo to seme shashin ni tsuite (Reflections on my time in the army: concerning male nudity and sadistic photographs)." *Kitan kurabu*, March (1953): 94–97.

Moriya Sōzō. "Danshō no seitai (Male prostitute lifestyles)." *Bungei yomimono*, February (1949): unpaginated photo section.

Morris, John. *The Phoenix Cup: Some Notes on Japan in 1946*. London: Cresset Press, 1947.

Morton, Leith. "The Concept of Romantic Love in the *Taiyō* Magazine 1895–1905." *Japan Review*, no. 8 (79–103).

Murata Ichirō. "Nami o oyogu pan pan bōi (The pan pan boys who swim in the black market)." *Surirā*, January (1948): 27–28.

Murata Toshiko. "Dōsei no koi (Same-sex love)." *Chūō kōron* 28, no. 1 (1913): 165–68.

Muto Unjuro. "Democracy and Chastity." Submission to the collection "Japan Looks Back on the Occupation" by Victor Otake and Douglas Haring. *Far Eastern Survey* 22, no. 3 (1953): 26–32.

Nagae Akira. "Adaruto-kei shuppansha no rūtsu o sagase (Looking for the roots of adult publishing houses)." *Sei media 50 nen*. Tokyo: Takarajimasha (1995): 11–22.

Nakajima, Sei. "Nenrei sa no tadashii fūfu no sei seikatsu (Proper sex life for couples according to age)." *Fūfu seikatsu*, December (1949): 22–23.

Nakamura Mitsuo. "Senryōka no bungaku (Literature under occupation)." In *Shōwa hihyō taikei*, vol. 3, edited by Endō Sasuke. Tokyo: Banmachi Shobō, 1968 [1952]: 305–13.

Nakamura Shigeki. *Kindai teikoku Nihon no sekushuariti* (Recent imperial Japan and sexuality). Tokyo: Akashi shoten, 2004.

Nakano Eizō. "Dōseiai hiyaku: To ichi ha ichi (*To ichi ha ichi*: a homosexual secret)." *Amatoria*, December (1953): 61–65.

———. "Seppun tsuya goroku (A glossary of sayings about kissing)." *Amatoria*, September (1953): 22–35.

———. "Seppun no gogen (The etymology of kiss)." *Ningen tankyū*, October (1950): 48.

Nanbu Kōichirō. "Sutā no seishun to kekkon to seiyoku (The adolescence, marriage and sexual desires of movie stars)." *Abekku*, July (1948): 36–38.

Nanri Hiroshi. "Danshō o tsuku (Poking at male prostitutes)." *Kitan kurabu*, January (1948): 12–14.

Narumigi Ichirō. "Sekkusu kaihō no ayumi: tenbō 1945–1953 (Steps toward sexual liberation: a perspective 1945–1953)." *Amatoria*, June (1953): 40–51.

Nihon seiteki fūzoku jiten (Dictionary of Japanese sexual customs). Tokyo: Bungei shiryō kenkyūkai, 1929.

Ningen tankyū. "Abekku kenkyū dai ikka (Couple research part 1)." August (1951): 77–80.

———. "Amerika no seiai sōdan (American sexual love advice)." November (1952): 106–11.

———. "Eiga (Movies)." June/July (1950): unpaginated section.

———. "Zadankai: Onna gakusei no seitai o tsuku (Roundtable: a discussion of the situation of female students)." March (1952): 66–77.

Nishi Toshio. *Unconditional Democracy: Education and Politics in Occupied Japan 1945–1952*. Stanford University: Hoover Institution Press, 1982.

Nomura Ayako. "Hana hiraku hatsu yoru (Opening the flower on the first night)." *Fūfu seikatsu*, September (1952): 128–33.

Norgren, Christiana. *Abortion before Birth Control: The Politics of Reproduction in Postwar Japan*. Princeton, NJ: Princeton University Press, 2001.

Ōba Masafumi. *Seppun*. Tokyo: Raifusha, 1958.

Ochi Hiromi. "What Did She Read? The Cultural Occupation of Post-War Japan and Translated Girls' Literature." *F-Gens Jyānaru* 5 (2006): 359–63.

Ogino Mie. "Kindai Nihon no sekushuariti to hinin (Modern Japanese sexuality and contraception)." *Joseigaku renzoku kōenkai* no. 11 (2006): 74–103. Online accessed May 11, 2011: http://hdl.handle.net/10466/10005.

Ohnuki-Tierney, Emiko. *Kamikaze: Cherry Blossoms, and Nationalisms*. Chicago: University of Chicago Press, 2002.

OK. "Danshō zadankai: mondai no kokuhaku (Male prostitute roundtable: confessions of a problem). August (1949): 6–12.

Oka Masahirō. "Ryōsei dōbutsu: danshoku yobanashi (Amphibious animals: a night tale about male eroticism)." *Kitan kurabu*, October (1953): 100–02.

Okamoto Shiro. *The Man who Saved Kabuki: Faubion Bowers and Theater Censorship in Occupied Japan*. Honolulu: University of Hawaii Press, 2001.

Omori Kyoko. *Detecting Japanese Vernacular Modernism: Shinseinen Magazine and the Development of the Tantei Shōsetsu Genre*. PhD diss., The Ohio State University, 2003.

Ōnishi Kōichi. "Ren'aigaku kōza: raburetā no kakikata ni tsuite (Romantic-love studies seminar: on how to write a love letter)." *Bēze*, December (1948): 31.

Onnasuki Hakase. "Ren'ai gakkōshitsu: ai suru mono no shinri ni tsuite (Romantic-love schoolroom: on the psychology of the lover)." *Bēze*, October (1948): 16.

Ono Jiyōtoku. *Angura Shōwashi* (Underground Showa history). Tokyo: Shūe shobō, 1981.

Osaki Shinzō. "Sei no shisō senkakusha: Takahashi Tetsu no baai (Pioneers of sexual philosophy: the case of Takahashi Tetsu)." *Shisō no kagaku* 77, July (1968): 58–61.

Ōta Tenrei. *Dai san no sei* (The third sex). Tokyo: Ningen no kagakusha, 1989 [1957].

Ōta Tenrei and Kabiya Kazuhiko. "Wakai sedai no sei ten: Pettingu wa ryūkō suru (Young generation sex dictionary: petting is a fad)." *Fūzoku kagaku*, March (1954): 79–83.

Ōtsuka Meiko. "The Dualism of Love and 'Wago' (Harmony) in Japanese Modern Family in the Pre-war Period." *Ningenkagaku kenkyū*, no. 26 (2004): 39–53.

Ōwada Kiyoshi. "Danshō o hadaka ni suru (Male prostitutes revealed)." *Shinsō to jitsuwa*, June (1946): 74–81.

Ōya Masatake. "Fūfu seiai tokuhon: hana kara mita sei seikatsu (Married couple sexual love reader: sex life from the perspective of the nose)." *Shin fūfu*, August (1949): 25–28.

Ōya Sōichi. "Ero guro nanasensu jidai (The erotic, grotesque nonsense period)." *Bungei shunjū rinzō*, July (1954): 64–69.

Pacific Stars & Stripes. "Delinquency Group Attempts Kissing Ban." May 25, 1948.

Park You-Me. "Comforting the Nation: 'Comfort Women': The Politics of Apology and the Workings of Gender." *Interventions* 2, no. 2 (2000): 199–211.

Pharr, Susan."The Politics of Women's Rights." In *Democratizing Japan: The Allied Occupation*, edited by Robert Ward and Yoshikazu Sakamoto. Honolulu: University of Hawaii Press (1987): 221–52.

Pratt, Mary Louise. "Arts of the Contact Zone." *Profession 91*, New York: MLA (1991): 33–40.

Procida, Richard, and Rita Simon. *Global Perspectives on Social Issues: Pornography*. Lanham MD: Lexington, 2007.

Reichert, Jim. *In the Company of Men: Representations of Male-Male Sexuality in Meiji Japan*. Stanford: Stanford University Press, 2006.

Report of Government Section Supreme Commander for the Allied Powers, *Appendices: Political Reorientation of Japan, September 1945 to September 1948*, vol. 2. US Government Printing Office: Washington, D.C., 1949.

Richie, Donald. "The Japanese Kiss." In *A Lateral View: Essays on Culture and Style in Contemporary Japan*, edited by Donald Richie. Berkeley: Stone Bridge Press, 1992.

Robertson, Jennifer. "Blood Talks: Eugenic Modernity and the Creation of New Japanese." *History and Anthropology* 13, no. 3 (2002): 191–216.

———. "Dying to Tell: Sexuality and Suicide in Imperial Japan." *Signs* 25, no. 1 (1999): 1–35.

———. "Japan's First Cyborg? Miss Nippon and Wartime Technologies of Beauty, Body and Blood." *Body and Society* 7, no. 1 (2001): 1–34.

———. *Takarazuka: Sexual Politics and Popular Culture in Modern Japan*. Berkeley: University of California Press, 1998.

Rubin, Jay. "From Wholesomeness to Decadence: The Censorship of Literature under the Allied Occupation." *Journal of Japanese Studies* 11, no. 1 (1985): 71–103.

———. "The Impact of the Occupation on Literature or Lady Chatterley and Lt. Col. Verness." In *The Occupation of Japan: Arts and Culture*, edited by Thomas W. Burkman. Norfolk, Virginia: General Douglas MacArthur Foundation (1988): 167–74.

Ruoff, Jeffrey, and Kenneth Ruoff. *The Emperor's Naked Army Marches On*. Trowbridge: Flick Books, 1998.

Ryang, Sonia. *Love in Modern Japan: Its Estrangement from Self, Sex and Society*. London: Routledge, 2006.

Saitō Hikaru. "Abekku wa kappuru ka? (Is *abekku* a couple?)" In *Sei no yōgo shū*, edited by Inoue Shōichi and Kansai Seiyoku Kenkyū Kai. Tokyo: Kōdansha gendai shinshō (2004): 176–84.

Sakai Kiyoshi. *Nihon kanrakukyō annai* (Guide to Japan's pleasure districts). Tokyo: Chikusui shobō, 1931.

Sakurai Rin and Kurosaka Yoshihiko. "Danna sama ga kapuri tsuku: utsukushii okusama no tanjō (Husbands getting greedy: the birth of a beautiful wife)." *Fūfu seikatsu*, January (1952): 131–38.

Sakurai Rōrando. "Kōshite nyūbō wa utsukushikunaru (This is how to make breasts beautiful)." *Fūfu seikatsu*, July (1950): 127–30.

Sandē Mainichi. "Nihonjin no sei kōdō gakuseihen (Japanese people's sexual activities: student edition)." October (1953): 3–11.

———. "Sei no tōsaku dai san otoko demo onna demo nai watashi tachi (Sexual perversion part 3: we who are neither men nor women)." October (1948): 24–25.

Sanders, Holly. *Prostitution in Postwar Japan: Debt and Labor*. PhD Thesis, Princeton University, 2005.

Sasama Yoshihiko. *Zuroku sei no Nihonshi* (An illustrated history of Japanese sex). Tokyo: Yūzankaku, 1996.

Sato, Barbara. "Contesting Consumerisms in Mass Women's Magazines." In *The Modern Girl around the World: Consumption, Modernity and Globalization*, edited by Alys Weinbaum, Lynn Thomas, and Priti Ramamurthy. Durham: Duke University Press (2008): 263–87.

Schaller, Michael. *The American Occupation of Japan: The Origins of the Cold War in Asia*. New York: Oxford University Press, 1985.

Schattschneider, Ellen. "The Bloodstained Doll: Violence and the Gift in Wartime Japan." *Journal of Japanese Studies* 31, no. 2 (2005): 329–56.

Schonberger, Howard B. *Aftermath of War: Americans and the Remaking of Japan, 1945–1952*. Kent: The Kent State University Press, 1989.

Scott, A. C. *The Flower and Willow World: The Story of the Geisha*. New York: Orion Press, 1960.

Sedgwick, Eve Kosofsky. *Epistemology of the Closet*. London: Penguin, 1990.

Seidensticker, Edward. *Tokyo Rising: The City since the Great Earthquake*. New York: Alfred Knopf, 1990.

Seishun romansu, "Kekkon hatsu yoru o kataru (Talking about the first night of marriage)." July (1949): 25–27.

Shakai tanbō. "Danshō bakari no zadankai ijō shinri to hentai seiyoku o kaibō (A roundtable of only male prostitutes: an analysis of perverse psychology and perverted desires)." April (1949): 32–37.

Shamoon, Deborah. "Misora Hibari and the Girl Star in Postwar Japanese Cinema." *Signs* 35, no. 1 (2009): 131–55.

Sherif, Ann. *Japan's Cold War: Media, Literature and the Law*. New York: Columbia University Press, 2009.

———. "The Politics of Loss: On Etō Jun." *Positions* 10, no. 1 (2001): 111–38.

Shibusawa Naoko. *America's Geisha Ally: Reimagining the Japanese Enemy*. Cambridge, MA: Harvard University Press, 2008.

Shibuya Tomomi. "*Dōtei* (Virginity)." In *Sei no yōgo shū*, edited by Inoue Shōichi and Kansai Seiyoku Kenkyū Kai. Tokyo: Kōdansha gendai shinshō (2004): 59–71.

———. *Nihon no dōtei* (Virginity in Japan). Tokyo: Bungei shunjū, 2003.

Shikita Minoru and Shinichi Tsuchiya. *Crime and Criminal Policy in Japan from 1926 to 1988: Analysis and Evaluation of the Showa Era*. Tokyo: Japan Criminal Policy Society, 1990.

Shimamura Teru, ed. *Korekushon modan toshi bunka dai 15 kan: Ero guro nansensu* (Modern city culture collection, vol. 15: erotic, grotesque nonsense). Tokyo: Yumanishobō, 2005.

Shimizu Akira. *Sensō to eiga senjichū to senryoka no nihon eiga-shi* (War and film: a history of Japanese film during the war and occupation). Tokyo: Shakai shisōsha.

Shimokawa Kōshi. "Gaitō no ero shashin uri wa doko ni kieta? (Where have the erotic photo street sellers gone?)." *Sei media 50 nen*. Tokyo: Takarajimasha (1995): 32–36.

———. *Nihon ero shashinshi* (History of Japan's erotic photographs). Tokyo: Shōkyūsha, 1995.

———. *Sei fūzoku nenpyō: Shōwa sengo 1945–1989* (A sexual customs almanac of the postwar period 1945–1989). Tokyo: Kawade shobō shinsha, 2007.

———. *Shōwa seisō shi: sengohen* vol. 1 (Showa history of sex: postwar collection, vol. 1), Tokyo: Dentō to gendaisha, 1980.

———. *Shōwa seisō shi: senzen, senchūhen* (Showa history of sex: prewar and wartime collection). Tokyo: Dentō to gendaisha, 1981.

Shimura Miyoko. "'Dai ni no seppun' arui wa 'Kyōko to Wako': ren'ai eiga no poritikusu ('The second kiss' or 'Kyōko and Wako': the politics of romance movies)." *Departmental Bulletin Paper 6*, Engeki kenkyū sentā, Waseda University (2006): 107–14.

Shin fūfu. "Sei ai kyōshitsu: seiyoku wa kenkō no kagi. Naze eiyū wa iro o okonomu ka? (Sexual love classroom: sexual desire is the key to health. Why is it that strong men like sex?)." August (1949): 53.

Shin jiyū. "Danshō no kokuhaku (Confessions of a male prostitute)." September (1949): 52.

Shin Young-sook and Cho Hye-ran. "On the Characteristics and Special Nature of the Korean 'Military Comfort Women' under Japanese Rule." *Korea Journal*, Spring (1996): 50–78.

Shinozaki Nobuo. *Nihonjin no sei seikatsu* (Japanese sex lives). Tokyo: Bungei shuppan, 1953.

Shinsō jitsuwa. "Onna gakusei no himitsu kokuhaku zadankai (A roundtable about the secret confessions of girl students)." July (1949): 38–51.

Shinsō shimbun, "Onna bakari de henshūshita ai no sekai (The world of love edited solely by women)." April 15 (1948): unpaginated.

Shioda Eijirō. "Kimi shiru ya danjo kyōgaku S gakuen tanbōki (What you need to know about co-education: a report on S campus)." *Modan Nippon*, July (1946): 42–45.

Shūkan asahi. "Ibu no subete: Kinzei hōkoku joseihan (All about Eve: the Kinsey report female edition)." September (1953): 14–17.

Shūkan shinchō. "Kanzen naru kekkon: Ban de Berude kara no shinpō (Perfect marriage: in the footsteps of Van de Velde)." June (1959): 28–34.

Shūkan shinchō henshūbu. *Makkāsā no Nihon* (MacArthur's Japan). Tokyo: Shinchōsha, 1970.

Silverberg, Miriam. "Constructing a New Cultural History of Modern Japan." In *Japan in the World*, edited by Masao Miyoshi and H. D. Harootunian. Durham: Duke University Press, 1993.

———. *Erotic Grotesque Nonsense: The Mass Culture of Modern Times*. Berkeley: University of California Press, 2006.

Simon, William, and John Gagnon. "Sexual Scripts: Origins, Influences and Changes." *Qualitative Sociology* 26, no. 4 (2003): 491–97.

Slaymaker, Doug. "When Sartre Was an Erotic Writer: Body, Nation and Existentialism in Japan after the Asia-Pacific War." *Japan Forum* 14, no. 1 (2002): 77–101.

Smethurst, Richard. *A Social Basis for Prewar Japanese Militarism: The Army and the Rural Community*. Berkeley: University of California Press, 1974.

Smith, Robert. "Making Village Women into 'Good Wives and Wise Mothers' in Prewar Japan." *Journal of Family History* 8, no. 1 (1983): 70–84.

Smulyan, Susan. "Using Hollywood Films to Teach Democracy: SCAP Film Policy in Occupied Japan." Tōkyō Daigaku Amerika Taiheiyō Kenkyū, no. 7 (2007): 50–61.

Sofue Takao. "Japanese Studies by American Anthropologists: Review and Evaluation." *American Anthropologist* 62, no. 2 (1960): 306–17.

Spencer, Colin. *Homosexuality: A History*. London: Fourth Estate, 1995.

Standish, Isolde. *Myth and Masculinity in the Japanese Cinema: Towards a Political Reading of the "Tragic Hero."* Richmond, Surrey: Curzon, 2000.

Steiner, Kurt. "The Revision of the Civil Code of Japan: Provisions Affecting the Family." *The Far Eastern Quarterly* 9, no. 2 (1950): 169–84.

Streitmatter, Rodger. *Unspeakable: The Rise of the Gay and Lesbian Press in America*. Boston and London: Faber and Faber, 1995.

Sumi Tatsuya. *Danshō no mori* (Grove of male prostitutes). Tokyo: Hibiya shuppansha, 1949.

———. "Danshō no mori (Grove of male prostitutes)." *Bungei yomimono*, February (1949): 10–11.

———. "Danshō no sekai: sōsaku nōto (Grove of male prostitutes production notes)." *Sekai hyōron*, February (1949): 59–65.

———. "Ueno e iku (Going to Ueno)." *Junkan nyūsu* no. 32, January 1 (1947): 8–12.

Suzuki Masahiro. "Senso ni okeru dansei sekushuariti (Men's sexuality during war)." In *Nihon no otoko wa doko kara kite doko e iku?* Edited by Asai Haruo, Itō Satoru and Murase Yukihiro. Tokyo: Jūgatsusha (2001): 98–119.

Suzuki Michiko. *Becoming Modern Women: Love and Female Identity in Prewar Japanese Literature and Culture*. Stanford: Stanford University Press, 2010.

Tachiki Takashi. *Seppun no hakubutsu shi* (Natural history of kissing). Tokyo: Seikyūsha, 2004.

Tajima Tarō. *Senetsushitsu noyami ni tsubuyaku* (Murmurs from the shadows of the censor's office). Tokyo: Yumani shobō, 2006 [1938].

Takahashi Tetsu. *Abu rabu* (Abnormal love). Tokyo: Seikyūsha, 1966.

———. *Arusu amatoria: Seikō taii 62 gata no bunseki, seiai funiki 86 hō no bunseki* (Ars amatoria: an analysis of the 62 positions of sexual intercourse and the 86 laws for creating a sexual atmosphere). Tokyo: Amatoriasha, 1953.

———. "Dokushinsha no nayami kaibō (Analysis of single people's worries). *Ningen tankyū*, December (1951): 52–59.

———. "Edo enbon kenkyū (Study of Edo erotic books)." *Amatoria*, May (1951): 16–23.

———. *Kekkon ai kaiwa jiten* (Marital love conversation dictionary). Tokyo: Amatoriasha, 1951.

———. "Kekkon ai no gijutsu mondō (Questions and answers about marital love techniques). *Amatoria*, May (1951): 50–57.

———. *Kinsei kindai 150 nen sei fūzoku zushi* (Illustrated history of the past 150 years of sexual customs). Tokyo: Kubō shoten, 1969.

———. "Nihon fūzokushi ni okeru seppun 'fukkō' ron (An argument concerning the 'revival' of kissing in Japan's history of sexual customs)." *Aka to kuro*, October (1946): 18–24.

———. "Tengoku ka jigoku ka? danshi dōseiaisha no tsudoi (Heaven or hell? A gathering of male homosexuals)." *Ningen tankyū*, January (1951): 70–83.

Takeda Hiroko. *The Political Economy of Reproduction in Japan: Between Nation-State and Everyday Life*, London: RoutledgeCurzon, 2005.

Takeda Toshiko. "Mai asa shukkin mae no hōyō to seppun (Every morning before leaving for work a hug and a kiss)." *Fūfu seikatsu*, October (1949): 70.

Takemae Eiji. *The Allied Occupation of Japan*. New York: Continuum, 2002.

Takemae Eiji and Nakamura Takafusa, eds. *GHQ Nihon senryōshi*, vol. 17, *shuppan no jiyū* (GHQ/Japan Occupation history, vol. 17, freedom of the press). Tokyo: Nihon tosho sentā, 1996.

———. *GHQ Nihon senryōshi*, vol. 18, *rajio hōsō* (GHQ/Japan Occupation history, vol. 18, radio broadcasting). Tokyo: Nihon tosho sentā, 1996.

———. *GHQ Nihon senryōshi*, vol. 19, *engi, eiga* (GHQ/Japan Occupation history, vol. 19, theater, film). Tokyo: Nihon tosho sentā, 1996.

Takenaka Ryō. "Takahashi Testsu sensei ni tsuite (Concerning Takahashi Tetsu)." *Erochika* (1972): 270–73.

Tamura Yasujirō. "Nikutai ga ningen de aru (The flesh is human)." In *Shōwa hihyō taikei*, vol. 3, edited by Endō Sasuke. Tokyo: Banmachi Shobō, 1968 [1947]: 455–58.

Tanabe Kenji. "Hatsu yoru no kanzen seikō echiketto (Perfect etiquette for first nights)." *Kōdan hiwa*, November (1952): 10–20.

Tanaka Taizō. "Ren'ai no hyōgen gikō: Rabu shiin no hanashi (Technique for expressing romantic love: talking about love scenes)." *Eiga fan*, no. 1 (1946): 22–25.

Tanaka Yuki. *Japan's Comfort Women: Sexual Slavery and Prostitution during World War II and the US Occupation*. London: Routledge, 2002.

Tatsumi Kōta. "Sei ai no gikō (Sexual love techniques)." *Raburii*, December (1947): 35–37.

Timm, Annette. "Sex with a Purpose: Prostitution, Venereal Disease, and Militarized Masculinity in the Third Reich." *Journal of the History of Sexuality* 11, nos. 1/2 (2002): 223–55.

Tomioka Naokata. "Hensō to dōseiai (Strange dressing and homosexuality)." *Ryōki*, May (1947): 23–24.

Tomita Eizō. "Danshō hoteru: danshō no seitai no isshō (Male prostitute hotel: a first chapter on the lifestyles of male prostitutes)." *Ōru shōsetsu*, June (1949): 14–28.

———. *Gei* (Gay). Tokyo: Tōkyō shobō, 1958.

———. "Josō otoko-tachi: Tōkyō no yoru no ichi shō setsu (Cross-dressing men: chapter and verse on night-time Tokyo)." *Hōpu*, December (1948): 34–35.

Tomita Kōichi. "Sei kyōiku no kadai (The issue of sex education)." *Jurisuto zōkan sōgo tokushū: ningen no sei, kōdō, bunka, shakai*, no. 25 (1981): 147–52.

Tosaka Yuji. "The Discourse of Anti-Americanism and Hollywood Movies: Film Import Controls in Japan 1937–1941." *Journal of American-East Asian Relations* 12, nos. 1/2 (2003): 59–80.

Treat, John Whittier. *Great Mirrors Shattered: Homosexuality, Orientalism and Japan*. Oxford: Oxford University Press, 1999.

Tsubaki Bunya. *Seppun nendai ki* (Kissing annals). Tokyo: Kindai bunkōsha, 1949.

Tsuge Hideomi, Ishigaki Ayako, Yasugi Ryūichi, Abe Tsuyako, and Minami Hiroshi. "Kinzei hōkoku joseihan zadankai (Roundtable on the female Kinsey report)." *Chisei*, September (1954): 114–23.

Tsuneyasu Tazuko. *Wakaki joi kiroku* (Records of a young female doctor). Tokyo: Dai Nihon yūbenkaikōdansha, 1950.

Tsurumi Kazuko. *Social Change and the Individual: Japan before and after Defeat in WWII*. Princeton, NJ: Princeton University Press, 1970.

Tsurumi Shunsuke. *A Cultural History of Postwar Japan: 1945–1980*. London: KPI, 1987.

Umehara Masaki. "Zasshi 'Gurotesuku' no shūhen (The limits of the magazine Grotesque)." *Dentō to gendai*, September (1972): 140–50.

Uno, Kathleen. "The Death of 'Good Wife, Wise Mother'?" In *Postwar Japan as History*, edited by Andrew Gordon. Berkeley: University of California Press (1993): 293–321.

Van de Velde, Theodore. *Ideal Marriage: Its Physiology and Technique*. New York: Covici Friede, 1930.

Vocabularia Erotica et Amoris. Tokyo: Kōbunsha, 1928.

Vogal, Ezra. *Japan's New Middle Class*. Berkeley: University of California Press, 1963.

Wagatsuma Hiroshi and George De Vos. "Attitudes toward Arranged Marriage in Rural Japan." *Human Organization* 21, no. 3 (1962): 187–200.

Walthall, Anne. "Masturbation and Discourse on Female Sexual Practices in Early Modern Japan." *Gender and History* 21, no. 1 (2009): 1–18.

Wani Saburō. "Kuchi ni jō ge no hedate ari (The distinction between upper mouth and lower mouth)." *Amatoria*, September (1954): 44–49.

Ward, Robert, and Yoshikazu Sakamoto, eds. *Democratizing Japan: The Allied Occupation*, Honolulu: University of Hawaii Press, 1987.

Watanabe Tsuneo and Jun'ichi Iwata. *The Love of the Samurai: A Thousand Years of Japanese Homosexuality*. Trans. D. R. Roberts. London: GMP, 1989.

Watt, George. "The Postwar in Mishima's Early Fiction." *NUCB JLCC* 7, no. 2 (2005): 79–94.

Westbrook, Robert. 1990. "'I Want a Girl Just Like the Girl that Married Harry James': American Women and the Problem of Political Obligation in World War II." *American Quarterly* 42, no. 4 (1990): 587–614.

Whiting, Robert, *Tokyo Underworld*, New York: Vintage Books, 2000.

Wildes, Harry Emerson. *Typhoon in Tokyo: The Occupation and its Aftermath*. New York: Octagon Books, 1978.

Yamagami Teiichi. "Hisokana geki wa tsuzuku (The secret drama carries on)." *Shin fūfu*, August (1949): 14–18.

Yamamoto Akira. "Kasutori zasshi" (Pulp magazines). In *Shōwa no sengoshi*, edited by Saburō Ienaga. Tokyo: Chōbunsha, 1976.

———. *Kasutori zasshi kenkyū: shinboru ni miru fūzoku shi* (Pulp magazine research: the history of sexual customs seen as a symbol). Tokyo: Shuppan nyūsusha, 1976.

———. *Sengo fūzokushi* (Postwar customs). Osaka: Ōsaka shoseki, 1986.

———. *Shisō toshite no fūzoku* (Customs as philosophy). Tokyo: Asahi shimbunsha, 1974.

Yamamoto Akira and Ozawa Shōichi. "Kisu o suru koto wa minshushugi no shinboru datta (Kissing was a symbol of democracy)." *Kasutori fukkoku han* (1975): 82–87.

Yamamuro Sei. "Dekadansu no bungaku (Decadence literature)." In *Shōwa hihyō taikei*, vol. 3, edited by Endō Sasuke. Tokyo: Banmachi shobō, 1968 [1947]: 144–53

Yarita Ken'ichi. "Ikoku seppun kō (Considering kissing in various countries)." *Amatoria*, July (1952): 26–33.

Yokota-Murakami Takayuki. *Don Juan East-West: On the Problematics of Comparative Literature*. Albany: State University of New York Press, 1998.

Yoneyama, Lisa. "Liberation under Siege: U.S. Military Occupation and Japanese Women's Enfranchisement." *American Quarterly* 57, no. 3 (2005): 885–910.

Yonezawa Yoshihiro. *Sengo ero manga shi* (Postwar erotic manga history). Tokyo: Aobayashi kōgeisha, 2010.

Yoshida Kenkichi. "Gaitō abekku sanpuru (Sample of couples on the street)." *Raburii*, May (1948): 29–30.

Yoshimi Shunya. "'America' as Desire and Violence: Americanization in Post-War Japan and Asia during the Cold War." *Inter-Asia Cultural Studies* 4, no. 3 (2003): 433–50.

Yoshizawa Norio. "Sengo no shingo ryūkō go (Postwar new words and popular words)." *Gengo seikatsu*, April (1959): 50–55.

Index